REGIONS OF THE BRITISH ISLES

EDITED BY W. G. EAST M.A.

LANCASHIRE, CHESHIRE
AND THE ISLE OF MAN

LIST OF TITLES

SOUTHEAST ENGLAND	E. M. J. Campbell, M.A., F.S.A.
WESSEX	R. A. Pelham, M.A., Ph.D.
SOUTHWEST ENGLAND	A. H. Shorter, M.A., Ph.D., F.S.A.
	W. L. D. Ravenhill, M.A., Ph.D.
	K. J. Gregory, M.A., Ph.D.
THE BRISTOL REGION	F. Walker, M.A.
THE EASTERN LOWLANDS OF ENGLAND	B. T. Bunting, M.A.
	P. G. Hall, M.A., Ph.D.
THE EAST MIDLANDS AND THE PEAK	G. H. Dury, M.A., Ph.D., F.G.S.
THE WEST MIDLANDS	R. H. Kinvig, M.A.
	M. J. Wise, M.C., B.A., Ph.D.
LANCASHIRE, CHESHIRE, AND THE ISLE OF MAN	T. W. Freeman, M.A.
	H. B. Rodgers, M.A.
	R. H. Kinvig, M.A.
YORKSHIRE	W. G. East, M.A.
	H. C. K. Henderson, M.A., B.Sc., Ph.D.
NORTH ENGLAND	A. E. Smailes, M.A., D.Lit.
WALES	E. G. Bowen, M.A., F.S.A.
SOUTHERN SCOTLAND	A. C. O'Dell, M.Sc., F.R.S. (Edinburgh)
THE HIGHLANDS AND ISLANDS OF SCOTLAND	A. C. O'Dell, M.Sc., F.R.S. (Edinburgh)
	K. Walton, M.A., Ph.D.
IRELAND	J. H. Johnson, M.A.

REGIONS OF THE BRITISH ISLES
EDITED BY W. G. EAST M.A.

Lancashire, Cheshire

and the Isle of Man

T. W. FREEMAN M.A.
Reader in Geography, University of Manchester

H. B. RODGERS M.A.
Reader in Geography, Keele University

and

R. H. KINVIG M.A.
Emeritus Professor of Geography, Birmingham University

NELSON

THOMAS NELSON AND SONS LTD
36 Park Street London W1
P.O. Box 336 Apapa Lagos
P.O. Box 25012 Nairobi
77 Coffee Street San Fernando Trinidad

THOMAS NELSON (AUSTRALIA) LTD
597 Little Collins Street Melbourne

THOMAS NELSON AND SONS (SOUTH AFRICA) (PROPRIETARY) LTD
P.O. Box 9881 Johannesburg

THOMAS NELSON AND SONS (CANADA) LTD
81 Curlew Drive Don Mills Ontario

THOMAS NELSON AND SONS
Copewood and Davis Streets Camden 3, N.J.

——

© T. W. Freeman, H. B. Rodgers, and
R. H. Kinvig   1966

Printed in Great Britain by
Thomas Nelson (Printers) Ltd, London and Edinburgh

CONTENTS

ILLUSTRATIONS
FIGURES

PLATES

The Plates will be found at the end of the book.

TABLES

COLOUR MAP

A full-colour map of Lancashire, Cheshire, and the Isle of Man
will be found at the end of the book, arranged to open out so
that it can be consulted simultaneously with the text.

PREFACE

A century ago, the Northwest was the leading industrial area of Britain, having more people in towns than any other, apparently capable of unlimited expansion, possessing an agricultural landscape brought to richness by the certainty of sales for its produce. Until the 1920s it seemed likely to grow in strength for ever. The towns were crowded, in many cases ugly with poor houses lacking amenities, and some of its industries left deep scars on the landscape and smoke blackened the towns so successfully that an Italian visitor to Manchester asked, 'And where do you get your beautiful black stone?' Visitors and new residents from areas of fairer complexion may wish to pull down all the towns and build new ones, but the warmhearted utopianism of their ideas is exceeded only by the economic impossibility of carrying them out. The present authors, both of whom were born in the Northwest and have lived in it for many years, naturally wish to see vast improvements in its appearance and in the living conditions of its people.

Battle-scarred by its industrial history, the Northwest has men and women of undefeated spirit, for even in the grimmest towns there are plans for rehabilitation, especially in the town centres. Changes are constant, and the need is so to direct the changes that a brighter environment develops. Long-developed agricultural richness is seen in a flourishing and scenically attractive countryside, much of it apparently far too precious for use as building land. There are also limited areas of recreational value, not necessarily agriculturally rich, that the Northwest possesses. Of these the main examples are the Furness area, Bowland Forest, the Pennine fringe, the hills of central Cheshire and some smaller rural areas valued largely for accessibility rather than any unusual scenic quality. A walk through woods or footpaths across fields may be of great recreational value to townspeople: equally the coasts are valued. To preserve such areas is desirable if not always possible, as the essential urban renewal involves the outward spread of settlement for both the present population and those likely to be added in the near future.

Professor R. H. Kinvig has written a chapter on the Isle of Man, of which he is a native. The County Planning Office has provided some useful material, and among students of Manchester University we owe much to Mr K. L. Wallwork, M.A., now of Leicester University, and Mr R. L. Holt, M.A. For photographs we have been able to draw on the resources of *The Guardian* (Plates 1, 5, 6, 8–11, 14, 15, 19, 24, 37) Airviews Ltd (Plates 2–4, 7, 12, 13, 16–18, 20–23, 25, 26–36, 38, 39), and the Isle of Man

Tourist Board and the 'Times Press'. (Plates 40-43.) Thanks are due also to the staff of the Central Library, Manchester, who provided copies of some of the old maps reproduced as Plates. The maps have been drawn by Miss E. A. Lowcock and the manuscript has been typed by Mrs M. J. C. Steele, both of the Department of Geography in Manchester University.

T. W. Freeman
H. B. Rodgers

February 1966

CHAPTER 1

In the Northwest

HUMAN activity has made the Northwest an area of varied landscapes, ranging from devastated industrial wastes to serenely agricultural country-sides. England's Northwest is here taken to mean the counties of Lancashire and Cheshire, and therefore corresponds to one of the subdivisions made in the 1851 Census. A hundred years ago its industrial resources seemed limitless, provided that raw materials could be acquired from overseas producers generally ready to supply them. Its coalmines were expanding in productivity; its towns were growing rapidly—indeed, as everyone now realises, too rapidly—with only a slight semblance of lip-service to planning and the maintenance of a good standard of domestic architecture. And agriculture had been brought to a productivity undreamed of before the town demand induced its intensification through various means of fertilisa-tion and drainage. Just as canal builders of the eighteenth century had regarded the Northwest as a rich field for enterprise, so the railway builders of the nineteenth century were eager to seize comparable opportunities. And by the 1880s there was talk of the new great canal to Manchester, comparable with the great Continental waterways or the long canalised stretch of the Clyde to Glasgow. Now, in the later part of the twentieth century, agriculture is still prosperous; but despite great industrial achieve-ment, there is much to regret in the appearance of the towns, notably in out-of-date housing and industrial premises as well as in the areas devastated by mining and industries. Coal and cotton are no longer inexhaustible employers of labour, and the need for regeneration is all too clear.

The northwestern division of England was unique in 1851, as it already had 63% of its people in towns: the provincial division nearest to it statistically was the West Midland, with 51% in towns. These subdivisions were redesigned in 1946, but at that time the only change in the Northwest was the addition to Lancashire and Cheshire of northwest Derbyshire, comprising two boroughs, Buxton and Glossop, the urban districts of New Mills and Whaley Bridge, and the rural district of Chapel-en-le-Frith. These Derbyshire areas were presumably included in 1946 with the Northwest standard region (a more ambitious term than the 'subdivisions'

1

of 1851) because they are closely linked in their industrial and residential qualities to the industrial area focused on Manchester: they are not included in this book. The term Lancastria is sometimes used for the Northwest, but it might be regarded unfavourably by the people of Cheshire as implying hegemony over them. To some extent the regional unity of the Northwest lies in its industrial development during the past two hundred years, for with the Industrial Revolution there has also been an intensification and expansion of agriculture that has markedly changed the appearance of the rural landscape.

The present problems of the Northwest are well known, and have been simply expressed in the Preliminary Report of the 1961 Census as 'a continued movement of industry to the south, or drift from the coal-mining and textile areas of the north, growth of population in areas of the midlands where iron and steel, brickmaking, chemical industries are thriving, industrial expansion in southern areas with good communications with London or around south coast ports'. It might perhaps be objected that few industries actually leave the Northwest, though the removal of Ford's motor works from Trafford Park (Manchester) to Dagenham (Essex) in 1929 is of some interest. The real concern is that an insufficient number of new industries are attracted to offset the decline in the old and long-successful trades. A long period of population increase has been followed by one of stability: for much of the eighteenth century and virtually all of the nineteenth, the Northwest had a high natural increase of population and considerable immigration from other areas, but now it has a net outward movement of population and even, in most of the older textile towns, a natural decrease of population through the dominance of the elderly in a population which has lost many of its active members to more attractive work elsewhere. Short-term problems have been expressed in high but temporary unemployment rates: the long-term anxiety lies in the apparent loss of attractive power, combined with uncertainty about the future in the event of Britain's entry to the Common Market.

As a unit for geographical study, the Northwest is not clearly and unequivocally separated on its margins from other regional units: its present limits are primarily due to historical chance. In the north, Lancashire includes, in the Furness area, part of the Lake District and lowlands that are diversified though not enhanced by the iron-working districts and the nineteenth century town of Barrow-in-Furness. In the east, Lancashire and Cheshire include part of the Pennines, though the boundary runs on their western side almost everywhere. Even Bowland Forest is partly in Yorkshire, but the whole of Rossendale is in Lancashire. Rarely is the Pennine boundary a definite line of division between areas sharply different except in southeast Cheshire, where the North Staffordshire coalfield lies to the east and rural Cheshire to the west of the boundary.

2

In southwest Cheshire, and in the Welsh borderland, the boundary with Shropshire, Flint, and Denbigh runs through an agricultural countryside, though the Dee is followed for several miles south of Chester. From central Cheshire and from the Wirral peninsula the Welsh hills are clearly visible, and Cheshire forms a wide lowland between these hills and the Pennines.

Of the physical units in the Northwest, one of the most interesting but least known is the Forest of Bowland, which has remained non-industrial, primarily given to dairy and sheep farming. By contrast, the Forest of Rossendale has been strongly marked by industry, having developed domestic working long before the factory stage of economic growth, and having also a long tradition of coalmining both in the valleys and on the uplands. Originally spread widely through the Pennines, the textile industries were concentrated from the late eighteenth century into the areas which they now occupy, having cotton on the Lancashire side and wool in Yorkshire with some overlapping between the two; nevertheless there are still some cotton mills in Derbyshire and Nottinghamshire. The search for water, mainly for power but also for washing and other processes, gave the Pennine and Rossendale streams great significance. Once the steam engine became generally used, proximity to coal supplies was an obvious advantage, and many of the more remote mills, especially in the upper parts of river valleys, were abandoned; in the upper Rossendale valleys, for example, one can see many such forgotten mills. There was a steady trend towards the concentration of the textile industry into larger mills where coal was readily available. This led to the accumulation of activity in those areas of Lancashire and northeast Cheshire having coalmines and in places to the building of mills beside canals, formerly used extensively for carrying coal. Many of the villages and towns in Lancashire and Cheshire were built around mills, and the patriarchal attitude of some millowners is seen in examples of a mill, cottages, the millowner's house and possibly some houses for managers, with a church or chapel, all in one compact group.

As the textile industry continued to flourish during the late eighteenth century and into the nineteenth, so many more mills were added, especially beside canals and rivers, and what in modern times would be called an industrial zone developed. By this time the millowners were moving to suburbs, increasingly distant from their work as communications became easier. Whole blocks of small houses, cottages in fact, were erected to house the workers in new industrial quarters of towns that, in the case of the larger towns, eventually surrounded the inner suburbs and initiated their decay. Thousands of houses were built on pieces of land between the mills. The very marked success of industry in the Northwest during the early nineteenth century has left acute problems for a later time. Along with the growth of the cotton industry, engineering developed, much of

3

it initially intended to provide machinery for the mills but expanded into a far wider range of activity. On the Mersey and in the St Helens area the chemical industry grew through the use of Cheshire salt brought along the Weaver navigation, and Lancashire coal taken along the Sankey Canal. And from the early eighteenth century Liverpool, having eclipsed Chester as a port, became the great overseas trading centre for a growing industry that, both for its raw materials and its finished goods, depended on the world overseas.

Having water, coal, and an industrious population, the Northwest was a leading industrial area of Britain, and indeed of the world, by the early nineteenth century. It is therefore not surprising that efforts were made to improve its communications, both by roads and canals and later by railways. Far less fortunately endowed than Yorkshire with rivers that could easily be made navigable, except for the Weaver, the Douglas, and the Mersey–Irwell, the Northwest was penetrated by canals that crossed the lowlands and climbed through flights of locks into the Pennines to connect with the Yorkshire rivers. If the eighteenth century travellers are to be believed, the roads were badly maintained, perhaps in consequence of over-use. When railway construction began, the promoters were anxious to reach Liverpool, Manchester, and Birmingham, the major provincial cities of that day as of this. Within twenty years from 1830 the present elaborate, indeed over-elaborate, system of railways was almost completed and most of the towns grew rapidly, though some were showing signs of stability, such as Stalybridge by the 1880s and Macclesfield even earlier. Only three of the factory towns, Crewe, Widnes, and Barrow-in-Furness, were virtual creations of the railway period, though many such as Oldham had been very small, in fact villages, before the nineteenth century. The most urbanised part of Britain by the mid-nineteenth century, the Northwest already had its grave problems of town living, though various municipal boards were set up to deal with these, notably during the second quarter of the nineteenth century.

Town growth involved a growing demand for farm produce, and from the eighteenth century efforts were made to fertilise the existing farmlands, to develop new rotations of crops, and to reclaim new land for agriculture. Fertilisation involved not only the addition of a wide variety of manures and natural soil constituents to the land, but also the provision of drains in the fields. Reclamation of new land was most permanently profitable in the various peatmosses that were drained and cultivated from the late eighteenth century, and in some places provided excellent land for market gardening. On the uplands the combination of domestic textile working with farming carried the limit of farming to considerable altitudes; indeed, Manley has suggested that many of the Pennine enclosures were made late in the seventeenth or in the early eighteenth century, when the rainfall may have been lower than at present. On the sandstone uplands of central

4

Cheshire, including Delamere Forest with the Peckforton and Bickerton hills, there had been some reclamation during medieval times; but some more land was gained during the eighteenth and nineteenth centuries, though fortunately patches of heathland or forest still remain. The present pattern of land use with dairy farming in south Cheshire, crop farming with a varying amount of dairy and cattle raising in north Cheshire, some rich crop farming in south and especially southwest Lancashire, and cattle farming farther north, gradually emerged during the period of industrial expansion.

The railways gave the population more mobility than ever before, and on the lines around Manchester and Liverpool suburbs began to grow around convenient railway stations almost as soon as they were built. This movement was merely the advance guard of a suburban army of occupation that came later, and most notably in the motor-bus and private-car period after the First World War. By various means, including coach and canal packet services, people went to the coast for sea bathing, and the railways gave a rich opportunity to Southport and Blackpool, both of which became popular holiday centres, though Southport was destined also to attract a residential population, including retired people as well as commuters working in the Merseyside area, and even in Wigan or Manchester. Blackpool became the largest of a whole group of coastal towns, at once holiday centres with residential attractions, in time possessing also a variety of industries and even, in Southport, national government offices. Morecambe developed on comparable lines, but was always much smaller. The Lancashire coast has been actively developed as an area able to provide holidays for the industrial masses.

When Patrick Geddes looked at Lancashire in *Cities in Evolution* (1915), he obviously held the view that the growth of population would be both continuous and rapid, and the same assumption occurs in the Planning Reports on Lancashire and Cheshire published shortly after the First World War, which forecast an industrial growth far greater than subsequent years have seen. The main changes of the years since 1919 have been the outward spread of houses due to an increase in the number of households rather than of population, though there have been heavy increases in population in such areas as the favoured Cheshire fringes of the Merseyside and Manchester conurbations, and in the coast towns. Many of the older industrial towns of the Pennines and Rossendale have entered a period of decline. The real need, slowly appreciated, has been to raise living conditions by clearing the slums of the industrial towns and, of necessity, rehousing many of their people in new suburban housing areas or even in new industrial towns like Kirkby on the margins of Liverpool; it is impossible to rehouse the population of a cleared area (including the new families requiring homes) on the site, even in tall flats. In virtually all the towns, too, more land is needed in the central areas for

5

non-residential uses, which may include new roads, open spaces, schools and colleges, central offices, car parks, bus stations, public halls, and the like. And nowhere is this more vividly seen than in the extension of the universities of Manchester and Liverpool; the new university of Lancaster, following Keele and Brighton, is beginning on a site outside the town.

In the chapters that follow it is hoped to give some impression of the Northwest as it is now and in a modern historical context. Writing at a time when the assumptions of unending growth once held, for example by Patrick Geddes, seem naive, one must not fall into the opposite error of assuming that perpetual decline is to be expected, for numerous new industries have been attracted to the Northwest in the past and are being brought in at the time of writing; the region's assets include factory sites, even old mills for conversion, and abundant labour of varied skills. The cotton industry, severely rationalised, may have reached the lowest limits of employment and show advance or at least some degree of stability. In the Manchester district, and along the Ship Canal as a whole, the effects of this late-nineteenth century enterprise have borne and are bearing fruit, and it may be that the new Birmingham–Preston motorway will prove stimulating to industrial growth, perhaps especially in the problem area of the central Lancashire coalfield through which it passes. One of the biggest social problems is the virtual rebuilding of a large part of the two major cities, Manchester and Liverpool, and in both cases the construction of centres more worthy of their past—and one hopes future—contribution to the economic life of Britain and, perhaps less certainly, to its cultural life. Within the rural areas, agriculture remains prosperous, and one main concern is the preservation of rich land against suburban growth. Green belts have been defined around the conurbations, but in 1966 they were still *de facto* rather than *de jure*. Part of the need for houses for Merseyside people is to be met by new towns at Runcorn on the Mersey and at Skelmersdale, west of Wigan, and for Manchester by the extension of some existing towns such as Westhoughton and also a number of planned overspill schemes. At a later stage in the dispersal of population from the two northwestern conurbations, it is probable that an overspill town of 'new city' size will be developed in the Leyland–Chorley area, beside the M6 motorway.

6

CHAPTER 2

Physical Regions of Lancastria:
an Economic Appraisal

FEW provinces of Britain contain such profound yet simple contrasts in the character of their physical landscape as Lancastria, a region divided neatly and clearly between morphological units of radically different types. On the west, flanking the coast and broadening progressively southwards, the soft landscapes of the drift-smeared lowlands are developed chiefly on Permo-Triassic rocks. To the east rise the slab-sided and level-crested plateaux of the Pennine and Rossendale moorlands, modelled entirely from the harder grits and limestones of the Carboniferous series. But the distinction between upland and lowland in Lancastria is not merely a reflection of geological age: the Middle Coal Measures are comparatively weak rocks, so that the plains of Lancastria are in part floored by Carboni-ferous material. Here, indeed, are the richest sections of the coalfield and some of the thickest population clusters.

The physique of the uplands

About one-third of the area of Lancastria consists of the high moor-lands of the western flank of the Pennine system, which extends seawards as the upland salients of the Rossendale and Bowland Fells. Nowhere can these be described as mountainous: apart from their abrupt terminal scarps and the deep valleys of the short, vigorous streams, the dominant features are level summit plateaux—a peat-covered and rain-sodden wilderness—whose slopes to the valley-flats are broken by extensive benches. The scenic value of the moorlands cannot be rated as uniformly high. At their best, in autumn and far from the smoking caverns of the textile valleys, they are attractive. High Bowland has one of the best-preserved (and least accessible) moorland landscapes in England, better fitted perhaps than the Peak District for the status of a National Park. In 1963, however, Bowland Forest was designated as an 'area of out-standing beauty'. But at their worst—scarred by mining and quarrying, strewn with the rubble heaps of abandoned farms, and veiled by the industrial haze which blackens even the sheep—the moors are as unsightly as the towns that have despoiled them. Yet even here the uplands provide

7

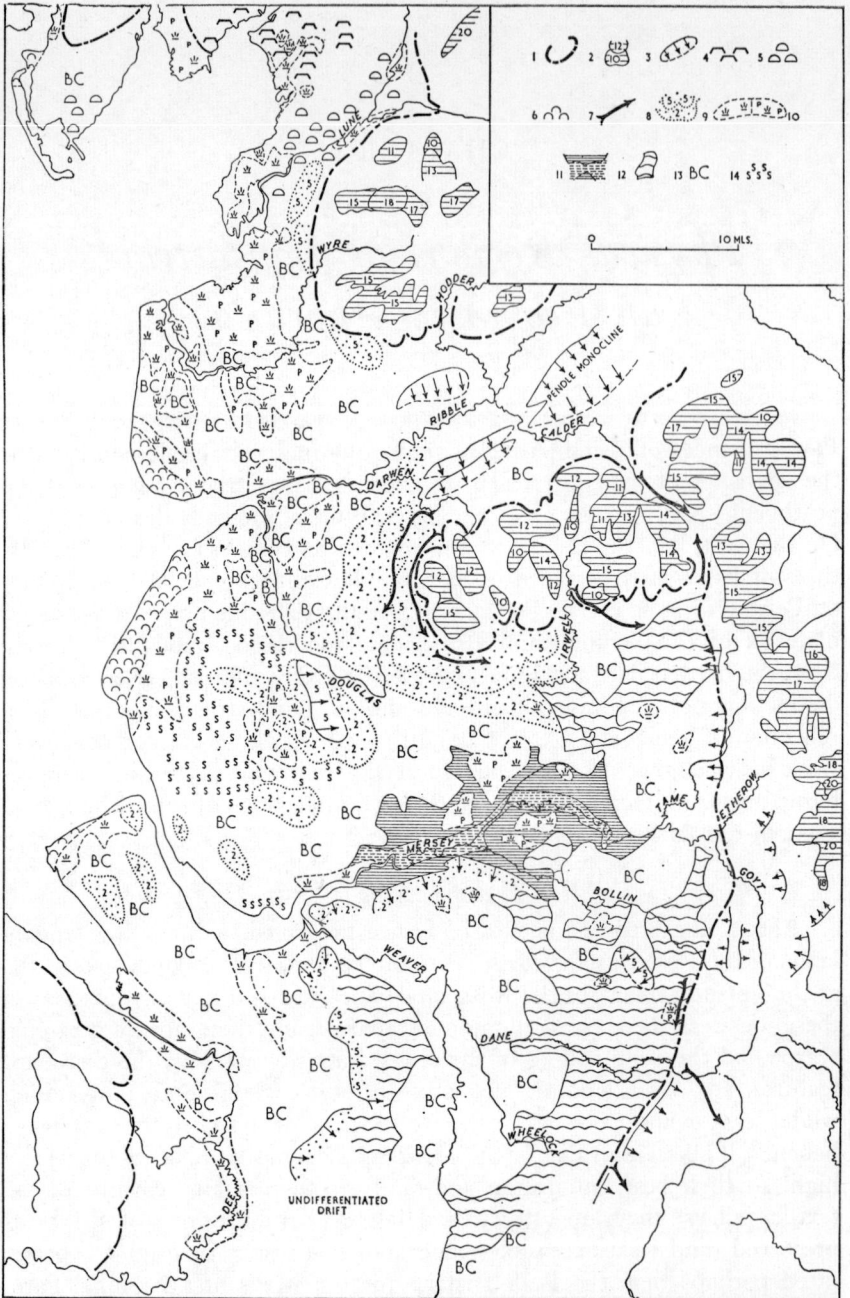

Fig. 1 THE GEOMORPHOLOGY OF NORTHWESTERN ENGLAND. 1: Generalised limits of the main moorland masses. 2: Main plateau summits, approximate altitudes in hundreds of feet. 3: Principal cuestas, arrows indicating dip. 4: Low tabular limestone hills of north Lancashire. 5: Chief drumlin fields. 6: Sand dunes. 7: Chief glacial drainage channels. 8: Low plateau remnants at *c.* 500 and *c.* 250 feet, in part drift-covered. 9: Salt marsh and chief areas of river alluvium. 10: Peatmosses. 11: The Mersey high terrace and flood plain. 12: Dissected glacial sand-spreads. 13: Boulder clay plains. 14. Main deposits of Shirdley Hill Sands.

recreational space to the populations of two of England's most congested industrial regions on either side of the Pennine axis (Plate 1).

The structural foundations. In upland Lancastria an almost complete section through the Carboniferous series is revealed. The massive limestones at its base are seen in our region only in far northern Lancashire and in the Ribble valley, where they are used in cement manufacture. Above these lies an alternating sequence of sandstones, grits, shales, and impure limestones: once given a variety of titles—for example the Yoredale

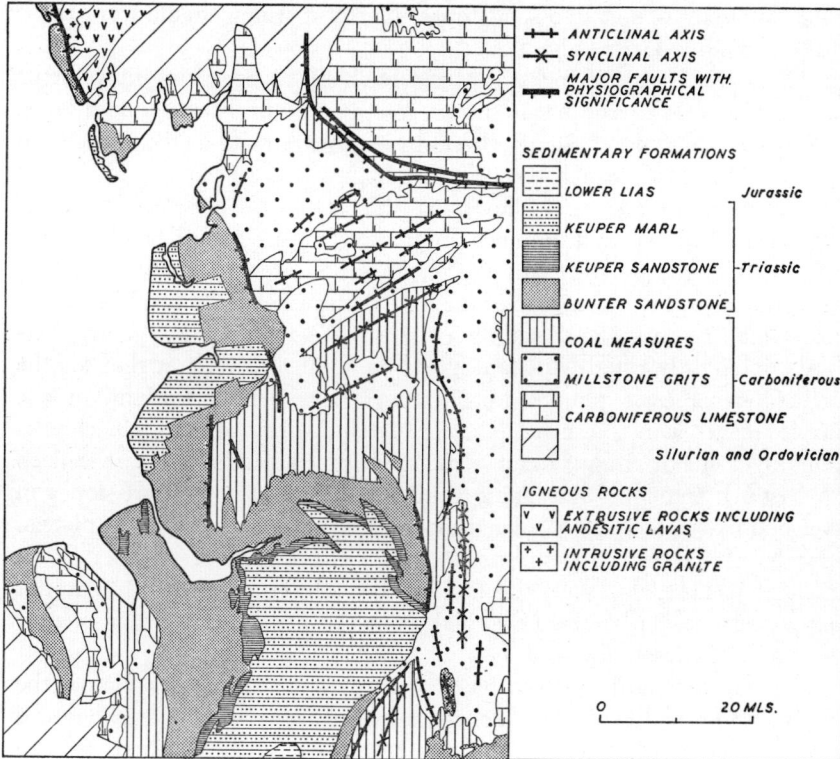

Fig. 2   GENERALISED GEOLOGY AND THE MAJOR STRUCTURES.

series—these are now regarded as a lower division of the Millstone Grits. They are significant in Lancastria chiefly because they make the main mass of Bowland Forest. But the Millstone Grits proper are the characteristic rock of the uplands of Lancastria. They consist of hard, cemented gritstone bands separated by soft, quickly rotting shales; and the differential erosion of grit and shale produces the 'stepped' profile so typical of the moorland landscape. The Millstone Grit series has a considerable, though declining, economic significance. It yields a hard, durable building stone, honey-coloured when fresh, though darkening quickly in industrial smoke.

9

At some horizons the grits are so finely bedded that they provided stone 'flags', the traditional roofing material of eastern Lancastria. Coal, too, was available from the top of this series, in thin seams once worked sporadically at great altitudes. But it was from the youngest of the upland rocks, the Lower Coal Measures, that most of the little pits scattered across the moors were mined for fuel. On a small scale the Lower Coal Measure seams are still worked, in many places in association with beds of fireclay and ganister which support a brick, tile, and heavy-pottery industry. But the coal resources of this series were always limited, for it consists chiefly of massive sandstones, hardly distinguishable from those of the Millstone Grits (Fig. 2).

This varied suite of rocks has been buckled, by recurring movements beginning in late Coal Measure times, into a series of broad, faulted folds. The master structure is the north–south monocline with a steep, fractured western limb, from which the central Pennines have been moulded. The three sections of Figure 3 show that this structure is simplest in the north, near Burnley, and becomes progressively more complicated towards the south. In the north it is a classic, uncomplicated monocline: the axis forms the abrupt western edge of the high plateaux of the central Pennines, from which the moorland interfluves of the West Riding fall gently east-wards on slightly tilted Millstone Grits; while to the west of the axis the Carboniferous beds plunge steeply into the synclinal lowland of the Burnley coal basin. Near Manchester the simplicity of the monocline is spoilt by a major fracture and a minor fold. The fault guides the deep north–south trench of the Tame valley, east of which stepped slopes in level-bedded grits rise in a magnificent staircase to the highest plateau summits of the central Pennines, Bleaklow (2,060 ft.) and Kinder Scout (2,088 ft.). To the west of the faulted monoclinal axis a band of minor east-facing cuestas has been worked from the gritstones dipping steeply into the Manchester lowland.

Still farther south, on the flank of the broad Derbyshire Dome, the minor folding of the western Pennines intensifies. Parallel anticlines and synclines have been etched out by a complex drainage system to form England's finest example of a cuesta-form landscape worked out from folded rocks of unequal resistance to erosion. The breached anticline of the valley of Todd Brook and the 'perched' syncline of the Goytshead moors are two classic features. But this minor folding has had strong economic as well as morphological effects, for example in carrying a salient of industrial and urban population along the synclinal middle Goyt valley, where Coal Measures were preserved from erosion in the valley floor.

Of the two uplands which are westerly extensions of the Pennines—the Rossendale and Bowland Fells—the former is structurally as simple as the latter is complex. Rossendale is the surface expression of a broad

BLACKSTONE EDGE

K.G.

R.R.   K.G.

K.G.

i) Section across Pennine Monocline N.E. of Rochdale
|———— 1 Mile ————|

L.C.M. LOWER COAL MEASURES   R.R. ROUGH ROCK   K.G. KINDERSCOUT GRIT

BUCKTON
MOOR
K.G.

LUZLEY HILL
R.R.   TAME
L.C.M.   K.G.   K.G.

ii) Section across Mossley Anticline E. of Manchester
|———— 1 Mile ————|

M.G. MILLSTONE GRITS (UNDIFFERENTIATED)   C.L. CARBONIFEROUS LIMESTONE

TODD   GOYT
BROOK   VALLEY
L.C.M.   M.G.
TRIAS   M.G.   M.G.
                                C.L.

iii) Section across S.W. Pennines, Buxton to Macclesfield
|— 1 Mile —|

P.G. PENDLE GRIT   B.S. BOWLAND SHALE

BOWLAND   BURNLEY
FELLS   LONGRIDGE   PENDLE HILL   BASIN
             FELL   P.G.   L.C.M.
             M.G.   RIBBLE   B.S.   P.G.
B.S.   B.S.
                         C.L.

iv) Section across Ribblesdale Fold Belt
|— 1 Mile —|

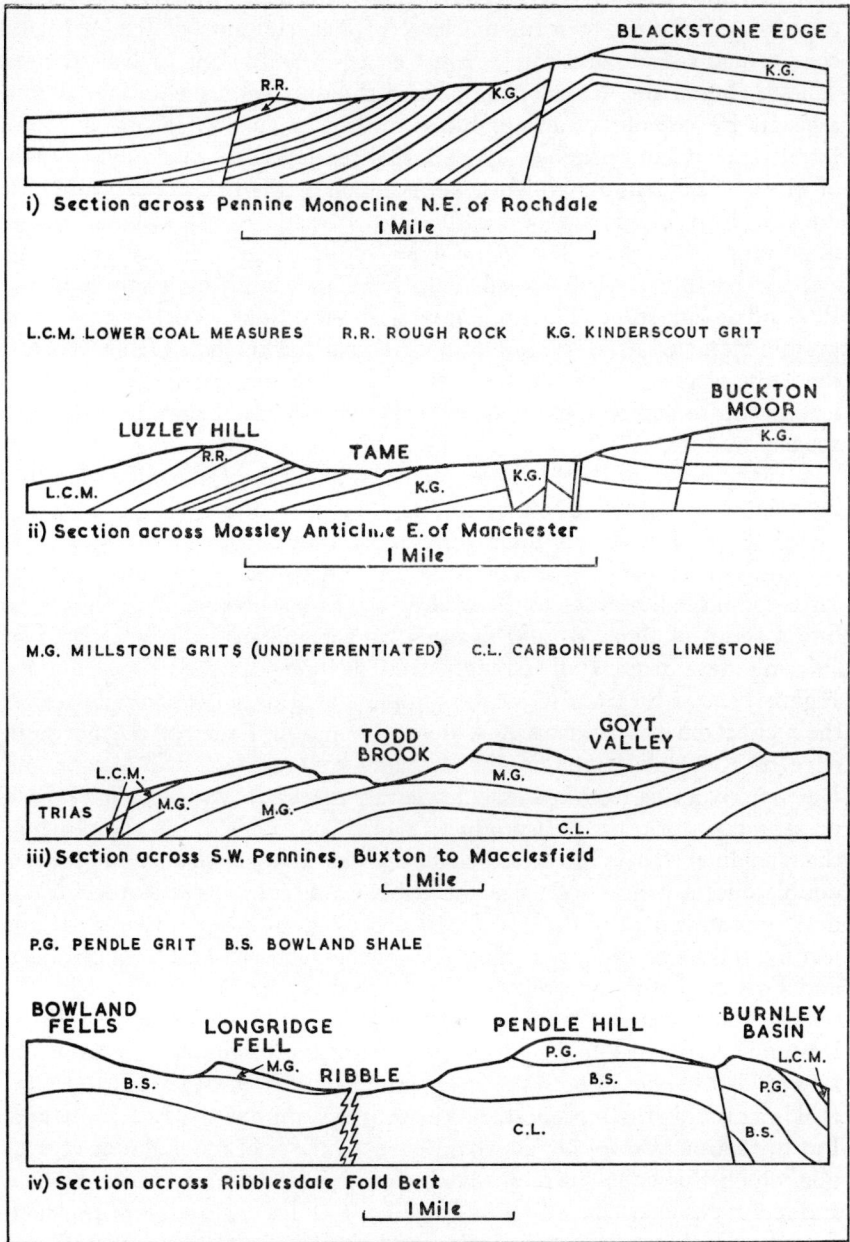

Fig. 3   GEOLOGICAL SECTIONS ACROSS THE PENNINE UPLANDS AND THE
RIBBLESDALE FOLDS.

11

flattened anticline of ENE–WSW trend. Untilted Millstone Grits are exposed at its crest to form the level plateau summits of the moorland core, which rises to altitudes as great as 1,700 feet and is gashed by deep valleys. Round the flanks of the upland the dips from the anticlinal axis, assisted by complex faulting, bring in Lower Coal Measures to form lower plateaux and benches. The entire structure is shattered by a system of NNW–SSE faulting which governs much of the minor relief and—by downthrowing fragments of Middle Coal Measures—has some economic importance. The long horizontal lines of its plateau summits and the stepped profiles of its grit-shale slopes are the dominant features of the Rossendale landscape. The uppermost grit—the Rough Rock—is the most prominent plateau-former, and from it rise isolated knolls of Coal Measures, sandstone-capped almost in the fashion of miniature mesas. 'Coal lanes', leading up to some of these, once served the tiny adit mines driven into the exposed seams.

To the north of the high core of Rossendale the Carboniferous rocks become so disturbed by tight folding that any attempt to outline the morphology of northern Lancashire must be set against the structural background of the Ribblesdale fold belt. In this area the whole of the series from the limestone to the Middle Coal Measures has been deformed into a series of tight, regular flexures, so that here, too, is one of Great Britain's few regions of strongly folded topography. The section in Figure 3 shows these structures in simplified form and roughly illustrates their effect on the landscape. A deep syncline lies against the northern edge of Rossendale, and in this trough—excavated by the Calder and Darwen rivers to form a broad lowland—the Coal Measures have been preserved to form the still productive Burnley coalfield. To the north of this synclinal valley Millstone Grits are raised to form a bold ridge, a double cuesta which overlooks the Ribble and culminates in the magnificent gritstone mass of Pendle hill, Lancastria's most spectacular landscape feature. This line of scarps (Fig. 1) is on the southern limb of a breached anticline, eroded into a broad valley-lowland by the Ribble.

On the southern flanks of Bowland, as on the northern flanks of Rossendale, parallel folds govern the character of the relief. Anticlinal axes guide the lines of both the Hodder and Loud valleys, while Longridge Hill is a classic gritstone cuesta on the southern limb of the Loud anticline. But the southern slopes of Bowland have a variety of relief and of vegetation which Rossendale cannot match, for here limestones of both bedded and reef types alternate with grits and shales. In the main mass of Bowland Forest the folding becomes gentler, and the level plateaux are modelled from gently warped gritstones and shales in a landscape little different from that of any part of upland Lancastria except for its complete wildness and perfect preservation. Farther north, however, the corrugations of the Ribblesdale fold belt become sharply evident again, for both the ridge of Quernmore and the limestone knolls of Lonsdale pick out the most northerly of these anticlines.

The erosional record. Throughout upland Lancastria the rocks have been folded and faulted so strongly that the relief clearly reflects their deformation, and thus it is possible to interpret the pattern of landforms in structural terms. Many features in these landscapes which are not tectonic but purely erosional in origin yield evidence of the complex denudational history of the uplands. The high cores of Bowland, Rossendale, and the Pennines all have summits so flat and so little adjusted to either structure or lithology that they have long been suspected to be erosional plains uplifted to altitudes approaching 2,000 feet O.D. In the Pennines proper there are widespread summit surfaces between 1,600 and 1,800 feet, above which the impressive monadnocks of Bleaklow and Kinder Scout rise to heights of more than 2,000 feet. A lower surface, between 1,200 and 1,400 feet, similarly interrupted by monadnocks, has been widely identified in the southwest Pennines, where it is often so well developed that it masks the cuesta-vale pattern of relief which expresses the tightly folded structure of this region. Valley benches are common features in all the upland valleys and mark later, shorter cycles in the evolution of the moorland relief. In Rossendale, too, the summit plateaux tend to be concordant in altitude: those of the southwest approximate to 1,250 feet, and a particularly widespread bench is found at 1,000 feet. But in Lancastria not every 'flat' may be taken to be a remnant erosional feature; for as the layering of grits and shales gives every slope a stepped profile it is not easy to distinguish the work of erosion from the direct influence of structure.

The evolution of the drainage pattern is a key to the physical history of any region. Though little detailed work has yet been completed in Lancastria, it is clear that many of the region's streams had suffered complex changes even before the general derangement of drainage in the Pleistocene period. To quote two examples, both the Loud of north Lancashire and the Etherow of east Cheshire apparently adopted their present courses only recently. The former is the region's best example of capture: it was once part of a Hodder–Loud system which flowed north of the Ribble to an independent entry to the plain and, ultimately, the sea. A vigorous Ribble tributary—the modern lower Hodder—cut back quickly to behead it, reversing the Loud and leaving, north of Preston, a broad dry or misfit valley. The Etherow, a 'consequent' east–west stream flowing off the Pennine uplift east of Manchester, makes an inexplicable turn southwards to become a tributary of the Goyt. Almost certainly it once followed a more direct course through the 'dry' and drift-choked Broadbottom gap to reach the Manchester lowland independently.

Glacial modification of the upland landscape. Many of the minor details of the upland landscape, though few of its major elements, are the recent work of glacial processes; indeed, most of the physical details which have had the greatest economic influence are the consequences of glaciation. Though these uplands were not themselves centres of ice accumulation and had ice-free cores, they were surrounded by and almost buried beneath the Irish Sea, Lake District, and Ribblesdale ice-sheets. A thick coating of drift choked many valleys, causing stream diversions, and extended as a veneer of varying depth on the moorland slopes to heights of 1,700 feet. The upper drift limit, now fretted by recent erosion, is a significant line in the agricultural geography of the uplands, for beyond it soils are merely loose accumulations of sand and rubble, while the heavy drift clays can be improved at high altitudes if adequately limed and drained. The contrast in land use between the pastures on the drift and the rough grass-heath beyond is obvious on countless Lancashire moorland slopes.

Glaciation had also a profound influence on Lancastria's industrial evolution. Scarcely a single major upland stream escaped diversion by drift accumulation in its old valley. In many cases the stream was deflected so far from its old course that, in incising its bed anew, it has cut a deep and narrow slot into the gritstone flanks of its old valley. Such diversion gorges are almost invariably ungraded, and they therefore provided a natural head of water to power the mills of the infant cotton industry. But between the gorges the upland rivers are well graded and their gentle gradients restricted their use for power; thus both industry and settlement were located at the power sites of the diversion gorges. Summerseat and Waterfoot on the Irwell, New Mills and Marple on the Goyt, Broadbottom on the Etherow, all of them among the earliest of the industrial villages created by the growth of the cotton industry, owed their location to glacial accident. Figure 23 (p. 102) shows the detail of typical diversion gorges.

Glaciation assisted Lancastria's early economic growth in another way, for the canals, roads, and railways which grew to serve the expanding industries were guided by a most complicated system of meltwater channels cut during the retreat phase. As the ice-front fell away from the hill-masses towards the plain progressively larger areas of upland were exposed, and here normal drainage began once more. But the valley mouths were still blocked, so that ephemeral systems of lakes were formed in all the major and many minor valleys. Such lakes naturally found the lowest point of overspill and cut channels now left as misfit or dry valleys in the modern landscape. Many of these provide low-level routeways between different valley systems which were exploited in the development of communications. The railway from Macclesfield to Leek follows, first, a minor channel which drained Lake Macclesfield, and then the much longer Rudyard Gorge cut by Pennine drainage deflected southwards to the Trent. Even more significant, both to the late-glacial history of the Pennines and to the progress of communications, was the Walsden Gorge between Rochdale and Todmorden, cut by the deflected drainage of eastern Rossendale, which for a time crossed the Pennine watershed and escaped to the Yorkshire Calder. In use long enough to be deepened to c.500 feet O.D., it provided a trans-Pennine routeway for a turnpiked highway (c.1760), the Rochdale Canal (opened in 1799–1804), and the Manchester–Leeds railway (1840). The earliest firm link between Lancashire and Yorkshire, it had immense industrial significance, not least in facilitating the invasion of the West Riding by the cotton industry. Almost all the north–south routes across Rossendale are guided in part by the lines of spillways, of which the most spectacular is the Cliviger gorge between Burnley and Todmorden, cut by the escape of drainage southeastwards to the Humber, though direct ice action may have been responsible for its initiation.

The physique of the lowlands

Between the Carboniferous uplands and the coast the drift lowland, tapering northwards, dominates Lancastria both physically and economically. Commonly but loosely termed the Triassic plain, it is neither a plain in the strictest sense nor is it floored entirely by Triassic materials. Rather it is a lowland of considerable lithological contrast and great structural complexity: its surface has been planed in several cycles of erosion and finally covered by an intricately varied overlay of superficial deposits now in the course of dissection.

Structure and the sub-drift surface. In its extent the Lancastrian lowland reflects the earth movements which, beginning in Coal Measure times, deformed the Carboniferous rocks to form a tectonic depression deepest in western Lancashire and central Cheshire. This basin was slowly filled by the desert and inland-sea deposits of the Permo-Triassic series, a varied suite of rocks ranging from the soft Keuper Marls (industrially important for salt beds) through the friable Bunter sandstones to hard, scarp-forming rocks like the Keuper sandstones and the Bunter conglomerate. Later, these sediments were gently folded by renewed earth movements, so that the basins of western Lancashire were deepened and the strata between—in southwest Lancashire and Wirral—was raised as a low saddle.

Though the Lancastrian plain is essentially a tectonic lowland it would be naive to suggest that its relief may be interpreted simply in structural terms. The plain has passed through at least three denudational cycles, and traces of the work of all three are preserved in its landscape. Extensive plateau remnants occur consistently at roughly 500 and 200 feet above sea level, and both are developed indifferently on a variety of both Permo-Triassic and Carboniferous rocks. Below the lower of these levels steep-sided valleys were cut far below the modern sea level, but these are now plugged and lost beneath the drift. Indeed, the plain has a strong, even a rugged, sub-drift form in which bold ridges and platforms rose many hundreds of feet above the old, lost valley floors. Though much of this preglacial landscape is entirely buried, it is more often masked than obliterated by the drift sheet, so that the modern relief of the lowland is still, in part, a softened reflection of the earlier physique. This is true, certainly, of the major regional contrasts in the lowland relief, although the complex superficial mantle is the key to minor, local variations. The relief of the Cheshire plain, despite its thick drift cover, is still directly related to the structures of the shallow, saucer-like depression in the New Red Sandstones. Round the lip of the basin, especially on the north and west, the older, harder members of the series outcrop to form a fragmentary peripheral cuesta. Half buried in drift, this can be traced as the southern bluff of the Mersey valley westwards from Lymm to the bolder headlands overlooking the estuary at Runcorn and Helsby. Here the trend of the ridge changes abruptly: it continues southwards, overlooking the alluvial flats of the Gowy and Dee valleys in the scarped edges of the Delamere, Peckforton, and Bickerton uplands. In general, these are west-facing cuestas, accentuated and modified by faulting: on their eastern slopes the rocks dip gently eastwards so that the soft Keuper Marls are brought in to form the structural foundation of the rolling drift plain of the Weaver–Dane basin. Fragments only of a peripheral cuesta may be identified on the eastern, Pennine flank of the Cheshire basin. The east-facing cuesta of Alderley Edge is the clearest example, though there is also, beneath the Stockport drift sheet, a cuesta-form Permian ridge.

In southwest Lancashire and the Wirral the influence of geological structure on the landscape takes a different form. Here the rocks of the lowland have been gently warped into an upfold which continues the trend of the Rossendale anticline southwestwards. This structure has immense economic significance, for it throws a broad salient of Coal Measures southwestwards almost into the suburbs of Liverpool, where it is shorn off by faulting. Farther west this gentle warping may be traced in the fault-assisted uplift of Bunter and lower Keuper sandstones to form the 'saddle' of Wirral and Merseyside. Here the solid rocks make a substantial contribution to the modern landscape, but in the coastlands farther north they are nowhere seen, for drifts deeply conceal the Keuper Marls of the west Lancashire basin.

On both sides of the Mersey estuary the dominant landforms are low plateaux cut from Keuper sandstone which preserve, on their summit-flats, remnants of a 200-foot erosion surface. They rise directly from the estuary and give Liverpool a noble site, sadly spoilt by Victorian slum housing and the decayed Georgian terraces which climb their slopes. Both in Lancashire and in the Wirral some of the low sandstone plateaux are defined by faults, but that they are essentially erosional features is shown both by their consistent summit altitudes—for all approximate to

200 feet O.D.—and by the passage of this erosional surface from Trias to Coal Measures at Skelmersdale without any topographical break.

The erosional history of the lowland is seen most clearly in the relief of the coalfield of central and southern Lancashire, for here the patchy drift rarely obscures the strong preglacial landforms. Both in the west and in the south of this area traces of a 'staircase' of erosional levels occur. The bold Coal Measure cuesta of the Ashhurst–Billinge ridge rises to summit-flats at 500 feet from the eastern edge of the 200-foot level of the Skelmersdale platform. Farther east drift-smoothed remnants of the 500-foot surface are widely developed on both the middle and the lower Coal Measures and even on Millstone Grits near Haigh, Bolton, and Ainsworth. Indeed, the 500-foot platform that girdles Rossendale from Hoghton in the west to Bury in the south, provides clear evidence that the scarps of the upland, which rise directly from this lower surface, are purely erosional in origin. The 500-foot plateau remnants to the south of Rossendale descend, southwards, by a marked break of slope to lower surfaces at c.250 feet, and these in turn fall to the level of the low drifts and alluvium of the Mersey valley. Since the remnants of the 500-foot surface are almost drift-free and are deeply dissected by vigorous streams, their outcropping coal seams were easily accessible with primitive mining techniques; Haigh, Blackrod, and Little Hulton—all close to such features—were among the earliest important mining centres. Later, the smoothly stepped southwards fall of the surface facilitated coal transport, for it made possible the construction of gravity tramroads to the canal and railway along the northern lip of the Mersey valley (Fig. 17, p. 91).

The key to much of the minor relief of the lowlands lies in the varied overlay of soft, superficial deposits covering the 'solid' landscape of pre-glacial times. Where complete, the glacial series consists of upper and lower boulder clays partly covered by lenses of water-borne sands, which suggests that in Lancastria there were two glacial advances during which ground moraine was laid down and subsequently covered during the retreat phases by sand and gravel deposits, mostly deposited as deltas in ephemeral ice-dammed lakes. Both the sands and the clays are associated with distinctive types of landscape. The clays are, in general, monotonously flat, especially where they have been smoothed by submergence in periglacial lakes, as in the Manchester lowland. In Cheshire and in the Fylde the boulder clay spreads are more uneven, for the drainage has dissected them more deeply and moulded the surface into rounded interfluves. Sand caps form infrequent knolls, and in some areas— especially in the south Fylde—the clay has the form of low, indistinct drumlins. But clay landscapes are always smoothly rounded, while those of the sands are dissected deeply and intricately cut into ragged forms. The thick deltaic masses north of Manchester consist of soft, rubbly material easily carved by even the slightest brooks into deep gullies rising by steep unstable slopes to hills which reach the 500-foot contour. The sands capping the Delamere plateau accentuate the roughness of its surface and the poverty of its soils, while the arcuate sandspreads of east and south Cheshire, in appearance strongly suggestive of recessional moraines, form similarly ragged landscapes. The only belt of classically 'morainic' topography in Lancastria—the Ellesmere moraine of the Cheshire–Shropshire border—lies in the extreme south.

On the glacial débris rest younger deposits, each of which has its characteristic landscape. All the mainstreams of the region run in broad valleys choked by their own alluvium, which has been cut into a system of terraces by postglacial changes in sea level. The Mersey and Irwell are typical; while still braided and heavily loaded in immediate postglacial times, they deposited a broad spread of flood gravels, now left 25 feet above river level as a high terrace. Monotonously flat, this feature accommodated most of Manchester's suburban expansion to the south and west and so contributed to the extreme topographical dullness of the city's suburbs. Fragments of two low terraces rise indistinctly above a true floodplain, which is regularly awash in winter. These lower, damper surfaces, avoided by the builder, interpose a green belt between the inner and the outer suburbs.

Two of Lancashire's superficial deposits are directly due to coastal change—the broad spreads of tidal alluvium of 'Downholland' type and the Shirdley Hill Sands. The former occurs as low coastal flats in west Lancashire and the Fylde standing scarcely 10 feet above mean sea level. This Downholland silt is beach material laid down when the coastline lay several miles inland from its present position. The slow advance of this old 'Hillhouse' coastline westwards and the later formation of the modern dune belt converted these saltflats into freshwater marsh and thus initiated the growth of an unbroken and impenetrable belt of peatmosses which flanked the coast from the Ribble to the Alt. Much the same sequence of events was involved in the evolution of the similar mosses and marshes of the Fylde, though these also cover much recent tidal alluvium reclaimed from the sea. The Shirdley Hill Sand is a wind-borne sand blown from the Hillhouse beach and deposited inland as a veneer which thickens locally to fill hollows and to smooth the drift surfaces and Triassic platforms of west Lancashire. A fine, sharp sand of great purity, it has great economic importance as a raw material of the St Helens glass industry.

Of all the landscape types of the Lancastrian lowland the peatmosses which once covered so large a part of it were perhaps the most distinctive; certainly in their influence on the settlement and agricultural evolution of the region they were the most important. Empty and desolate until two centuries ago, they were progressively drained and converted into first-class arable land with organic soils so rich that they are now among the

18

most intensively cropped land not merely in Lancastria but also in Great Britain. In these wet western coastlands, where rainfall ranges up to 35 inches and where cloudiness reduces evaporation, soils on any flat surface tend to become water-logged, and peat accumulation ensues. Bogs have therefore developed on several of the superficial deposits in several types of location. First, there are the coastal mosses on the flat surfaces of tidal silt (p. 8). Second, peat has accumulated on level but slightly higher boulder clay plains, for example at Longton Moss, near Preston, and in the mosses north of the Wyre. Third, on the flat high-terrace plains, chiefly on the north side of the Mersey, another belt of mosses of great size extended from Warrington almost to Manchester and Altrincham. Fourth, depressions in the clay surface have become peat-filled to form small, enclosed mosses, both in the Manchester embayment and in the drift plain of north Cheshire, and similar examples occur in the silty valleys between the limestone knolls of the coastlands of Lonsdale. Fifth, some broad, misfit valleys of periglacial origin contain small mosses covering indeterminate watersheds, like Red Moss at Horwich. Sixth, in southwest Lancashire, a large group of mosses stands at 60–200 feet on drift and Triassic surfaces levelled by a veneer of Shirdley Hill Sands. These, like some of the lower mosses, are raised bogs of clearly convex form. There has been little systematic study of the Lancastrian peats; but it is probable that the coastal bogs and the 'hollow mosses' of Cheshire are 'flush' peats not of strongly acid character. In contrast the raised bogs at higher elevation receive little local drainage and are certainly highly acid. But all types of peat have been successfully reclaimed, and a recent survey showed that only tiny remnants of unimproved mossland survive.

The coast, estuaries, and seaports

Few coastlines in Great Britain have been so fully exploited in the economic growth of their region as that of Lancastria, for few others serve such dense masses of urban population in their immediate hinterland. Of the 135 miles of coast between the Dee and Kent rivers 70 miles are built up. This comparatively short coastline has not only the country's largest provincial port-city in the Merseyside conurbation, but also several smaller specialised ports such as Fleetwood and Preston. Between the estuaries and away from their mudflats, groups of resorts have grown on open, sandy shores: on the Fylde coast a 12-mile-long resort-ribbon stretches from Fleetwood to Lytham, while in the Wirral and southwest Lancashire the coast has attracted dormitory settlement, so that Liverpool's suburban expansion has been largely coastwise. Only rarely is this shore-line cut into solid rocks. Its boldest features are crumbling boulder clay cliffs and the belts of unstable dunes in the south Fylde and near Southport. In the Wirral, Triassic sandstones make their only coastal exposures, in a wave-cut platform at New Brighton and in the low islands off West Kirby.

Here sandstone bluffs rising immediately behind the shore shape the angles of the peninsula and give it greater relief than any other section of the coast, except for the hilly shorelands of Morecambe Bay.

The Mersey and Dee estuaries, on either side of the Wirral peninsula, are totally contrasted in physical character. The former narrows to a tight constriction at its mouth between the Triassic bluffs of New Brighton and Great Crosby, so that the tidal and river water impounded in the broad spread of the upper estuary pours through the bottleneck twice daily, cleansing it of silt. Dredging is necessary only at the bar blocking the seaward approaches and, at very heavy cost, in the approach to the Manchester Ship Canal at Eastham. The Dee estuary is broad and bell-mouthed. No tidal scour is possible, and progressive estuarine accumulation has strangled the ancient port of Chester, which until the fifteenth century enjoyed a lively trade, especially with Ireland. Not even the development of successive outports and the canalisation of the lower Dee in the New Cut of 1735–7 could save the port, and today there is little traffic even on the lower estuary.

Until the late nineteenth century Preston seemed likely to share Chester's fate; for the Ribble estuary is V-shaped and was choked by mudflats which merged into salt marshes on both its banks. The winding channels from the open sea were unstable, and even the little vessels of the seventeenth century rarely attempted the passage to the decaying wharves below the town. But Preston was revitalised as a port after the 1840s when the Ribble was put within training walls to the open sea off Lytham. The reclamation of the saltmarshes for cultivation was a secondary but equally successful aspect of the scheme. Lancaster, unlike Preston, has given up the battle against silt accumulation. The winding Lune estuary gradually narrows, so that there is no effective scour, and since its golden age in the late eighteenth century Lancaster has slipped into insignificance as a port. Attempts to establish outports were failures: both the little village of Sunderland and, later, Glasson Dock on a branch of the Lancaster Canal enjoyed brief periods of prosperity, but they could not save this old trading town on a sand-choked estuary as a port, though it flourishes as an industrial and commercial centre.

Two other small Lancashire ports, Fleetwood and Heysham, have sites physically more favourable than Lancaster and have acquired specialised functions. Fleetwood is on the Wyre, a Mersey in miniature, for the estuary is constricted and scoured at the tidal changes. At flood tide the depth is adequate for the considerable trawler fleet which is the port's chief traffic; but the packet service to the Isle of Man was abandoned in 1961 because of the movement of an offshore bank. Heysham is an artificial harbour, sited on a low wave-cut platform in Carboniferous rocks and developed by the old Midland railway which opened the dock in 1904 to obtain a share in the Irish trade. The construction of an oil refinery close by has varied and enormously enlarged the trade of this young port, in effect the successor to Lancaster.

The estuaries of the Lancastrian coast have provided sites for ports, but the mud and silt accumulation inevitable on their shores has deflected resort growth to the open coasts between. Here wide sandy beaches, some backed by dune belts, make an attractive physical setting for resorts. Yet all the large holiday towns face problems rooted in coastal geomorphology. Southport is on a coastline of rapid accretion and has been abandoned by the retreating sea. Coast-building materials supplied abundantly from the Dee and Mersey estuaries and—more locally—by the erosion of Formby Point are laid down as a series of long sand-ridges aligned in echelon and at right angles to the waves of maximum fetch. Consequently the shore has been pushed seawards, leaving behind a broad dune belt and, at Southport, a beach of immense width, much of which has been reclaimed for gardens, lakes, and an amusement park.[1]

Blackpool's problems are the reverse of Southport's, for the town has fought an expensive battle against erosion. From the Ribble to the South Shore beaches at Blackpool the coast is one of accretion and dune development, but farther north rapid erosion is the natural tendency. Until defence works were built, the clay cliffs here were suffering erosion at the rate of several feet each year: the saga of lost farms and hamlets of the Fylde is not wholly legendary. But a change is slowly occurring in depositional conditions on the Fylde shore. The accreting sector is extending northwards, and the spread of mud from the Ribble may prove to be a threat to the basis of Blackpool's holiday industry, the broad, clean beaches of mud-free sand. The third and smallest of the Lancashire resorts, Morecambe, has already faced such a threat. Paradoxically, though Morecambe Bay is choked by immense sandbanks, the shore at Morecambe itself is shingly, for there is a pronounced local longshore drift. Sand has been spread on the shore here by the town authorities, but this may only add to the banks in Morecambe Bay.

Climate and water supply

Lancastria's mild, damp climate, typical of the west of Britain, is unpleasant but useful. Although it may be doubted that high humidity of the air ever had much influence on the growth of the textile industries, there is no doubt that high and reliable rainfall, through its effect on stream flow, has been an industrial asset of first importance. The weather of Lancastria has many moods, few of them genial. Most of the vigorous fronts of fresh Atlantic depressions may be expected to trail a rain belt across the two counties, and a warm front will generally bury the lowlands beneath a heavy cloud pall and clothe the uplands in thick hill fog. A

---

[1] In 1965 there were reports that the tides had begun to wash the coast at Southport more vigorously.

stable westerly airstream may leave the plain under clear skies, but its abrupt uplift against the moorland flanks will produce a blanket of thick wet cloud and perhaps moderate rain. The climatic reputation of the coastal resorts probably rests on the frequency of days like these, for it is not uncommon for the coasts to be sunny and the interior cloud-covered. Unstable westerly and northwesterly airstreams, too, bring more vigorous weather and greater rainfall to the hills, for uplift provokes the development of violent showers. Fortunately, serious snowfall is uncommon at high levels. Atlantic air masses are rarely cold enough to bring much lasting snow, and northeasterly streams of Continental air dampened by the North Sea must cross the Pennines before affecting Lancashire, where snowfall is usually much slighter than in Yorkshire. Both in depth and duration, Lancastria's snowfalls are usually too slight to cause widespread disruption of traffic except on the higher trans-Pennine routes.

The climatic contrasts between upland and lowland rest on rainfall rather than on temperature. Contrasts in warmth between hill and plain are slight and subtle. Mean monthly temperatures are only a few degrees lower at the upland stations. For example, Buxton (1,007 ft. O.D.) has a July mean of 58° F, two degrees lower than Bolton (342 ft.) and Liverpool (198 ft.) but three degrees lower than Ringway (240 ft.). In winter the contrast is greater: Buxton averages 36° F in January while most lowland stations are from two to four degrees warmer. The winter differences are rather a matter of warmer lowland days than cooler upland nights: surprisingly, the mean minima for January and February at Buxton (almost exactly 31° F) are scarcely different from those of hillfoot stations like Macclesfield and Stonyhurst and only a degree or two lower than those on the coast. Nor is the frost risk much greater in the upland than on the plain: both at Buxton and at lowland stations like Rochdale and Ringway there are about 83 frosty days each year. Indeed some Pennine-slope stations record fewer frosts, because of their effective cold air drainage, than many lowland stations. Even so, these several slight contrasts are cumulative, and they delay the onset of spring in the hills. If the common garden plants are a true guide the difference is perhaps two or three weeks, a significant one to an upland agriculture which, in any case, is faced with problems of slope, drainage, inaccessibility, and a host of related limitations.

Cloudiness and the lack of sunshine are other climatic problems to the upland farmer and townsman alike. Sunshine totals vary, very broadly, with altitude and degree of urbanisation. They are highest in the non-industrial areas of the plain (and especially on the coast), where annual values of roughly 1,530 hours are recorded. Even in non-industrial upland areas less sunshine occurs, for example 1,310 hours at Stonyhurst and 1,146 hours at Buxton. In the most congested of the lowland cities totals of about 1,000 hours are characteristic, the penalty of gross air pollution and the frequency of fogs. There is a difference of some 300 sunshine hours annually between central Manchester and the Cheshire fringe of the conurbation. In the deepest of the town-choked valleys of the moors few pollution or sunshine records are kept, but they would show, if they existed, an alarming situation. Steep slopes make these narrow slots natural fog traps, for cold air pours into them on clear nights, and smoke pollution soon stains these fogs a filthy grey-brown. So deep are some of these valleys that there is scarcely a true dawn on mid-winter days, for the southern wall may totally exclude the low sun even at noon. The condition of a fog which persists for several days in these circumstances may become acutely dangerous to health. But there is some hope for the future in the present trend of sunshine data. The conversion of factories to electric power, the closure of many of the most antiquated mills, and the creation of smokeless zones are all reflected in a significant increase in recorded sunshine in industrial east Lancashire. Bolton averaged only 981 hours of bright sunshine annually beteeen 1901 and 1911 but 1,288 hours in the decade 1951–61; and this upward trend has been consistent for sixty years.

It is chiefly the incidence of rainfall which distinguishes the upland from the lowland climate, for there is a steep precipitation gradient against the hill flanks, which stand full in the path of wet Atlantic airstreams. Over most of the plain rainfall totals are between 32 and 36 inches. A few of the Triassic plateaux and cuestas are high enough to receive slightly greater amounts; but a considerable area of southwestern and southern Cheshire lies in the rainshadow of the Welsh hills and has less than 30 inches. On the ascent to the moorland plateaux, especially on their exposed western flanks, rainfall totals quickly increase. The 40 and 45 inch isohyets follow the lower slopes of the fells, and on their summits totals of 60 or even 70 inches are recorded. But this is an oversimplification of the rainfall pattern. Totals increase not only with altitude but also northwards, partly a consequence of the high proportion of southerly winds, which is especially marked in southern Lancashire. The details of upland rainfall distribution are complex. The highest falls are not on the true summits but are displaced some distance down the direction of prevailing wind, and may thus occur on significantly lower ground. And some valleys are deep enough, with enough 'up-wind' shelter, to be local rain shadows with totals as low as 40 inches. Though the uplands are so much wetter than the plains, they have only slightly higher totals of rain-days (an average of 210 compared with roughly 190–200 for most parts of the plain). Upland rainfall is obviously more violent; indeed, occasional storm-showers of exceptional intensity cause flash floods which have done damage to property in the crowded industrial valleys.

But in one respect the excessive upland rainfall is a distinct economic advantage, for it provides an ample surface water-supply. Of an annual total of 50–60 inches as much as 50–60% may be runoff, for slopes are steep and the rocks impermeable. The spongy peat stores the excess precipitation of wet spells and stabilises stream flow by regulating the discharge into the headstreams. Deep, narrow valleys are easily dammed, and water flows under gravity from these high reservoirs to the industrial towns of the lower valleys and the plains. Since limestone is so rare in Lancastria south of the Ribble, most of the runoff is soft; indeed, the peat water is distinctly acid, and even the Bowland reservoirs yield soft water. But it is incorrect to describe eastern Lancastria as a soft-water region. Certainly the public supply drawn from the high reservoirs is soft, clean, and unpolluted; but the river water used so widely by industry in the lower valleys and in the plain has been made hard through pollution for more than a century, for most Lancashire rivers become industrial sewers when they pass through their first large town. The argument that eastern Lancashire owed its dominant position in the British cotton industry to its soft-water resources is one which requires great qualification (p. 98). Despite its deterioration in quality, the upland water of Lancastria is an important economic resource which has been tapped increasingly for more than two centuries. Canal companies built the earliest substantial reservoirs —at Hollingworth and Foulridge, for example—and many tiny millponds were constructed in the late eighteenth century to safeguard watermills in times of drought. Though a few smaller town-supply reservoirs had been built earlier, Manchester and Liverpool pioneered the use of upland water for domestic purposes. They both turned to their nearest upland valley; Liverpool to the Anglezarke–Rivington valley in 1847 and Manchester to Longendale, where the first of a chain of reservoirs was built in 1851. Both were fortunate in finding valleys with little industrial settlement, which could be completely drowned. Very few other valleys south of the Ribble could be similarly treated, for their water power had previously given industry too firm a foothold. Thus most other Lancashire urban-supply reservoirs are small and are sited high in the 'cloughs' of the minor headstreams. Only the upper Goyt and the upper Hodder (the latter in the Yorkshire part of Bowland Forest) offered reservoir sites of substantial size to supply Stockport and the Fylde respectively.

Inevitably, through the sterilisation of most suitable valleys by close settlement, most of Lancastria's water resource must be allowed to escape down the stream courses, where it is not wasted but well used by industry. Paradoxically, one of Britain's wettest regions is a heavy 'importer' of water. Both Manchester and Liverpool (and through them 49 other dependent undertakings) rely on distant sources in the Lake District and North Wales respectively for the bulk of their supply. Many smaller towns, unable to tap these aqueducts from distant sources, now face recurrent summer water crises. The prospects for increasing the yield of nearby upland areas are slight, for both Rossendale and the Lancastrian Pennines are more fully exploited than any other British uplands; 17% and 21% respectively of their available and effective rainfall is already gathered, and these represent the maximum practicable yields. A few potential reservoir sites are still available—for example east of Macclesfield and in Bowland—but for various reasons these have not been developed, in most cases because they would involve considerable disturbance not only to farming but also to industry and communications. But a small reservoir is under construction in a minor valley to the west of Rochdale, and Stockport is now constructing a second reservoir in the valley of the Goyt to end its recurrent water shortages.

On the plain surface water resources are slight. Both rainfall and run-off are lower, streams are smaller and less regular in volume, and their slight valleys are much too thickly populated to be dammed. Most of the master streams of the lowland have passed through industrialised upland valleys and are grossly polluted; significantly, the only river which supplies a sizeable town is the relatively clean Dee, which provides Chester's supply. Many lowland towns have depended chiefly on underground supplies from the heavily water-charged Triassic series. This is hard water—in west Lancashire among the hardest in the country—and it usually needs softening for industrial use, though it is said to make excellent beer, notably at Warrington. But the yield of the underground sources is limited, and if the supply is overdrawn the water table falls and the quality may deteriorate. Through the years Birkenhead's supply from five bores became progressively harder and more saline, forcing the town to turn to a reservoir in the Alwyn valley; at Northwich a difficulty is seasonal variation in the water table. Many of the water authorities of the lowland, unable to increase local supplies in pace with demand, now tap the 'imported' water of the Manchester and Liverpool aqueducts. Paradoxically south Cheshire 'exports' underground water to augment the north Staffordshire supply (p. 167). In general, it seems clear that in those parts of the plain far from the aqueducts of the two great cities any substantial population increase through overspill or industrial dispersal will raise critical water supply problems. A regional water grid is the ultimate solution.

No systematic review of either the natural vegetation or the soil types of the Northwest has been attempted in this chapter. Little of the natural vegetation now survives, except as remnants much affected by human activity or in protected habitats such as the coastal saltmarshes. On the lowlands the surviving woods consist chiefly of planted copses with, at best, a seminatural association. On the moorlands the influence of human intervention has been more subtle but equally emphatic. The botanical evidence suggests that at one time sessile oakwood and oak-birch associations clothed all but the highest ground, where peat began to replace woodland during the wet Atlantic phase. Fragments of the oak-birch forest survive in the deep cloughs of the moors, but elsewhere clearance and grazing have removed it. The slopes and the shelves of the uplands now have a complex variety of poor grassland and heath associations. *Nardus* and *Molinia* cover much of the wettest ground below the summit peat-mosses, and bracken grows strongly on the protected lower slopes. Heather moors have developed, generally with human encouragement for shooting purposes, on many of the drier slopes and summits, while a distinctive association dominated by bilberry clothes the craggy gritstone edges. Even the peat has been affected by human agency, for the sphagnum which was once the chief peat-forming plant has been replaced in recent centuries by cotton grass, perhaps as a result of increasing air pollution. Since the native vegetation of the region has been suffering radical change for at least 1,500 years its importance to the present study is chiefly in an historical context, and a brief outline is presented in Chapter 3 as a preface to a survey of the progress of settlement. Since the Soil Survey has yet to extend its activities to any substantial part of the Northwest only the most general description of the region's soils can be given, and this is deferred to the regional chapters as part of a survey of the agriculture of the Northwest.

CHAPTER 3

Landscape Changes of the Pre-industrial Era

Northwest England is the most heavily urbanised and industrialised of the major regions of Britain: its modern personality was determined chiefly by the feverish economic growth of the eighteenth and nineteenth centuries. For this reason the historical geography of earlier periods is reviewed only very briefly here. So short an account cannot be comprehensive; all that can be attempted is a selective summary of the more important episodes in the shaping of the Lancastrian landscape as it existed on the eve of the Industrial Revolution.

The primeval landscape

Few parts of Britain retain so little of their landscape in a primitive, unmodified form as the Northwest, for even in its unsettled islands—the bleak summits of the upland plateaux—the modern vegetation is thought to be of quite recent origin and by no means natural in type. It is difficult to reconstruct the character of the landscape of the region as it was on the eve of the earliest Anglo-Saxon settlement, before any significant and widespread changes had resulted from human intervention and interference. Since neither prehistoric colonisation nor the Roman intrusion into the Northwest were strong enough to leave much permanent imprint on the landscape, it seems logical to adopt the beginning of Anglo-Saxon settlement as the date of this outline reconstruction.

That much the greater part of Lancastria was then thickly wooded is clear from both historical and ecological evidence. But there were exceptional areas without a forest cover, or with only patchy and scrubby woodland. On the lowlands the largest breaks in the forest cover were those of the great peatmosses. Developed in a broad belt along both flanks of the Mersey valley and continued northwards as a discontinuous belt of peat behind the coasts of southwest Lancashire, the Fylde, and Morecambe Bay (Chap. 2, pp. 18, 19), the mosses were the least attractive of the region's varied environments to primitive man. Soft, spongy, and saturated, they were avoided by settlement until a very late period. From pre-Roman times to the eighteenth century they were the largest of the completely unsettled areas of the region, though their drier parts were used for a little rough grazing during summer and peat was cut for fuel from their fringes. The peatmosses long impeded contact across the Mersey between the two northwestern counties. They may be partly responsible for the extreme paucity of Neolithic and Bronze Age settlement over much of the Lancashire lowland by insulating the plain from contact with the lively trade and traffic across the Irish Sea; and they certainly guided and deflected the spread of both Anglo-Saxon and Norse settlement. Where peatmoss gives way directly to saltmarsh and mudflats, for example along the Ribble estuary and in the northern Fylde, the coast of Lancashire must have seemed inhospitable in the extreme to the maritime peoples, from Neolithic to Norse times, whose life focused on the Irish Sea.

Apart from the peatmosses, the largest forest-free areas in Lancastria were the Carboniferous uplands of Rossendale, Bowland, and the Pennines. Both Rossendale and Bowland are still often referred to as 'forests', but this is a distant memory of their medieval use as 'chases' reserved for the hunting parties of their royal and noble owners. Large parts both of Rossendale and Bowland, and indeed of the Pennines proper, were legally 'afforested', but this term has nothing to do with their botanical character. Trees once covered much greater areas of the uplands than today, but most of the higher plateau has been peat-covered and treeless throughout historic times, indeed since the onset of damp 'Atlantic' climatic conditions in the sixth millennium B.C. when peat accumulation overwhelmed an existing forest cover. Detailed floristic changes have come to the upland peatbogs in the past two centuries, for cotton grass has replaced sphagnum as the dominant plant and the peat has suffered quick erosion, perhaps in consequence. But the highest ground has been peat-covered for as long as human societies of any size have existed in the region, and it has always been avoided by settlement of any type.

The lower slopes and shelves of all three moorland masses have had a more complex vegetational history, and here woodland clearance for cropping and grazing has radically altered the environment. The original altitudinal limit of woodland in the moorlands doubtless varied with slope, aspect, and exposure; but forest must have clothed the slopes to elevations much higher than those where remnant woods survive today. Mixed oak-ash and oak-birch forest in a stunted form has escaped destruction high up the Pennine cloughs, where it formerly extended to 1,300–1,500 feet over large areas, and hardy birch-ash woodland may have reached to 1,800 feet. High peatbogs have, by their pollen contents, yielded evidence of the existence and later destruction of this high woodland; but it clearly suffered progressive destruction throughout the medieval period from about A.D. 1200. The settler's axe, the grazing of his sheep and cattle, and, later, the burning of moorland to encourage heather have all contributed to the replacement of the natural vegetation of open, stunted woodland by a variety of other types. That the Pennine woodland was lighter and less continuous in character than the damp oak forest of the glaciated plain is shown by the very many discoveries of prehistoric artefacts and settlement sites from the Mesolithic to the Iron Age along the moorland slopes throughout the region.

Over the whole of the Lancastrian lowland, except only the peatbogs and the strips of riverine marsh, forest was the dominant covering. On the strong damp soils of the boulder clay country pedunculate oakwoods grew thickly, with massive individual trees and a dense shrub layer. An effective barrier to penetration and settlement by earlier and ill-equipped societies, the oakwoods were vigorously attacked by the earliest Anglo-Saxons during the seventh and eighth centuries. Little of this native woodland remains, for the present forests, for example Delamere, are composed mainly of introduced trees. Over parts of the plain the dense damp oakwood was replaced, where the soils were thinner, drier, and more siliceous, by sessile or durmast oak associations. More open in character, forest of this type covered many of the Triassic sandstone hills and platforms both of Lancashire and Cheshire, and it may have been present, too, on the poorer soils of the glacial sand-spreads, for example in east Cheshire. In all these areas of more open woodland prehistoric settlement sites and finds are more numerous than on the damp lowland clays with their denser forest cover. On the wettest ground, particularly on the alluvium of the major valleys, oaks were largely replaced by trees more tolerant of excessive moisture and the 'gley' soils of impeded drainage: here 'carr' woodland dominated by alder, willow, and birch grew thickly along the floodplains.

Attempts have been made to identify other variations in the density of the forest cover of the Lancastrian lowlands. It has been argued, partly from documentary evidence, that some parts of the plain were only lightly wooded, while elsewhere continuous forests of great thickness—many given local names—existed. Some of these supposed contrasts have been used to explain such features of the settlement history of the region as the apparent survival of groups of Celtic settlements long after the Anglo-Saxon penetration in parts of central Lancashire. But historical material is difficult to apply to the landscapes of earlier periods. One of the few general conclusions suggested both by documentary and by ecological evidence is that woodland was poorly developed in, or even possibly absent from, the most exposed coastlands. The Fylde coast may have been open country with only thin, stunted woodland. If so, this must have been a contributory factor in its particularly dense and early settlement by both Anglo-Saxon and Norse colonists.

Prehistoric settlement and the Roman occupation

Scattered groups may have peopled parts of the Northwest as early as Mesolithic times, for microliths have been found in the Pennine margin of Lancastria, though the harvest of sites and artefacts is meagre. With the exception of a few restricted areas, which possessed some significance for part of the span of prehistory, the Northwest was a region of little consequence compared with the scarplands of southeast England with their much greater populations continually replaced and replenished by the invasions which brought each new step in cultural progress. All the great cultural revolutions—except only the industrial—came late to Lancastria, which was a part of the 'Highland zone' characterised by stability and slow cultural absorption, rather than quick progress, as Sir Cyril Fox argued in his study of prehistoric Britain.

Within the Northwest there is a clear contrast, significant in prehistory, between the densely forested claylands of the plain and the more lightly wooded country of both the Carboniferous uplands and the Triassic hills and platforms. The drift-floored plain is archaeologically as barren as any part of Great Britain, but in contrast the hills and moors have yielded evidence of early penetration and settlement. The lower ground of the peninsula of Furness, rolling and lightly forested country based on a foundation of Triassic sandstones and Carboniferous limestone, has a settlement history reaching back to the Neolithic period. Farther south the limestones of Derbyshire, strictly outside Lancastria but of great importance to it, were strongly colonised by Neolithic and early Bronze Age man; and here is one of the great prehistoric monuments of England, at Arbor Low, 'the Avebury of the North'. Perhaps the founders of this new civilisation in the open country of the limestone plateau, megalith builders whose links were with Wales and Ireland, came to it from a landfall made on the Mersey estuary. If so, they pioneered a route across Cheshire which was of great importance to trade both in late Neolithic and Bronze Age times, when stone axes from Welsh factories near Penmaenmawr and bronze objects of Irish origin were carried across the county to the Trent basin.

The importance of the low hill-country of Triassic sandstones in the periods of the Bronze and Iron Ages is seen clearly in Cheshire. Along the gently tilted dipslopes of the mid-Cheshire ridge from Frodsham to Bickerton tumuli and artefacts of the Bronze period have been found in profusion, particularly in the Delamere area, where sterile glacial sands resting on Trias can have supported only light woodland. Over much of eastern Cheshire, not only along the Pennine flank but also on the glacial sands of the lower ground, evidence of Bronze Age settlement is almost as abundant, while the more scattered sites across northern and central Cheshire from the head of the Mersey estuary to the Pennine fringe have been taken to indicate the line of the trade route. This is a tentative suggestion, which has been put too strongly by some archaeologists; for the line of 'finds' picks out the north Cheshire arable belt, in which the chances of discovering evidence of early occupation are clearly much stronger than in the pastoral country to the south. But these same areas remained the chief centres of settlement in Iron Age times. The most important group of hill forts in the region is along the crest of the mid-Cheshire ridge, where the multi-ditched forts of Helsby and Eddisbury are the most elaborate examples. The Pennines are poorer in evidence of Iron Age occupation: there are a few hill forts, for example east of Macclesfield and at Combs Moss, and other scattered indications of occupation. The ridged landscape of Furness, combining defensible crags with rich limestone pastures, was another focus of settlement in immediately pre-Roman times, with two important camps at Urswick and Warton.

Despite its locally important clusters of settlement, the Northwest on the eve of the Roman conquest was so poor, backward, and unattractive that its occupation by the legions was prompted entirely by military necessity rather than commercial advantage. In the military geography of Roman Britain the plain of Lancastria had a strategic importance which far surpassed its trivial economic value. It separated the upland strongholds of native resistance in the Pennines and North Wales, and it commanded the western approaches to Scotland and Hadrian's Wall. In A.D. 61 ephemerally, and in A.D. 78 more permanently, Chester was established as the great legionary fortress of the region, the northwestern outpost of the Empire and a bastion against the tribes of Wales. From this secure base the conquest of the Northwest was soon completed. Expeditionary forces penetrated the region, cut their roads cleanly through its forests, and established fortified camps at commanding points (Fig. 4).

There is geographical common sense in the complex pattern of Roman roads in Lancastria. A road of first importance led northeast from Chester past the Iron Age settlements of Delamere to Northwich, where the brine was used for salt making, to Manchester, and thence across the Pennines to York. Joining the two great fortresses, this must have been one of the main lines of military communication in northern England. A second route of similar importance, with twin parallel roads, led northwards ultimately to Carlisle and the Wall. One of the great roads to the north ran through the plain, crossing the heads of the great estuaries where Warrington, Preston, and Lancaster now stand, while the other, almost parallel, road followed the western flank of the uplands from Manchester near Bolton to Ribchester and then across Bowland to the Lune valley. Many other roads of shorter length and more local importance were constructed; and Manchester, from which seven roads radiated, became a focal point in the network, an early demonstration of the site's nodality. No fewer than five trans-Pennine roads were built, some of which had economic as well as military value. One, to Buxton, served a tiny Roman spa, and another, through Brough to Doncaster, skirted the lead mines of the Peak and made possible the export of this valuable metal from the Humber. The

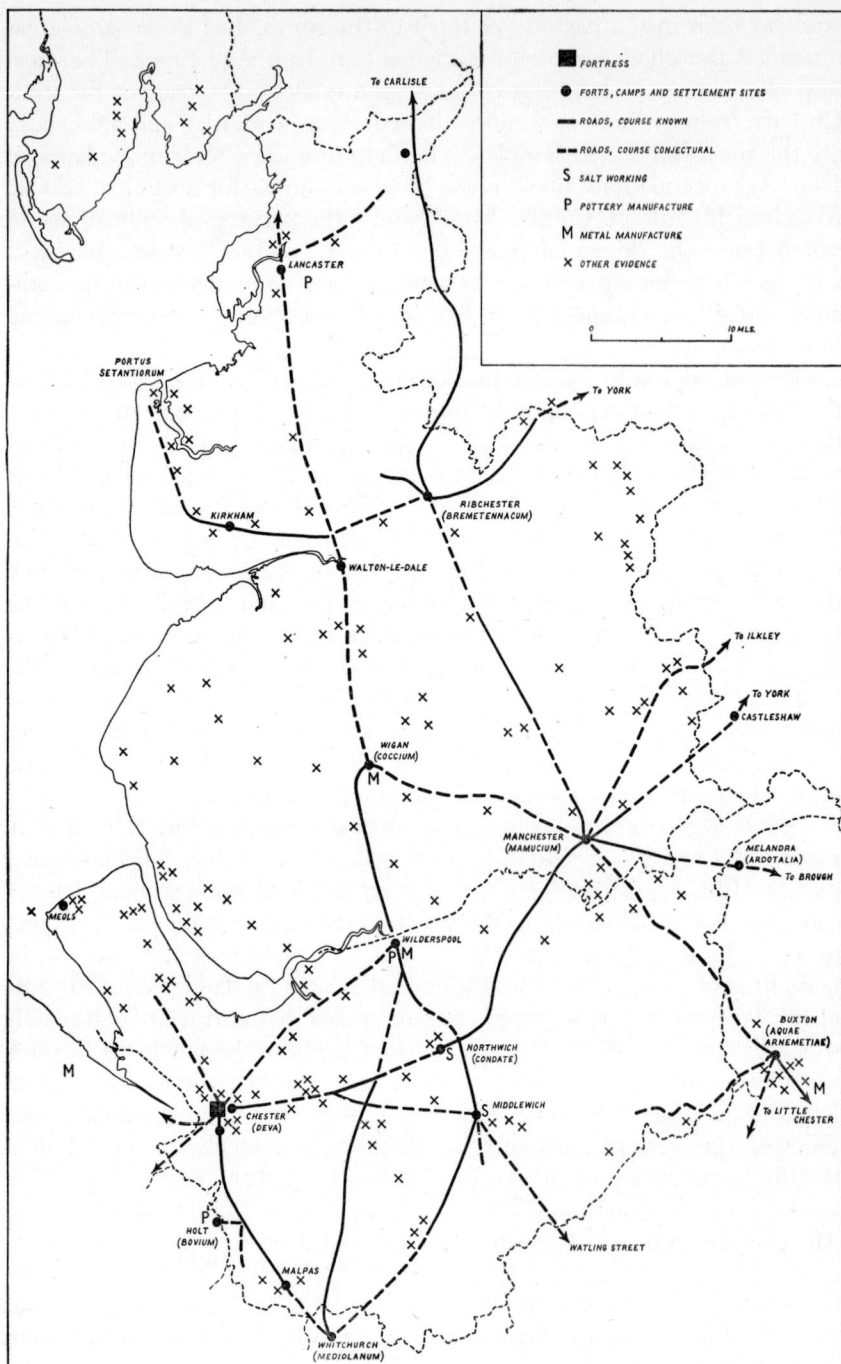

LEGEND

■ FORTRESS
● FORTS, CAMPS AND SETTLEMENT SITES
━━ ROADS, COURSE KNOWN
┅┅ ROADS, COURSE CONJECTURAL
S SALT WORKING
P POTTERY MANUFACTURE
M METAL MANUFACTURE
× OTHER EVIDENCE

0   10 MLS.

Fig. 4   THE ROMAN GEOGRAPHY OF LANCASHIRE AND CHESHIRE.
Based partly on the Ordnance Survey Map of Roman Britain.

road which crossed the Pennines by the easy routeway of the Ribble–
Aire gap had an interesting extension westwards. It has been traced from
Ribchester to Kirkham in the Fylde, and there is some evidence that it
may have continued westwards to the coast to serve a lost Roman port,
Portus Setantiorum, in a site now destroyed by the quick coastal erosion
in northwest Fylde.

It may be argued that Rome laid the foundations of the present urban
pattern of northwest England; for Chester, Northwich, Manchester,
Wigan, Warrington, Preston, and Lancaster, as well as many lesser places,
grew at or near sites chosen by the Romans for forts along their road
system. But in many cases the later, permanent settlements at these places
were sited, and the medieval towns grew, at some distance from the Roman
ruins. The camp at Manchester was at the Medlock–Irwell confluence,
whereas the medieval town grew at the Irk–Irwell junction, over half a
mile away. The Roman forts at the head of the Ribble and Mersey estuaries
were south-bank settlements at Walton and Wilderspool, whereas the later
towns of Preston and Warrington grew on north-bank sites. Not only was
there an obvious lack of continuity of occupation in these sites from the
collapse of Roman power through the Dark Ages, but also the later
founders of new settlements studiously avoided any surviving traces of the
Roman camps. Yet at Chester and Ribchester the Roman site became the
nucleus of later growth. The parish church of Ribchester occupies a corner
of the old fort, while the greater part of medieval Chester lay on the ruins
of the Roman fortress: the north and east walls were raised on Roman
foundations, and it is likely that the modern street pattern has a Roman
origin. It is not impossible that there has been complete continuity of
settlement at Chester and Ribchester since Roman times. Chester became
the closest approach to a Roman city in the Northwest: the fortress itself
acquired some civic graces, and a substantial civil settlement grew close
by, on the road to Manchester. With its temples, baths, and amphitheatre
and a port on the Dee under the western ramparts, it was the single
monument of Roman urban civilisation in the barbarous Northwest. But
not even west Cheshire has yielded any traces of Roman villas, despite
abundant evidence of a rural population of native stock. The evidence of
iron working near Warrington and Wigan and of a considerable pottery
factory at Holt on the Dee and at a smaller site near Lancaster suggests
that even in Roman times the economy of the Northwest may have been
industrial as well as agricultural.

The Anglo-Saxon and Scandinavian settlements

Most of the scanty evidence available, based almost entirely on the
analysis of place-names, suggests that before the Anglo-Saxon immigration
most of the Northwest had only a sparse and scattered population of Celtic
origin, though it has been argued that in western Cheshire, especially in

33

the strongly Romanised area near Chester itself, Celtic power and influence survived late and vigorously. An isthmus of Celtic influence between the much stronger kingdoms of Wales and Strathclyde, the Lancastrian lowland had a considerable strategical significance in the westward penetration of Anglo-Saxon colonists. It was invaded simultaneously from two directions. Northumbrian settlers pushed through the low gaps which bisect the central Pennines, while Mercian pioneers gradually extended the frontier of their colonisation northwestwards from their Midland base into and across Cheshire. In general, Lancashire became an outlying province of the kingdom of Northumbria, from which most of its colonists came, while Cheshire settlement was almost wholly of Mercian origin. There is inconclusive evidence, based on the forms of a very few place-names, that Mercians penetrated into southern Lancashire. But for most of the period of the Dark Ages the Mersey was a frontier, a function reflected in the name itself (the 'boundary river') and for which the valley—a line of peatbogs surrounded by dense 'carr' woodland—was particularly well suited.

The twin streams of Anglo-Saxon colonisation from northeast and south quickly eroded Celtic power in the Northwest except perhaps in the Dee basin; but place-name evidence suggests that groups of British settlements survived, chiefly in sites protected by their inaccessibility. The island settlements of Ince and Wallasey in the Mersey marshes, a line of settlements with Celtic place-names along the Pennine flanks, and a few clusters in remote corners of both Lancashire and Cheshire away from the main routeways of Anglo-Saxon colonisation (near Peover and Wigan) suggest a survival of Celtic communities. The Anglo-Saxon penetration of the lowlands was clearly quick and deep: place-names which have been ascribed to the early phases of the invasion (those with suffixes embodying the elements '-ingas', '-ingaham', and -'ingatun') are found widely over both counties. In Lancashire the distribution of these earliest names shows a rational pattern, for they are especially numerous in the Ribble valley—clearly the great routeway of Northumbrian penetration—and in the plain at the mouth of the valley. Perhaps, too, Northumbrian settlers passed through the low Calder–Walsden gap, for a group of names of early forms is to be found in the Manchester lowland. But in Cheshire the earliest Anglo-Saxon names have a less coherent distribution. They are most numerous on the southern threshold of the county, as one might expect, and there are lines or clusters along the foot of the Pennines and in the Weaver and lower Dee basins, which were clearly among the principal lines of colonisation. The isolated group on the Mersey high terrace southwest of Manchester may well be associated rather with the early settlements of the Lancashire section of the Manchester plain than with the other Cheshire groups (Fig. 5).

It is more difficult to follow the later stages of Anglo-Saxon colonisation from place-name evidence. Ekwall, in his studies of Lancashire names, has suggested that the suffixes '-ton', '-ham', '-bury', and '-wick' probably identify settlements of more ancient origin than the purely topographical and descriptive suffixes like '-ley' and '-ford'. Certainly names with endings in this group of four elements have a coherent distribution which may be explained, in part, by physical contrasts in the landscape. In Lancashire they are especially numerous in and near the areas of earliest Anglo-Saxon settlement, in the Ribble and Lune valleys and in the Fylde, in the Manchester lowland and in the higher peat-free areas of the south Lancashire plain in a broad crescent at the foot of the Rossendale upland. Very few are found in southwest Lancashire, half-isolated by the barriers of the peatmosses, and none occurs along the coast from the Douglas to the Mersey. In Cheshire names containing this group of four suffixes are widely distributed: they are common in the lower Dee valley, in the Wirral and along the mid-Cheshire ridge, and there are groups also along the Pennine foot, in the Weaver–Dane valley, and on the high terraces of the Mersey. These names occur mainly in or on the margin of areas of most ancient Anglo-Saxon colonisation and may reflect the spread of settlement from the primary nuclei. But in parts of Cheshire, particularly in the heart or the Delamere area and in the Bollin–Weaver interfluve, the Anglo-Saxon names are of probably later types, and there is a strong suggestion that for a considerable time Anglo-Saxon settlers avoided these dense forests.

In Lancastria the Danish incursion was so feeble and localised that it left few place-names except in the Dane and Mersey valley; and therefore the second great invasion was the tenth-century Norse colonisation of the coastlands. Scandinavian settlers had already established strong colonies in eastern Ireland, western Scotland, and the Isle of Man, and by extending their influence to Lancastria they settled one of the few lowland coasts on the shorelands of the Irish Sea. Norse place-names clearly identify the areas of this late sea-borne invasion of the Northwest: they cluster thickly in the Wirral and form a line along the dune coast of southwestern Lancashire, where the Norse settlements must certainly have been fishing villages, since the sterile dunes are backed immediately by peatmoss. Norse colonisation was especially strong in the Fylde, where the close juxtaposition of Scandinavian and Anglo-Saxon names has been taken as evidence that this invasion was peaceful, with the acceptance of the new settlers by the established communities. Along the entire length of the Morecambe Bay shorelands, especially in Furness, Norse names are more common than those of Anglo-Saxon origin.

From this belt of Scandinavian settlement along the coast salients reached inland along some, but by no means all, of the chief rivers, which were used as a means of penetration into the interior. There was little extension of Norse settlement from the Wirral up the Dee, and penetration

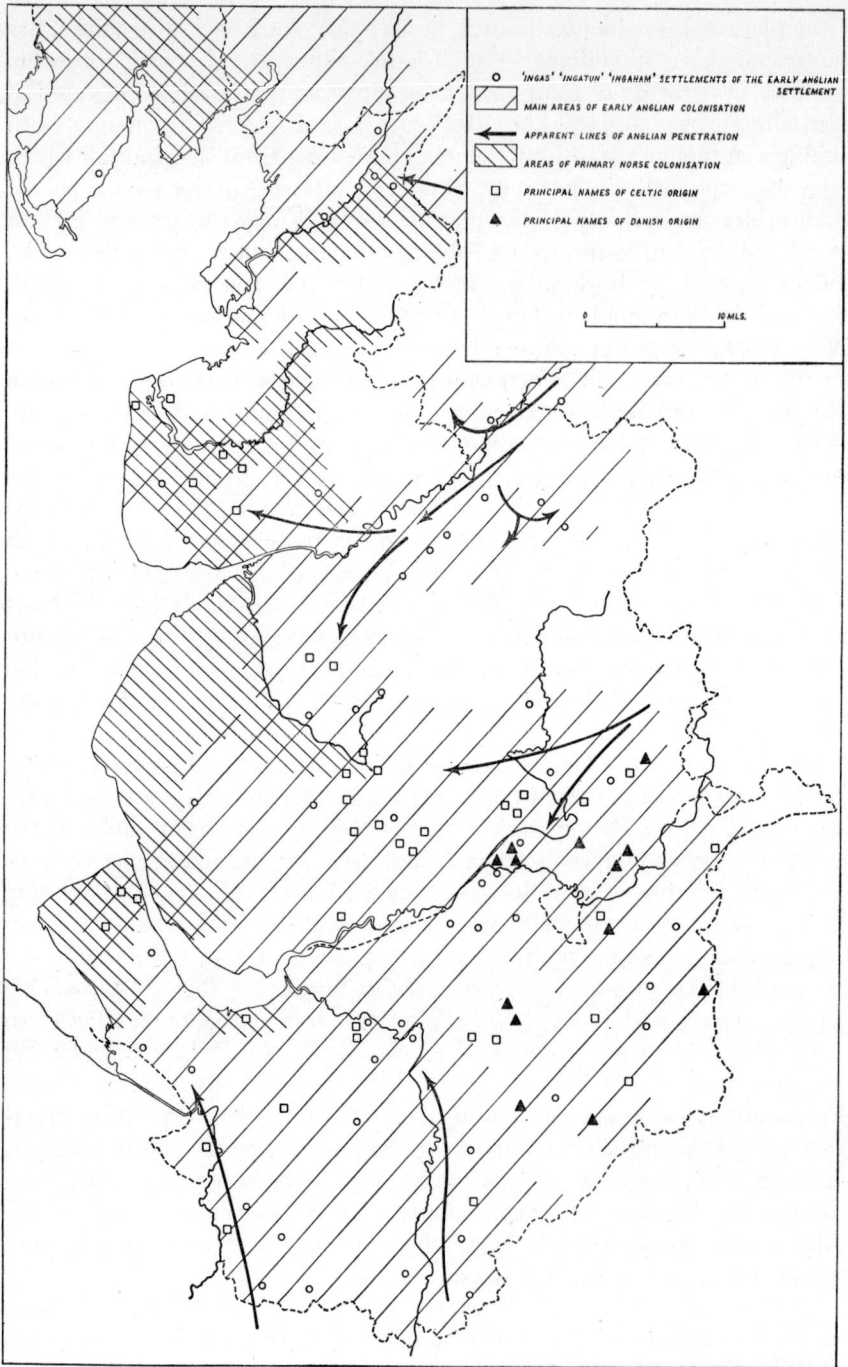

Fig. 5 PLACE-NAMES AND THE DISTRIBUTION OF EARLY ANGLIAN AND NORSE
SETTLEMENT.

36

along the Mersey scarcely reached beyond the head of the estuary. Yet on smaller streams like the Douglas and Wyre long lines of Norse names reach far inland, though on the Ribble few occur east of Preston. The Lune, in contrast, was clearly used as a major highway into the interior. It has been thought that the failure of the Norsemen to exploit the easy routeways of the Ribble, Dee, and Mersey may reflect the strength and resistance of the Anglo-Saxon settlements at the heads of their estuaries.

Over much of the moorland of eastern Lancashire Norse place-names outnumber those of any other ethnic origin: certainly these unattractive uplands had been ignored by the Anglo-Saxon colonists and were thus available to Scandinavian settlement. But it is unlikely that the Norsemen, in their initial expansion from the coasts, chose to people these inhospitable slopes and valleys. The Norse-named settlements of the hills probably indicate early medieval colonisation, for by then the common tongue of Lancashire had become almost a Scandinavian dialect; indeed many Norse words survive in the Lancashire vernacular, and Nordic ethnic characteristics are still common in the older families of the regions of Scandinavian settlement. Though the hill settlements of Norse origin may be comparatively late, the typical plan of the Scandinavian settlement is seen in a loosely knit scatter of farms and cottages with no pronounced nucleation, in sharp contrast with the compact, tightly clustered Anglo-Saxon vill.

The Domesday stocktaking

The great survey of England made by William I, a stocktaking of its taxable wealth and resources, is less comprehensive for the two north-western counties than for the more developed Midlands and South, but it provides the best available material for an outline of the economic geography at the close of the settlement phase and the opening of the medieval period. As the record for Cheshire is comparatively full, the major regional contrasts in the density of population and the development of agriculture may be identified with fair confidence; but the detail for Lancashire is too incomplete for geographical analysis. Lancashire has no identity in Domesday Book, for its northern Hundreds beyond the Ribble are treated as an appendage of Yorkshire, while south Lancashire, 'inter Ripam et Mersham', is reviewed as a border zone of dubious affiliation.

Some interesting and geographically rational contrasts are revealed by the mapping of Domesday Cheshire. The complete transformation that had taken place in the geography of settlement during previous periods of colonisation is demonstrated emphatically. In the later stages of prehistory the lightly wooded lands of the Triassic ridge of mid-Cheshire and the Pennine flank had contained most of the sparse population; but by the eleventh century these were comparatively negative areas and the clearance of the dense oak forests of the lower claylands had advanced so far that these lowlands had become the best-developed areas of the county. Much of the high ground of the New Red Sandstone hills, almost from the Mersey estuary to the Cheshire border, was recorded as woodland and waste in Domesday; it was not only thickly timbered in the true sense but also legally 'afforested' as the great hunting grounds of Mara and Mondrum. In the east, the Pennine 'Forest' of Macclesfield was also a hunting chase. The rest of Cheshire was by no means free from timber, for woods and waste are constantly entered in the record, but clearings for cultivation and settlement were more closely spaced away from these great survivals of the primeval forest.

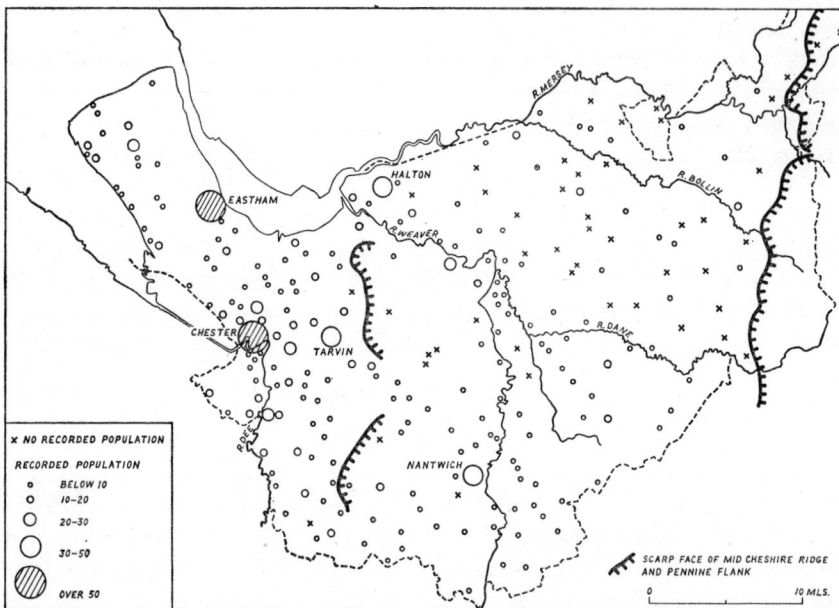

Fig. 6   DISTRIBUTION OF THE DOMESDAY POPULATION OF CHESHIRE. The map is not extended to cover Lancashire because of the unsatisfactory nature of the Domesday material for this county. Based on a map by D. Sylvester, page 21 in Sylvester, D., and Nulty, G. (eds.), *The Historical Atlas of Cheshire* (Chester 1958).

By far the greater part of the population and wealth of Domesday Cheshire was concentrated in three areas which stand out in Figure 6. In the west the lower Dee valley, the Gowy plain, and the Wirral formed the richest region of the county; in the centre the line of the Weaver–Dane valley formed a second, but less important, settled area, while in the northeast there was an even lighter and more scattered occupation of the Bollin basin to the hill fringe. The first of these districts, dominated by the city of Chester, contained the bulk of the county's wealth: virtually all the larger manors of Cheshire were in this area of close settlement which extended eastwards to the barrier of protected 'forests' along the ridge of mid-Cheshire. Some of the manors of west Cheshire were very large indeed by Lancastrian standards: Eastham, Halton, and Tarvin all had recorded populations of more than thirty, and both churches and priests are more frequently recorded here than in any other area, as were mills, smiths, and fisheries. With its dry climate in the Welsh rain-shadow and its varied soils, west Cheshire had agricultural advantages over the rest of Lancastria: a high proportion of its total area was productive ploughland, and the vills along both the Dee and Gowy recorded large acreages of meadow along the floodplain. Chester, the only true city in the entire Northwest, centrally placed in this prosperous area, was a town of almost 500 houses on the eve of the Conquest. It had a cathedral (then the church of St John) and several other religious foundations. It was a walled town, a port, and a considerable commercial centre with no fewer than seven moneyers.

Domesday settlement was close along the valleys of the Weaver and Dane from the Mersey estuary to the southeastern borders of the county. But most of the vills here were much smaller than those of the west: apart from Weaverham and Acton none had more than a score of recorded households, and most had fewer than ten. Churches were rare, especially in the upper valleys; but a few manors had priests. Mills and smiths, too, were recorded chiefly in the densely peopled section of the lower Weaver valley. Though it had not reached such a state of economic maturity as the Chester district, mid-Cheshire had a distinctive asset in its brine springs, which had long been used for salt manufacture and supported a well-established industry by the eleventh century. Three salt towns ('wyches') are mentioned in Domesday: Nantwich (where the works were valued for tax at £10), Northwich (valued at £1 15s.), and Middlewich (valued at £1 5s.). Refining was practised on a considerable scale, for the Earl of Chester alone had eight salt houses in Nantwich, and there were many more. The trade was clearly already widespread, for packhorses and even carts carried salt throughout Cheshire and even to other shires.

Of the last and much the poorest string of Cheshire vills, along the line of the Bollin, there is little to record except their poverty. Many lay entirely waste after the Norman march across Cheshire; only three had more than ten recorded families; and none had land for more than five ploughs, though there were extensive meadows. Large areas of the Bollin–Weaver interfluve seemed to be entirely empty, for the scattered villages here were mostly 'waste' without a population. In the whole of north Cheshire only Lymm and Bowdon had churches recorded.

Little may be deduced from the Lancashire survey. Doubtless the sketchy nature of the record for Lancashire itself indicates the poverty and backwardness of the county; but there were areas of close settlement and relatively intensive agriculture which appear to have rivalled the districts of most mature development in Cheshire. Lonsdale Hundred, in the extreme north of the county, had a higher total of ploughland than

39

the rich Broxton Hundred of Cheshire; and even the more backward Salford and Blackburn Hundreds of upland east Lancashire had about as much ploughland as the lowland Hundreds of north and central Cheshire. Lancashire had even greater contrasts in density of settlement (Fig. 7) than Cheshire. The rich and varied landscape of southwest Lancashire,

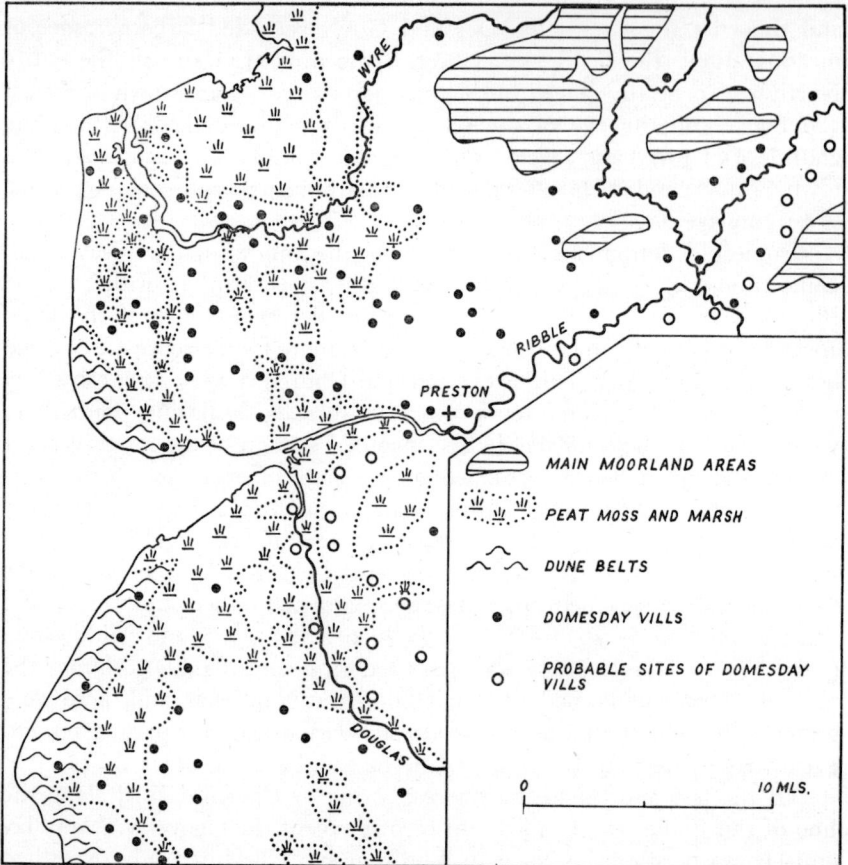

Fig. 7 DOMESDAY VILLS IN PART OF WEST AND NORTH LANCASHIRE. The 'probable' sites in Blackburn and Leyland Hundreds are those of villages known to have been well established within a century or two of the Domesday survey, and so very likely to have been the unnamed vills of these areas.

except for the bleak mosses, was crowded with little settlements, and most of the modern villages may be traced to Domesday origins. In the Fylde and in the fertile coastal lowlands and valleys of Morecambe Bay the density of occupation was even greater, for virtually every patch of well-drained land away from the mosses and marshes had its vills, many of which were substantial settlements with six or more ploughlands. It seems likely that the addition of Norse settlers to the existing Anglo-Saxon population of the coastlands had produced local overcrowding, while huge areas of the interior still lay forested and empty. The Newton, Warrington, and Leyland Hundreds, all of them small, had scarcely more than a hundred carucates in total, and much of this lay along the Ribble and Mersey estuaries. In contrast, parts of the eastern upland were surprisingly rich: though full details of the settlement pattern were not recorded for Salford or Blackburn Hundreds, they had considerable totals of plough-land, doubtless concentrated along the main valleys, which must have been quite thickly settled.

Lancashire lay far behind Cheshire in urban and commercial develop-ment. It had no town or port to compare with Chester, nor any industrial or trading asset like the Cheshire salt. Liverpool makes no appearance in the survey, and Manchester is mentioned only incidentally, though it had the unusual distinction of a church. Lancaster, like Manchester, was a small town with a church, but it acquired its status as the county town only in the following century. Preston had some significance as the chief manor of Amounderness, but little other detail is given. In fact not a single town in Lancashire was given an extended description, nor was there any trade or industry in the county which was thought worthy of attention by the king's surveyors.

The medieval landscape

The character of the medieval landscape of lowland England is neatly sketched in every lower-school history book: compact nucleated villages clustered about their little churches, surrounded by the two or three open fields of their collective agriculture and overlooked by the manor house in its enclosed demesne. At close intervals were the market towns which regulated the economy of the countryside and housed the craftsmen who laid the foundations of English industry. This simple concept cannot be applied to Lancastria, except perhaps for a few districts which were both maturely developed and typically English in their cultural heritage. The greater part of the Northwest was too backward in its economic evolution, too remote, and too diverse in its ethnic origins to share the same patterns of settlement and land tenure as the English Midlands.

Probably the essential feature of the medieval countryside, the open arable field, was never widespread throughout Lancashire; but Cheshire was, in large part, an open-field county. Documentary and cartographic traces of open ploughland have been assembled for most of the Wirral and the Dee–Gowy lowland and also for large tracts of the Weaver–Dane basin. In fact those advanced parts of Cheshire which contained the bulk of the Domesday settlement were closely similar to the English Midlands in the texture of their rural landscape. But it is doubtful whether the Midland two- or three-field system existed in Cheshire in a typical form. Most of the open-field townships of west Cheshire apparently had only one or two fields and may display Celtic influences. In part of the Weaver valley most townships had more than three fields, and villages with the three open arable fields of the classic model were rare. Over much of Cheshire there was never open arable cultivation. Evidence of common fields is clear on the lowlands with their heavy drift and alluvial soils, but the Triassic hill country of the mid-Cheshire ridge and the rougher, higher ground of east Cheshire had few—if any—open fields. These were areas of late colonisation and of dispersed settlement in which ploughland was enclosed from the first and worked not in common but in severalty. Thus the open-field system was limited by geographical factors chiefly to the areas of strongest soil and most genial climate where grain, the basis of the system, was easily cultivated. Perhaps these considerations explain the very scanty evidence of open-field arable in Lancashire. Some of the nucleated villages of the Lancashire plain, for example in the southwest, the Fylde, and lowland Lonsdale, are known beyond dispute to have had open arable land, so that here the landscape closely resembled that of the Midlands. But many records of 'townfields' in Lancashire refer not to arable land but to unenclosed pastures which provided common grazing to farmers who worked their own hedged arable fields. Even Preston had its 'townfield', in which the burgesses kept their animals; and the town's strip-meadows in the Ribble valley were widely repeated elsewhere in the county. Even if open arable land had ever existed widely in Lancashire, it disappeared earlier and more quickly than in Cheshire. By Tudor times Lancashire was an enclosed county. John Leland found 'closes all the way' in his journeys across it, and later Cromwell was to lament the difficulties of bringing his opponents to battle in the close-set fields and miry lanes of the Lancashire plain.

Late into medieval times considerable areas of both counties remained almost empty, and the modern landscape displays unmistakable traces of the slow progress of pioneer farmers into the forest wastes. Along the lower slopes of the Bowland Fells, on the higher bluffs of the Ribble valley, in the old Forests of Delamere and Mondrum, and throughout the broken country of Pennine and sub-Pennine Cheshire the compact nucleated village is a rarity, and settlement takes the form of dispersed farms joined by a tangled road and lane pattern of great complexity, the modern descendant of the system of trackways which joined the little forest clearings of the first farms. Documentary evidence occasionally illuminates the process of forest colonisation. Some of the grants preserved in the Cockersand Cartulary describe the penetration of the wild foothills of Bowland and the slow progress of the frontier of settlement northeast-wards from the Fylde plain near Preston. Both in Lancashire and Cheshire court rolls there are frequent fines for 'assarting', the establishment of 'squatter farms', without legal title, in land protected by forest laws. It was by this piecemeal progress that the Forest of Delamere was reduced and its twin, Mondrum, eliminated. In the Lancashire uplands the establishment of vaccaries was the spearhead of colonisation. The great medieval cattle farms, almost ranches, were the property of the chief landed families, who turned part of their hunting land to profit. Many Rossendale valleys and also Wyresdale and the larger valleys of the Bowland flank were first settled in this way. Rawtenstall was the site of such a vaccary, and high up the valleys leading to it summer settlements like Crawshaw Booth were established and later brought into permanent year-round use. The 'Booths' and the 'Folds' that are such common names in the Lancashire moors reflect the spread of this extensive medieval pastoralism in the uplands and their flanks.

The relative wealth of the regions of Britain in the Middle Ages can be judged by the number and spacing of their market towns and the stature of their trading cities. On either count the Northwest must be judged backward and unimportant, though there were areas in which markets clustered thickly, competing for the rich trade of well-settled rural regions. Lancashire had six royal boroughs with parliamentary privileges, thirteen market towns chartered by noble families, and an equal number of market villages, some of which had markets in name but not in fact. In Cheshire there were over twenty chartered or customary markets, but some of these, too, were mere villages with illusory commercial privileges. In a legal sense the royal boroughs were the great towns of the region, while the seignorial boroughs had lesser privileges; but in fact the distinction was meaningless. Preston and Lancaster, royal boroughs, were the chief towns of medieval Lancashire, and Wigan and Clitheroe, too, were substantial market towns. But although incorporation by charter was a necessary condition of urban existence, royal favour did not, in itself, create trade. Liverpool's progress from the thirteenth century to the seventeenth was scarcely spectacular, while Newton-le-Willows, though a royal borough sending members to Parliament, had little significance until the establishment of a railway works nearby in Victorian times. But some of the non-royal boroughs were among the great market towns of the Northwest, for example Kirkham, Bolton, Rochdale, and Manchester, though some noble foundations languished like the feebler royal towns. Although kings and lords might appear to create towns legally, by signing the parchment of the charter, geographical factors alone could induce true urban and commercial growth.

In Lancashire the spacing of market towns (Fig. 8) faithfully reflected the distribution of population. Along the northern shorelands, in the boulder clay country of the Fylde, in the dissected plain of central Lancashire, and along the Mersey valley markets were closely spaced: there were eight between Warrington and Liverpool and seven in a cluster in central Lancashire. But the whole of west Lancashire, still largely undrained peatmoss, was served by a single market at Ormskirk. Bowland

43

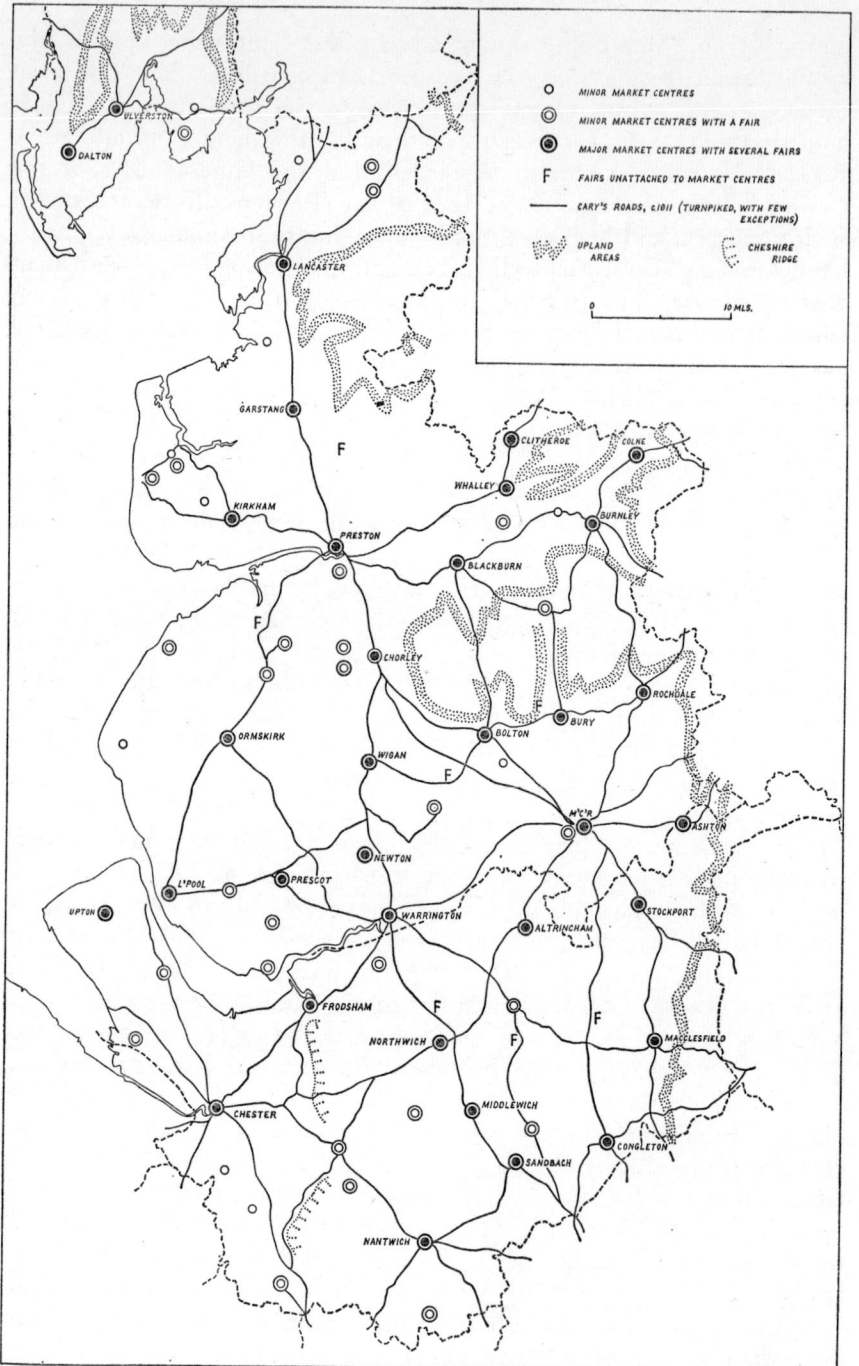

Fig. 8 THE DISTRIBUTION OF MARKETS AND FAIRS BETWEEN THE TWELFTH AND SIXTEENTH CENTURIES. Not all the centres plotted were active over the whole of the period. The distinction between 'major' and 'minor' centres depends both on the number of weekly markets held and their continuity.

and Rossendale were almost without markets, but the latter was served by a ring of peripheral centres—at Burnley, Chorley, Bolton, and Rochdale.

In Cheshire, too, there were marked regional contrasts in the distribution of markets. Though densely peopled, west Cheshire had surprisingly few, doubtless because of the overwhelming importance of Chester, which allowed few local rivals. But there were three important markets in Wirral, and two market villages in the Dee valley. Along the Weaver valley, from Frodsham and Halton at its mouth to Nantwich and Congleton, markets were closely spaced. The 'wyches' held markets and fairs, and there were lesser centres such as Over. But in north Cheshire the market towns were small and widely spaced: Altrincham was little more than a village, and both Stockport and Macclesfield served immense tracts of ill-developed country on the Pennine flank. Communications and accessibility were the keys to the growth of trading centres; a line of substantial markets lay along the great north–south highway, where the dominant centres (Warrington, Preston, and Lancaster) grew at the lowest bridge-points at the heads of the great estuaries. Other medieval highways, some of them following Roman roads, served market centres such as Northwich and Altrincham, on Watling Street.

Chester was the only town in the Northwest with the dignity and stature of a true city. Within the rectangle of the medieval walls, an enlargement of the Roman fortress, most of the symbols of civic status were to be found. Though Chester had no cathedral from the late eleventh century until 1541,[1] the site was dominated by the great Abbey of St Werburgh, the religious functions of which took a greater share of the space within the walls than in many cathedral cities. And, apart from the eight parish churches which served the several quarters of the town, the whole of its western edge was dominated by a line of monastic houses. In the south, perched on a bluff of the Bunter sandstone which floors the site, the castle was the symbol of Norman power and the base for the conquest of North Wales. As a seaport, medieval Chester was probably second only to Bristol along the western shores. In addition to their lively trade with Ireland, Chester merchants sent ships on bolder ventures to Gascony and Spain. Grain and wine were the principal imports, and there was a considerable traffic also in wool and cloth to the wharves and pool below the Watergate in the western wall. But already by the fourteenth century some cargoes were being unloaded at outports lower down the silting Dee—for example Shotwick and Burton. So quick was the deterioration of the estuary that by the mid-fifteenth century seagoing vessels were obliged to unload far below the city: a document of 1445 complained that 'for forty years now the great flow of water . . . is taken away by the wreck of sea-sand so that the said harbour is wholly destroyed [and] no vessel can approach within twelve miles'.

[1] St. John's Church was the cathedral from 1075–95.

45

Though Chester had its problems, it was long to remain the greatest town of the region; no Lancashire town was to rival it in size and significance until the close of the Middle Ages. Liverpool was a small port of little consequence: even in the late seventeenth century it consisted of a few streets some little distance from the creek—or pool—which served as a harbour. Manchester was a market town huddled under the shadow of its collegiate church which gave little promise of its future industrial greatness: much of the medieval core of Manchester now lies under a single office-block. Both southwest and southeast Lancashire were remote districts of a backward county in medieval times, removed from the major north–south axis of communications which was the main route of trade and movement until the revolution in transport created the new axis between Manchester and Merseyside. Preston and Lancaster, on the great road to the north, occupied more significant sites. The former was a royal borough and a market centre of unusual importance at the focus of the road system of north and central Lancashire. Already it was beginning to acquire the functions which made it, by Tudor times, the *de facto* county town of Lancashire. It contained the Hundred Court of Amounderness and occasionally housed the assizes; later, indeed, it was said to live 'chiefly by the quill'. But trade was the mainspring of Preston's growth: its port had close links with Ireland and ships were sent to more distant countries, for wine entered in considerable quantities. Preston's importance was chiefly commercial, and its large market-place, already inadequate for the town's trade, dominated its plan; but Lancaster's dominant function was strategic, and its castle, on a limestone knoll, overshadowed the town below. Though Lancaster had its markets and fairs it never rivalled Preston in importance, for its hinterland was much poorer.

Lancashire in transition: the sixteenth and seventeenth centuries

The period from Tudor times to the opening of the eighteenth century was one of accelerating change in the Northwest and particularly in Lancashire. It was a transitional period, almost a prelude to the Industrial Revolution, in which many of the features of the modern geography of the region were foreshadowed. The origins of industrial growth on a significant scale, of agricultural specialisation, of moorland enclosure, of substantial town-growth in southeast Lancashire and on Merseyside can all be traced to this period of quickening economic progress.

Over much of England the Tudor period brought a transformation of the rural landscape, for a great wave of enclosure reduced the number of open-field townships. But there is little evidence that the landscape of the Northwest was caught up in these changes: little of Lancashire remained in open fields even in the early sixteenth century, while in Cheshire some open fields disappeared earlier while some were to survive much later. By Tudor times, in Lancashire at least, the chief regional contrasts in agriculture had little to do with tenure but rather, were, differences in the type of farming and intensity of land use.

In Figure 9 these contrasts are summarised. Lancashire was divided between land use regions of sharply different characteristics. There were two upland regions of pastoral agriculture, the 'forests' of Bowland and Rossendale, in both of which vaccaries had been the pioneers of farming in medieval times. Arable land in both areas was restricted to the older-established townships of the larger valleys. But even here the sour, wet, and heavy soils often did not repay cultivation, and much of the best valley land was used as meadow. Of the improved land grassland covered about 60%, but the bulk of the land in both areas was the poor grazing of the upland 'waste', used as common pasture. Obviously this was a system of farming oriented towards the production of stock, not grain. In medieval times cattle had been the most numerous animals, but the growing importance of the county's domestic woollen manufacture stimulated a greater interest in sheep rearing, for which the grass heaths of the bleak moorland were better fitted.

South of Rossendale was a land use region of quite different character: in a crescent-shaped belt at the foot of the fells, reaching from the Manchester lowland to the Ribble estuary and covering most of central Lancashire: almost two-thirds of the improved land was arable, and a very low proportion of the total acreage was recorded as waste in the documents from which Figure 9 was compiled. This was a zone of rich and intensive farming, doubtless not without its stock kept on the fallow fields and on the stubble, but with grain production as its chief concern. Though wheat was grown here oats was the staple grain: Camden noted that the land towards the fells was 'not so apt to bear wheat' as the drier plain to the west, which yielded 'good store of wheat and barley'. The intensive arable cultivation of central Lancashire reached northwards into three other areas, the central Fylde, the Ribble valley, and the belt of well-drained boulder clay country at the foot of the Bowland Fells. The first of these, the drift surface of the central Fylde rising from the belt of coastal peatmoss and marsh, was to support an arable agriculture so specialised that it possessed almost the features of a grain monoculture by the opening of the eighteenth century, when this area became known as the 'granary of Lancashire', supplying great quantities of oats to the rest of the county. Unfortunately its soils were ruined in the process.

By no means the whole of the Lancashire plain supported a high proportion of arable land, for there were several districts in which pasture greatly exceeded the arable acreage, particularly in the north and west Fylde and over much of southwest Lancashire. These areas correspond with the great groups of coastal peatmosses. Little land was dry enough for cultivation, and though the wettest parts of the mosses were completely useless their drier fringes seem to have been used widely as pasture. At

47

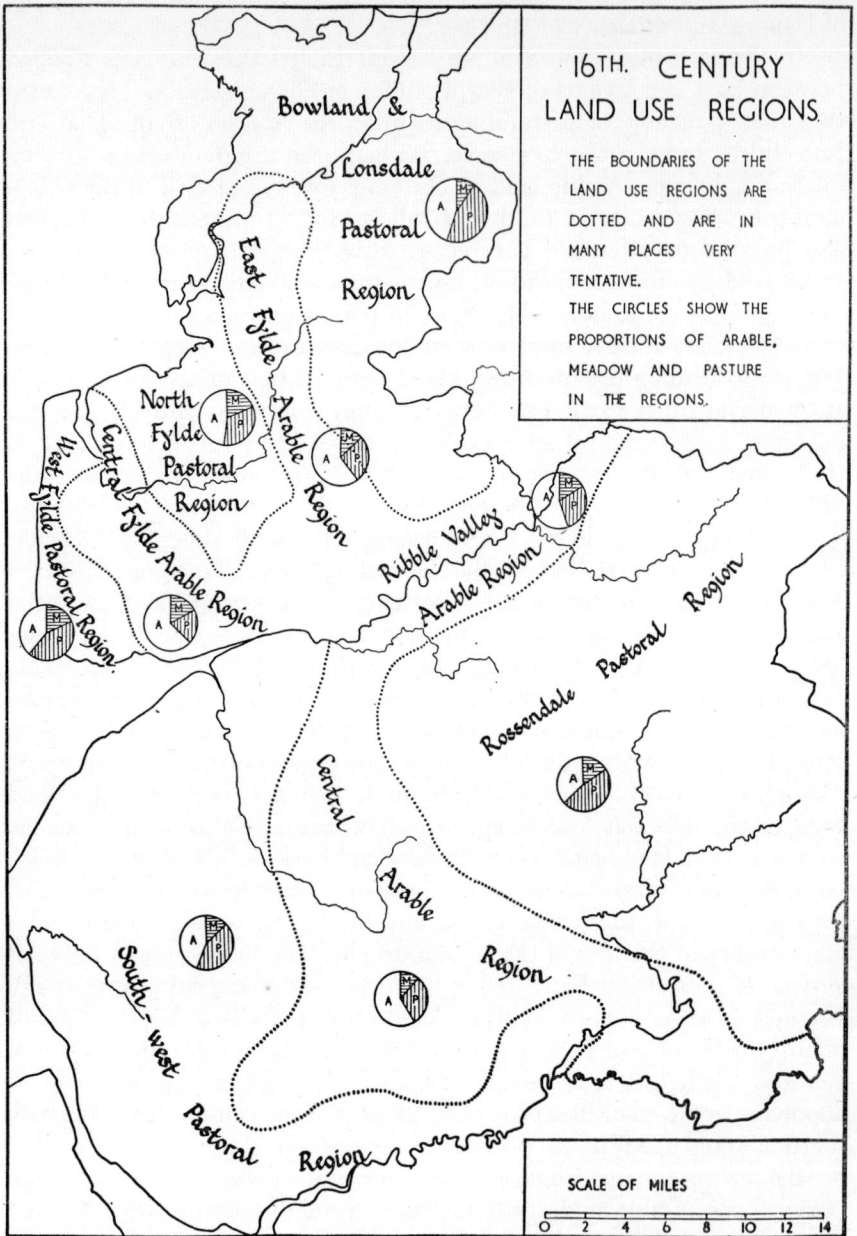

Fig. 9 SIXTEENTH CENTURY LAND USE REGIONS. First published in *Trans. Inst. Brit. Geogr.* **21** (1955), 85.

this time coastal Lancashire shared with the eastern uplands a strong tendency towards pastoral specialisation; but the attack of improving landlords on the mosses had already begun. Squire Fleetwood, the pioneer, financed the cutting of a sluice to drain part of Martin Moss near Southport in 1692; but the task proved to lie beyond the technical resources of the day, and the sea broke through the gates to flood the reclaimed area in 1755.

As agriculture improved market towns grew in strength and their domestic industries multiplied. The most significant feature of the urban geography of Tudor Lancashire was the increasing rivalry between competing markets and the emergence of a few dominant centres. There was, in fact, an incipient urban hierarchy of which the higher members were capturing the trade of their weaker rivals. Figure 10 illustrates the pattern of market towns over the greater part of north and central Lancashire, within which Preston was becoming increasingly dominant. This town was now a great inter-regional market centre, which gave it greater strength than such competitors as Kirkham, whose trade was limited to the Central Fylde, or Clitheroe, which depended on the Ribble valley. Through its nodal position at the focus of the contemporary road system, known to us in detail from the descriptions of a Preston man, Dr Kuerden, it was able to poach upon the trade of its rivals and extend its influence over a number of regions of contrasted agriculture. Preston drew oats and other arable produce from the Fylde and the Ribble valley to its markets, while sheep, cattle, and cheese came from the regions of pastoral specialisation. There is evidence that Preston's competition was proving too much for the smaller centres: the symbols on the map show that the town drew trade from the market areas of Kirkham, Garstang, Leyland, and Chorley, among other places. Some of these were in decline, and elsewhere markets had ceased to exist. By the seventeenth century Preston completely dominated the trade of a considerable district (the 'inner zone' of the market area shown on Fig. 10) and even beyond these limits it attracted part of the trade of districts up to twelve miles away (the 'outer zone' of the market area). Preston was now, at least as a commercial and social centre if not in the legal sense, the county town. Squires left their estates to build town houses here; and when the courts were in session the town's inns were thronged by litigants and their lawyers. Domestic industry grew to serve the needs of the expanding market area and the growing population. Woollen and linen weavers, leather workers, smiths, and tailors are frequently recorded in the Guild Rolls of the town, and more sophisticated industries like lock and gun manufacture were later to grow. The growth of Preston as a great regional centre culminated in the eighteenth century, the town's golden age, when the attractive squares and terraces overlooking the incised valley of the Ribble were built. The later growth of industry and the faster growth of Manchester and Liverpool not only

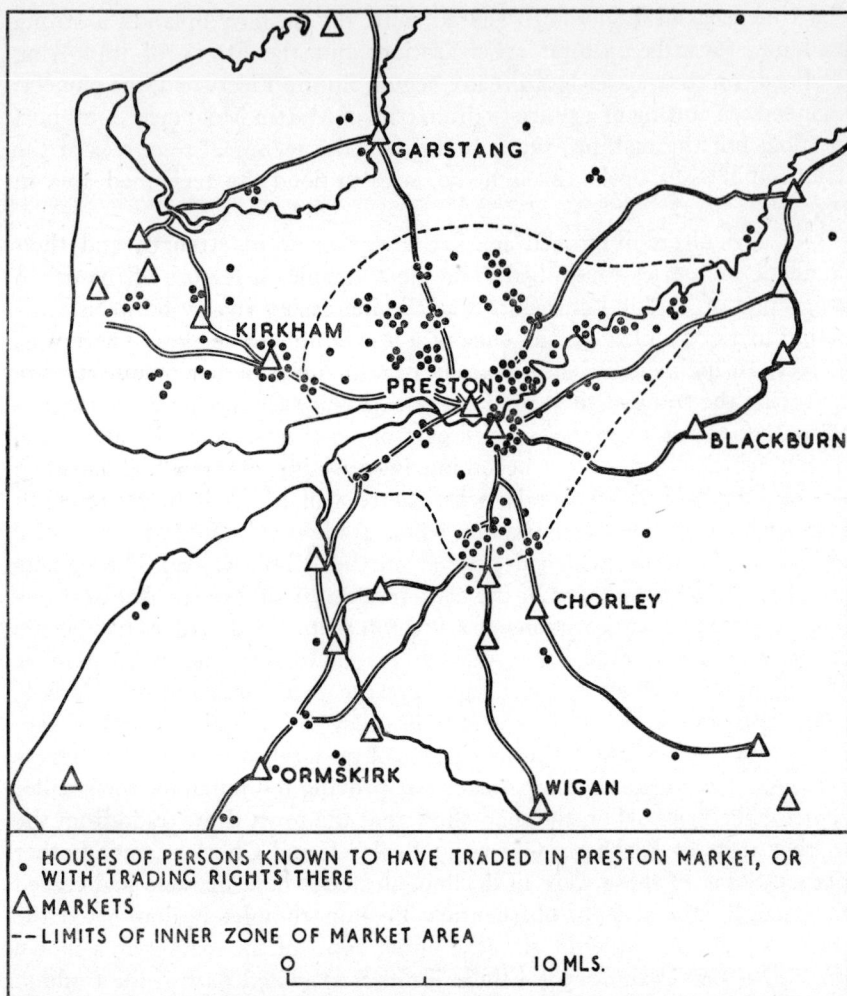

Fig. 10 MARKET AREA OF SEVENTEENTH CENTURY PRESTON. Redrawn from a map in Rodgers, H. B., 'The market area of Preston in the sixteenth and seventeenth centuries', *Geographical Studies*, **3**, (1956), 50.

transformed the personality of Preston but demoted it to a lower urban rank.

On a lesser scale these same forces of economic progress were at work in the other towns of Lancashire. Saxton's plan of late-sixteenth century Lancaster shows that the town was still small and compact and had scarcely spread away from the foot of Castle Hill, though it had a considerable market through which Lonsdale cattle passed southwards. But the town, as Defoe noted, lay 'upon its own ruins' and was distinguished chiefly by 'a decayed castle and a more decayed port'. Soon Lancaster was to make a brief adventure into American and African trade, quickly terminated by the shortcomings of its estuary; for it was clearly no match for Preston in its seventeenth century commercial importance. Although Manchester's trade had grown and its cloth merchants were already amassing fortunes, the medieval plan served the needs of the town until urban expansion began with the 'improvements' of the early eighteenth century.

Of all the changes of the sixteenth and seventeenth centuries the most important, in its future consequences, was the growth of these old and staple industries. By 1600, however, new industries were making progress in many regions of the county. Not all of these were in the textile group which was later so to dominate the economy of the county. Coal was already being won from the more rolling, dissected areas of the exposed fields, where seams outcropped along the valley sides and were worked in bell-pits and shallow adits. At Haigh, near Wigan, mining had expanded far beyond its medieval scale as the winter occupation of a few farmers. Pits clustered along the outcrops and a considerable drainage tunnel, the Great Sough had been built. To the south of Bolton, too, the exposed seams were being worked with increasing vigour, and by the late sixteenth century pits at Prescot were supplying coal to Merseyside, especially for the purposes of the salt-boiling industry. In Furness mining of a different type was growing. The charcoal 'famine' which was hampering the growth of the English iron industry was driving smelting to new areas, hitherto without any considerable tradition of metal working. In Furness iron-masters found not only ample timber but also magnificent hematite deposits, smelted near the ore quarries, and also 'exported' to other iron working centres.

Textile industries of more than merely local importance first began to develop in Lancashire in the sixteenth and seventeenth centuries. In 1600 it was possible to distinguish two provinces within the county: in the west the dominant textile industry was the manufacture of linen, while in the uplands of the east and along their flanks a domestic woollen trade—an extension of the West Riding hand-loom weaving area—was growing. The linen trade of the west was restricted in distribution. Preston was a principal centre; and linen cloth was one of the most important com-modities traded in its market. Kirkham, Warrington, Wigan, and Liverpool also engaged in the manufacture of linen, produced in part from flax grown on the wet Lancashire plain and in part from Irish imports. But the woollen industry of the east was more widespread and on a greater scale. It was carried on both by townsmen and by the farmer-weavers of the countryside; indeed, its prosperity greatly increased the density of settle-ment and population in the indifferent farmlands of the moorlands and their flanks. In Rossendale, particularly, a new pattern of rural settlement was evolving in association with the spread of hand-loom weaving. The

51

old open moorlands, used only for extensive grazing, were being divided into the walled enclosures of smallholdings, many of which, by subdivision, became far too small to provide a living for the families who struggled with the sour soils and insufficient sunshine. As in the West Riding, the small-holder turned to domestic weaving to supplement the miserable return from his few sterile acres. As the east Lancashire textile industry expanded, weavers' smallholdings spread more widely and clustered more thickly across the bleak slopes of the moors. In Rossendale, for example, they showed a distinctive pattern closely adjusted to the stepped relief. There was little settlement in the narrow slots of the valley floors or on the wet ribbons of the floodplains: the chief concentrations of population were along the broad benches which rise, separated by gritstone scars, to the moorland plateaux. Typically, each bench had a double line of small-holdings, one along its upper edge in the shelter of the steep slope leading to the upper levels and the other along the lower lip, overlooking a lower bench in the valley floor. Primitive trackways, typically flagged 'causeys' used by pack-horse trains, between each line of settlements, foreshadowed the modern road system. There was little tendency to nucleation, but chapels occasionally attracted a cluster of cottages to form a hamlet. And so the transformation of Rossendale from a 'forest' to an industrial region began.

As the seventeenth century advanced changes of immense future importance began in some of the towns along the south and west flank of the Rossendale upland, particularly in those which, like Manchester, stood on the overlap of the linen province of the west and the woollen area of the east. Here cotton began to be used in the manufacture of fabrics, though at first always in mixture with other fibres. It was natural enough that Manchester, a town on the margins of the woollen and linen zones, should take up the manufacture of smallwares, in which both yarns were used. Even more important was the quick growth of the fustian industry, a cloth in which linen was used for the warp and cotton for the weft. The great progress of Manchester during the late seventeenth and early eighteenth centuries was based chiefly on the expansion of this prosperous trade, which it shared with a narrow belt of country along the edge of Rossendale to Bolton and Blackburn. In fact the fustian trade, from which the cotton industry was soon to evolve, grew chiefly along the overlap between the linen and woollen areas, in districts which were fully com-mitted to neither of these older trades (Fig. 11).

Little of this industrial progress had spread to Cheshire, except to the parishes of the northeast which came under the influence of Manchester. Cheshire seemed destined for a career of stability, sustained by a pros-perous but conservative agriculture, in comparison with the brash enterprise and experiment, both in agriculture and in industry, breaking out north of the Mersey. Yet Cheshire was by no means wholly non-

industrial: the rich brine-springs of the wyches continued to support a distinctive group of towns, soon to become a cluster of industrial islands in the rich dairy country of mid-Cheshire. Indeed, a new phase in the growth of salt making opened with the discovery of the rock-salt beds near Northwich in 1670; this was to be a stimulus to the canalisation of

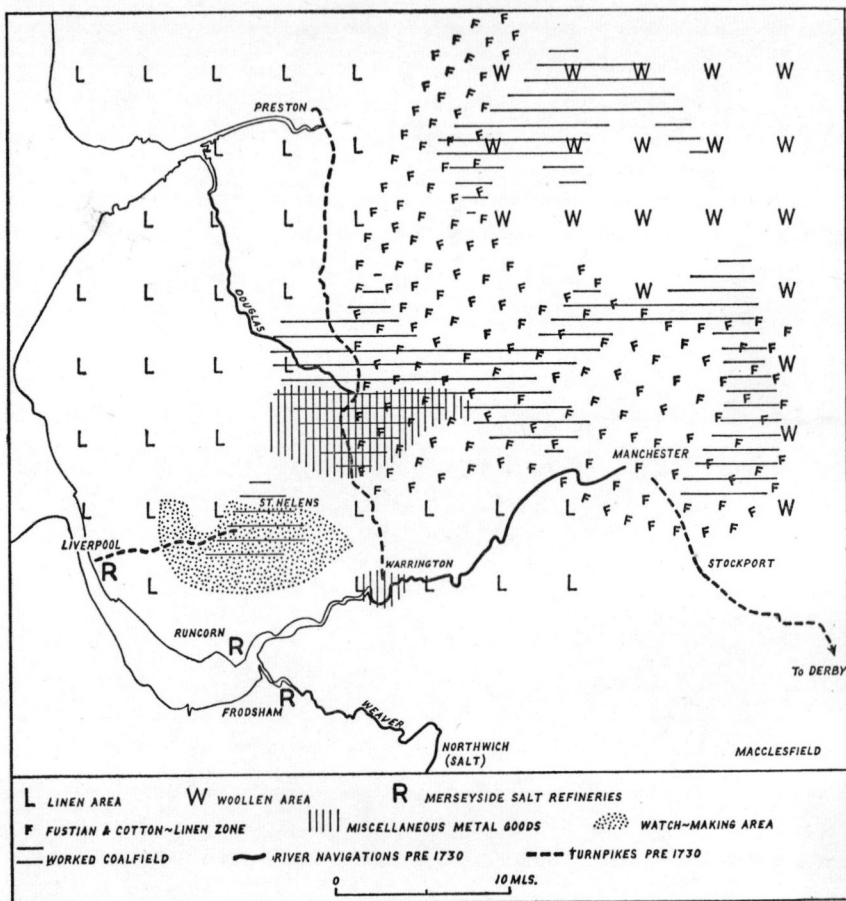

Fig. 11 INDUSTRIAL REGIONS OF SOUTH LANCASHIRE AND NORTH CHESHIRE IN THE EARLY EIGHTEENTH CENTURY. Silk working was restricted to Macclesfield and Stockport.

the Weaver in the early eighteenth century and thus to the accelerating development of the industry. Even the iron manufacture had come to Cheshire with surprising strength by the end of the seventeenth century. The great furnaces of Vale Royal near Northwich smelted Furness ore using local timber from the forested Weaver valley and supplied forges nearby. In fact the group of furnaces and forges, which extends from the Weaver valley to north Staffordshire, became an important supplier of

iron to the metal trades of the western Midlands. But agriculture was wholly dominant over most of Cheshire, with a growing specialisation in the production of cheese from farms on pasturelands rooted in heavy clays. Exported through Chester and its outports, the cheese had acquired wide fame before 1700.

Lancastria in the Eighteenth Century

THE eighteenth century was a time of great economic advance in Lancastria. Its textile industries, aided by new inventions, rose to greatness, its major mart at Manchester became powerful, and Liverpool developed as the great port of the Northwest, effectively surpassing possible rivals such as Chester, Preston, and Lancaster. Turnpike roads were built as modern additions to the packhorse trails or ordinary highways of the time, and the main rivers, notably the Mersey with the Irwell, the Douglas, and the Weaver, were improved to form 'navigations'. Before the end of the century there were also several canals, including three that traversed the Pennines. Inevitably a stimulus to industry, these waterways were constructed in the expectation of profit, like the railways of a later time. Not only was the cotton trade growing and coalmining expanding, but the long-established salt industry of Cheshire was using an increasing quantity of coal for the evaporation of brine. With the industrial expansion, agriculture became more productive through the increasing use of marl and lime and artificial drainage, and also with some expansion of cultivation into the uplands, on various peatmosses, and on heaths and forests such as Delamere 'Forest'.

The observations of Defoe

Defoe in his travels in the mid-1720s approached the Northwest[1] from Chester, 'the largest city in all this side of England that is so remote from London', and made many observations that could have been made by a modern visitor. He found the medieval walls in good repair, walked round them, noted the green sward of the Roodee on the river floodplain, compared the rectangular pattern of streets to that of Chichester: 'The best ornament of the city is that the streets are very broad and fair, and run through the city in straight lines.' He noticed that the cathedral, built of Triassic sandstone, was sharply attacked by the weather: while it was 'a very magnificent building', it was of a 'red, sandy, ill-looking stone'. All a matter of taste, perhaps, and many would not agree with his strictures on the Rows as 'certain long galleries, up one pair of stairs . . . to keep the people dry in walking along . . . but then they take away all the view of the

[1] The *Tour* at least says he did, but Defoe may have made his journey at some other time, or may have drawn on someone else's experience.

houses from the street . . . [and] . . . make the shops themselves dark'. On Defoe's visit a recent flood had destroyed a wharf and several warehouses, but much of the maritime trade of Chester was handled at Neston, described by Defoe as 'a long naze or nose of land which running out into the sea, makes a kind of quay'. The silting of the Dee made Shotwick useless by the eighteenth century, but the final eclipse of Chester as a port was due to the rise of Liverpool.

In the early eighteenth century cheese was a main export from Cheshire, and the London market was supplied by the 'long sea' route from Chester or Liverpool and by land carriage to Burton-upon-Trent, thence by the Trent to Gainsborough and Hull, and so by sea to London. Some was sent to Bristol by sea, or to York by the Trent and the Ouse; there was also sea-carriage of cheese to Scotland and Ireland. The making of cheese was widespread, not only in Cheshire but in the neighbouring areas of Shropshire, Staffordshire, and Lancashire. The Wirral peninsula was 'rich and fertile', according to Defoe, who, working perhaps on cause-and-effect reasoning, ascribes its prosperity to sales in the markets of Chester and Liverpool; although the Wirral had numerous villages (p. 74) there was no market town. Nothing is said of other market towns in the county; but Moll's map of 1727 picks out the 'wych' towns, Nantwich, Middlewich, and Northwich, with Sandbach, Congleton, and Macclesfield farther east, and Stockport, Altrincham, Knutsford, and Frodsham in the north, with Warrington on the north side of the Mersey and therefore in Lancashire.

Liverpool was a source of fascination to Defoe. Its first wet-dock was opened in 1715, and from this time any hope of the revival of Chester as a port faded. Liverpool's wide export trade was largely in salt, mainly supplied from Northwich, Nantwich, and Middlewich, but also from works which, before the end of the seventeeth century, were established at Frodsham and at Dungeon, near Hale (Lancashire). Defoe noted that the Liverpool shippers 'trade round the whole island, send ships to Norway, to Hamburg, and to the Baltic, as also to Holland and Flanders; so that, in a word, they are almost become like the Londoners, universal merchants'. Though foreseeing that Liverpool might become a greater port than Bristol, Defoe thought that each had its natural sphere of influence within the British Isles, in the north and south, with Wales naturally divided between them; in Ireland, Bristol traded with the ports from Dublin southwards, and Liverpool with the ports from Dublin northwards. Inland, too, each had its natural hinterland: Bristol with the southwest, South Wales, and the Severn basin as far north as Bridgnorth, even perhaps Shrewsbury; and Liverpool with all the northern counties, as well as North Wales, Cheshire, and Staffordshire. The town had many fine buildings, including a town house and exchange and a new church in addition to its historic parish church beside the Mersey (Plate 50).

56

Warrington was an 'old town' in the early eighteenth century, and regarded as of considerable strategic significance as the first and major crossing place of the Mersey. It had a linen market every week, as well as strong retail trade. Between Warrington and Manchester Defoe travelled beside Chat Moss, and described it as typical of all the various mosses of the Northwest: it looked 'black and dirty . . . frightful to think of, for it will bear neither horse or man, unless in an exceeding dry season, and then not so as to be passable, or that any one should travel over them'. Some peat was cut by cottagers, and the thickness of the peat was as much as eight or nine feet in places: but 'what nature means by such a useless production, 'tis hard to imagine. . . . The land is entirely waste except . . . for the poor cottagers' fuel, and the quantity used for that is very small'. Defoe could not foresee the potential agricultural richness of fertilised and drained mosslands (on which, see pp. 104–06).

Manchester was as startling a phenomenon as Liverpool: 'One of the greatest, if not the greatest meer village in England', for it was 'neither a wall'd town, city or corporation' and was unrepresented in Parliament. With Salford on the west side of the river, its population was probably 50,000 people, and there was 'an abundance, not only of new Houses only, but of new streets of Houses . . . a new Church [St Ann, 1712] and a fine new Square . . . so that the town is almost double what it was a few years ago'. The expansion was due to the advance of the textile industry, especially in the fustian branch (p. 52). On the north side of Manchester, Defoe visited Rochdale, Bury, and Bolton, and noted that the 'cotton' manufacture so strongly established in Manchester had spread to Bolton, but that in Bury and in the surrounding villages, as in Rochdale, wool was dominant. Coarse materials known as 'half-thicks and kersies' were made here and commanded a considerable sale even at Rochdale 'tho' otherwise the town is situated so remote, so out of the way, and so at the foot of the mountains that we may suppose it would be but little frequented'. Through Rochdale there was a post road which ran eastwards to Halifax, Leeds, and York, and westwards to Bury, Manchester, Warrington, and Liverpool, with a connecting road to Chester and so to the southwest through Shrewsbury, Gloucester, and Exeter to Plymouth. The postmaster-general had 'thought fit to establish a cross-post through all the western ports of England' to Lancashire, 'to maintain the correspondence of merchants and men of business'.

Coalmining was prevalent in the area between Bolton and Wigan, and the 'canell or candle coal' was much favoured; described as easily ignited, it was smooth and thick and 'the most agreeable fuel that can be found'; but though it was used in Lancashire and Cheshire the cost of transport to London was prohibitive. To the north, Lancashire narrows and, Defoe notes, becomes more mountainous, and industry becomes less prominent. Preston, for example, had among the inhabitants numerous lawyers and a strong trading fraternity; well into the nineteenth century, Preston had the aspect of a county town. Lancaster was less attractive, for the castle had decayed, few ships—and only small ones—came to its port and there was 'little trade and few people'. Later in the eighteenth century it flourished on the West Indian trade, chiefly from 1750 to 1800, though in Defoe's time the Gillow family, founders of the furniture industry, were living in the town. To Defoe the hills were 'high and formidable ... they had a kind of unhospitable terror in them'; lacking both rich pleasant valleys, or even such economic resources as coal and metals, they were 'all barren and wild, of no use either to man or beast'. Even at Windermere (then Winander Meer), at the northern extremity of Lancashire, Defoe makes no comment on what must then, as now, have been a sylvan scene, but expatiates on the delights of eating potted char fish (trout).

Communications and trade

Roads, rivers, and canals were the main means of communication in the eighteenth century, though Defoe and many other famous travellers of the time went on horseback. At the same time, the provision of better communications for coaches, carriages, and wagons, was regarded as desirable, and Defoe's comment on the cross-country route from Lancashire to Plymouth was true to its time. Ogilvy's *Britannia* of 1675, giving all the main roads of England, shows routes from London to Chester passing through Whitchurch and through Nantwich, and a route to Carlisle which enters Cheshire at Church Lawton and continues to Warrington, Preston, and Lancaster. There were cross-routes from Chester through Warrington, Manchester, and Rochdale to York, also between Manchester and Derby through Stockport and Buxton, and from Lancaster to Skipton and York. At this stage, Liverpool was not even mentioned, and though it grew considerably as a port in the early eighteenth century, it was badly served by roads until much later (pp. 60, 61, 84). The central road through Cheshire and Lancashire was first outlined in Roman times, and so too were the roads from Manchester to Carlisle and to Chester, as well as some of the trans-Pennine highways. Long before the period of the turnpikes Manchester was the meeting-place of several roads, and there were also pack-horse trails such as the Liversgate, used as a lime-carrying route (on ponies) between Clitheroe and Rochdale, or the ways through the Rossendales for carrying cloth to Manchester and Rochdale (Fig. 12).

Road maintenance depended on the common law and a statute of 1555 gave the main responsibility to the parish except where some individual or group of people could with justice be charged with the duty of maintaining roads. In many places soft roads were considered adequate, but causeways were laid across marshy ground to give a safer passage to horses; for these, slabs of millstone grit were used on the Pennines and pebbles or cobbles in southwest Lancashire. Many of these were kept in good repair, and pack-

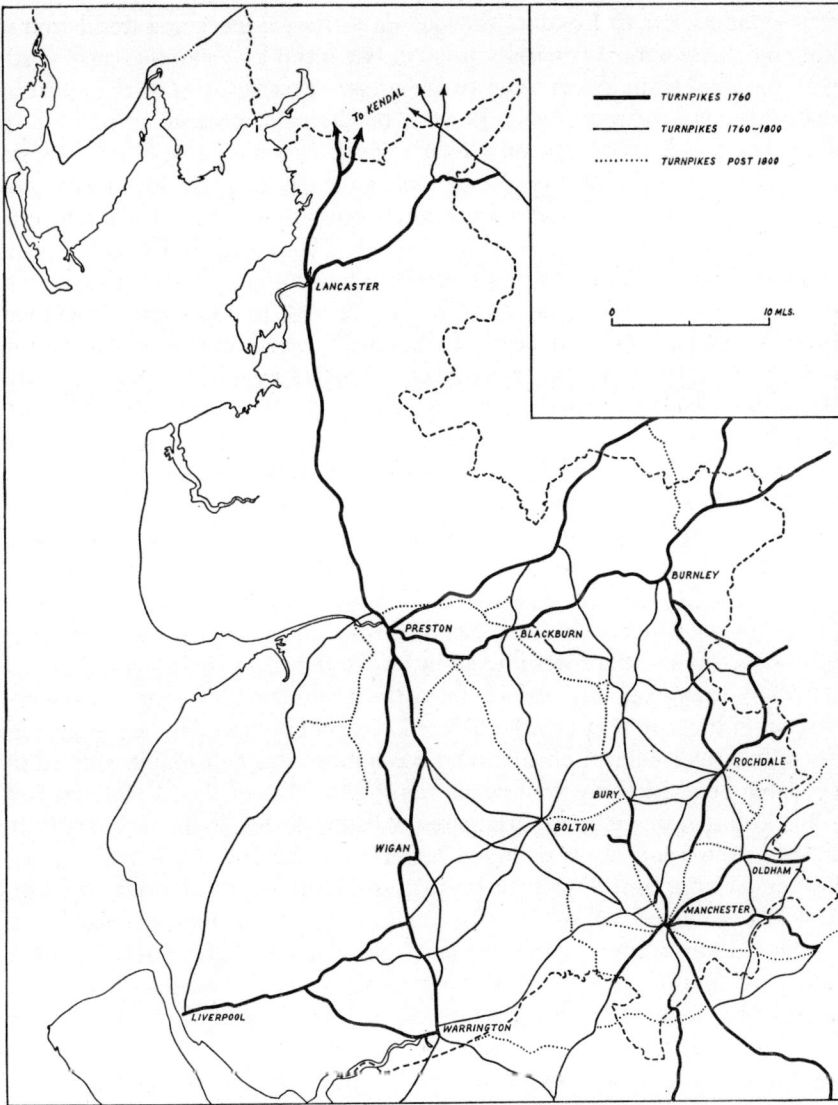

Fig. 12   THE GROWTH OF THE TURNPIKE SYSTEM IN LANCASHIRE.

horse travel survived well into the eighteenth century; but the increasing traffic on many of the roads made their maintenance too great a burden on the parishes, and Turnpike Acts were passed from 1663 under which tolls would be levied for road maintenance.

In Cheshire the first turnpike was on a section of the Whitchurch–Chester road, from Barnhill to Hatton Heath, under an Act of 1705. Some twenty years later the road from Buxton and Chapel-en-le-Frith to Manchester was turnpiked; described in the Act of 1725 as the nearest road

59

from Manchester to London, on account of its wildness and desolation it was not the one most generally used. In 1726 the Liverpool–Prescot road, with the road from Warrington to Wigan and Preston, and in 1730 part of the mid-Cheshire road, from Lawton to Cranage, became turnpikes. In some cases only a section of a road might be included, possibly due to hesitation about the best choice of route to the next town: Harrison notes that north of Cranage there were alternative roads to Warrington, one through Budworth and the other through Knutsford; but eventually in 1752 the Knutsford route was chosen and turnpiked, with a connecting road at Mere, north of Knutsford, to Altrincham. In 1750 part of the road from Altrincham to Manchester from the Mersey crossing at Sale to the city was turnpiked, and the remaining few miles were added in 1765 with the result that all the old post route to London, through Lichfield and Coventry, then became a turnpike. Another Cheshire road of significance was the route from Chester to Nantwich and onwards into Staffordshire, turnpiked in 1743. Meanwhile, in 1732 and 1735, two roads penetrating the Pennines were added—first, that from Manchester to Ashton, Mottram, and onwards into Yorkshire, and second, the main road to Oldham, which was extended later across the Pennines. In 1735 also a trust was formed to construct a road from Rochdale to Halifax and Elland; but for the next fifteen years there were no additions to the turnpike system.

Many turnpikes were added from the 1750s, notably that from Warrington to Prescot in 1752, which gave Liverpool better inland communications than ever before; on this road a coach service to London started in 1764, ten years after the first coach ran to Manchester. But Liverpool had only two turnpikes whereas Manchester had a dozen, some of which were added at this time: these included roads from Manchester to Warrington, Bolton, Wigan, and Duxbury (1752), and through Crumpsall to Bury, Radcliffe, and Rochdale (1754). In east Lancashire a network of roads was established to connect such towns as Rochdale, Todmorden, Burnley, Edenfield, Bolton, and Bury. Farther north, in 1754, two lengths of road united Skipton and Preston, one by Burnley and Blackburn and the other by Clitheroe. In Cheshire, too, substantial additions to the road system were made, notably from Chester southward through Whitchurch (1759), eastward to Northwich (1769), and northward to Warrington (1786) and Birkenhead (1787). And the cross-country traffic from Sheffield to Liverpool was facilitated by the turnpiking of roads through Macclesfield to Tabley in 1758 and 1769 and of the road from Whaley Bridge to Macclesfield in 1770. As noted above, the old route to London from Manchester ran through Altrincham, Lichfield, and Coventry; but in 1762 a turnpike was made from Macclesfield through Leek, which gave a connection through Derby and Leicester that became the main route, and supplanted both the old route and the rival way through Buxton. Another southward route was developed in 1752, at first from Didsbury, Manchester, to Wilmslow, and later, in 1781, by the road through Congleton to Church Lawton; in 1793 the road was completed to Ardwick Green, near the centre of Manchester (Fig. 12).

In the last great period of turnpike building, from 1789 to 1830, virtually every place that could be called a town acquired such roads. But though a considerable amount of constructive work was done in the early years of each road many were not kept in good repair; travellers such as John Wesley and Arthur Young noted that many turnpikes were no better than unturnpiked roads. The speed of communications increased, however, and more post or stage coaches as well as private conveyances were used. In 1772 Matthew Pickford's flying wagons took $4\frac{1}{2}$ days to reach London from Manchester, but by 1824 the journey was reduced to 36 hours. By then the influence of Telford and Macadam on road construction had become widespread, though by no means universal. Some interesting details of the earlier turnpikes have survived: in 1757 a road across Deerplay moor part of the Rochdale and Burnley trust, was to be 7 yards wide with a drain on each side 1 yard wide, and the middle 4 yards were to be paved with small broken stones to a depth of 12 inches on the crown, diminishing gradually to 6 inches at the sides. Four years earlier roads were made in much the same way for the Liverpool and Prescot trustees. Most roads were 'metalled' into a compact surface of small stones and gravel, and limestone was favoured because it bound together well. Stone from quarries in the Clitheroe district was used on the Bury, Blackburn, and Whalley road, and whinstones were also used, though they were said to be less durable. In southwest Lancashire some roads were made of pebbles from the river beds, not the most comfortable surface on which to travel; and slag from the copper works of St Helens and Liverpool was found to be a good and hard-wearing surface.

In the 1770s Arthur Young found that the roads left much to be desired: the way from Windermere to Lancaster was 'very bad, rough and cut up', that from Lancaster to Preston 'very bad', and from Preston to Wigan even worse: 'I know not, in the whole range of language, terms sufficiently expressive to describe this infernal road. . . . Let me seriously caution all travellers, who may accidentally purpose to travel this terrible country, to avoid it as they would the devil. . . . They will here meet with ruts . . . four feet deep and floating with mud. . . . The only mending it receives, is the tumbling in of some loose stones, which serve no other purpose than jolting a carriage in the most intolerable manner.' From Wigan to Warrington the turnpike was 'infamously bad . . . only wide enough for one carriage and therefore cut into ruts'. 'Any person would imagine the boobies of the country had made it with a view to immediate destruction.' From Wigan to Liverpool, the road was 'mostly a pavement' and 'as good as an indifferent pavement can be', and from Liverpool to Altrincham the turnpike was 'execrable', largely of 'heavily rutted sand turning to floods in rain'. There were similar conditions on the road to Manchester from Altrincham; but the southward road from Knutsford to Holmes Chapel was better, and thence to Newcastle-under-Lyme there was a paved causeway. As if he had not said enough, Young adds: 'Let me persuade all travellers to avoid this terrible country, which must either dislocate their bones with broken pavements, or bury them in muddy sand.' In short, do not travel north of Newcastle, as 'all between that place and Preston is a country one would suppose devoid of all those improvements and embellishments, which the riches and spirit of modern times have occasioned in other parts'.

Commerce in the eighteenth century was fostered by the construction of river 'navigations' and, later, canals. In Lancastria the main artery was the Mersey, especially as the Dee was silting up and Chester was no longer a significant port. In 1721 a company was formed to improve the Mersey and the Irwell, largely by making 'cuts' between the river bends and locks to regulate the flow of water. The company could only charge a fixed levy per ton for the goods carried, but was able to drive other carriers off the river by charging high rates for the use of its warehouses in Manchester. The Weaver, giving a connection with the Mersey vital for the salt and, later, the chemical industry, was navigable only in its tidal reaches up to the early eighteenth century, though possibly boats were used higher up the river. The accidental discovery, in the course of a search for coal, of a bed of rock salt, overlaid by a natural reservoir of strong brine, at Marbury near Northwich in 1670, opened the way to a considerable development of the salt industry. Salt is one of the oldest articles of commerce in the world and the springs are known to have been used before the Norman Conquest. The main mines worked in the eighteenth century were those at Northwich, at depths of 214 feet and 334 feet; and though pillars were left to support the overburden, funnel-shaped holes appeared, owing to the collapse of these pillars, largely through solution when water entered the roofs and shafts. From the 1790s natural brine pumping began, and subsidence was seen not only near the actual workings but also at a considerable distance from them. But these problems were scarcely appreciated in the eighteenth century, when a main concern of the salt manufacturers was to acquire coal cheaply since virtually all the available timber had been used, most of it by the end of the seventeenth century. Coal was brought from mines in south Lancashire and north Staffordshire; but as the cost of transporting coal was high, salt was carried to the refineries on Merseyside. In 1721 a Bill was passed to make the Weaver navigable to Winsford, largely to carry coal from Lancashire and salt to Liverpool for shipment. By 1732 the Weaver was navigable from Frodsham to Northwich for boats carrying 45 tons of rock salt and to Winsford for cargoes of 38 tons. The trade continued to expand and in the 1760s it was noted that salt accounted for 70% of the total by weight and coal for a further 20%, while the remaining tenth was industrial raw materials such as pipe-clay and pig metal, heavy building materials, and

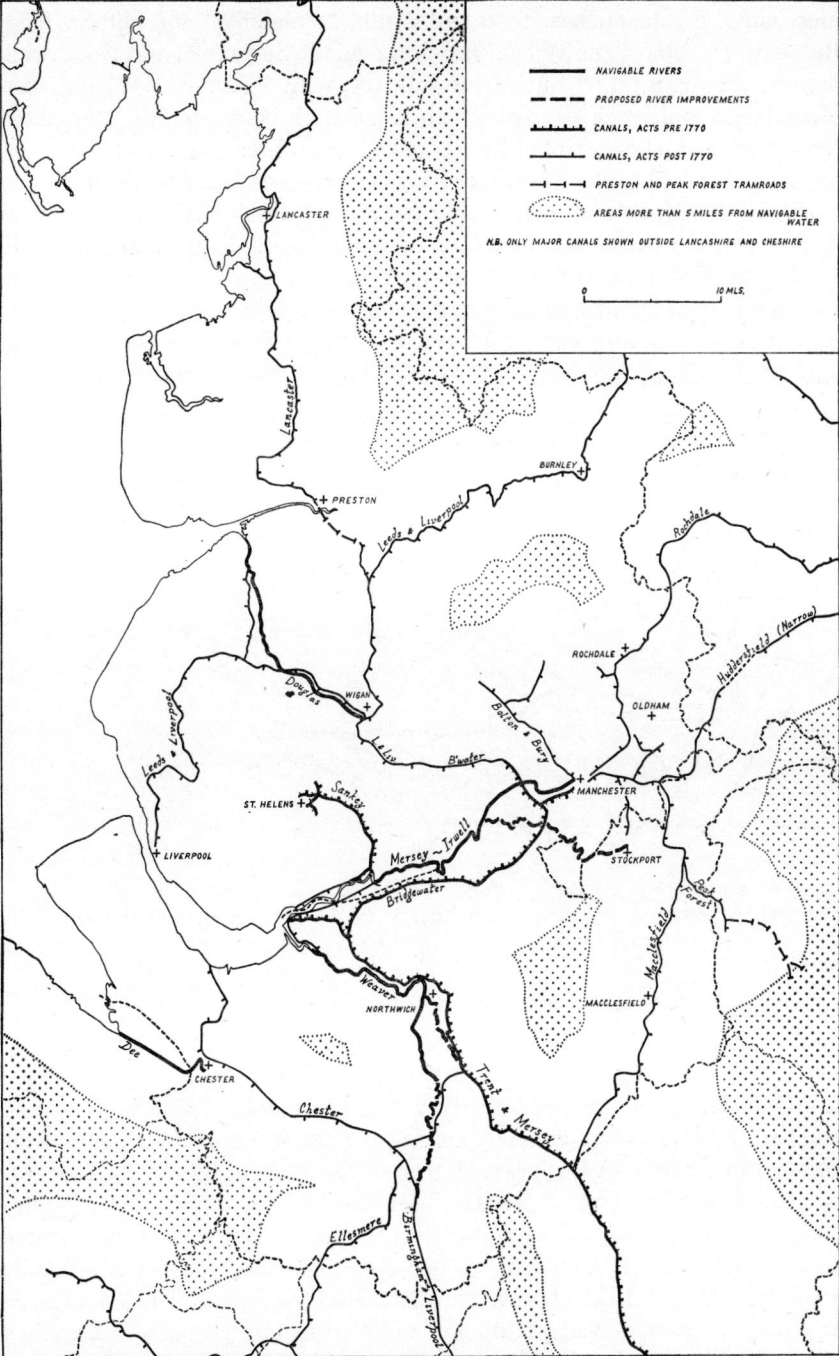

Fig. 13   RIVER AND CANAL NAVIGATION IN LANCASHIRE AND CHESHIRE.

merchants' goods, such as food and drink, furnishings, and pottery from Burslem. In 1764–5 the Witton Brook was made navigable, and Northwich became the main centre of the salt industry, with Winsford as a significant secondary supplier: at Middlewich and Nantwich brine was still evaporated for salt on a smaller scale, but both lacked water transport.

To bring coal to the Mersey the Sankey navigation was opened in 1757 from the Haydock and Parr collieries. A true canal rather than a river navigation, it runs along the valley of the Sankey Brook to the coalfield around St Helens, and from its earliest years it was used largely for the carriage of coal to Liverpool, Warrington, and Northwich, for the growing salt industry. Sailing barges known as 'flats' carried the salt down to

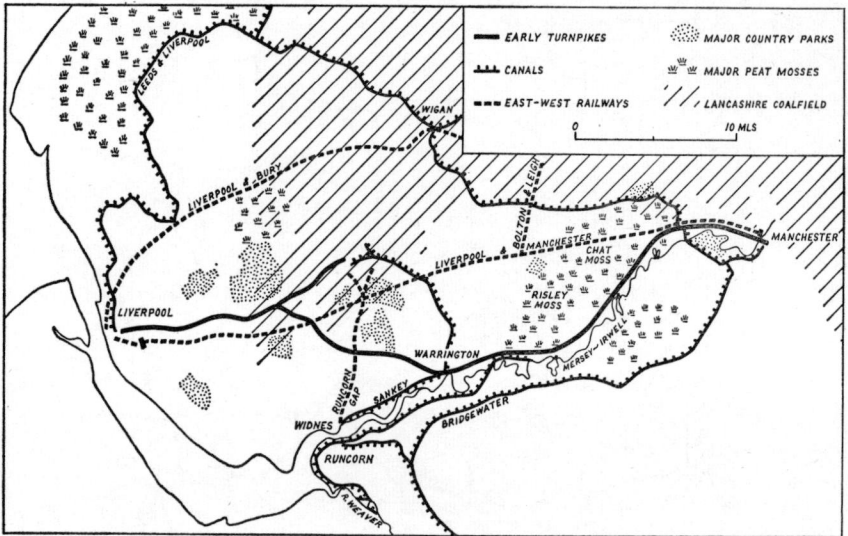

Fig. 14   THE GROWTH OF COMMUNICATIONS BETWEEN LIVERPOOL AND MANCHESTER TO 1830.

Liverpool for export and returned to mid-Cheshire with Sankey Canal coal as a return cargo: this initiated a trade triangle of considerable significance in the growth of Liverpool. The Sankey Canal was a stimulus to industrial development in the St Helens area, where mining prospered and the industries included glass and copper smelting before the end of the eighteenth century. A few years later in origin, the Bridgewater Canal was opened in sections from 1761. Of these the first, from Worsley to Manchester, drains a coalmine cut into a cliff face, and for many decades carried coal to Manchester. Constructed by James Brindley for the supposedly lovelorn Duke of Bridgewater, it was carried over roads and streams by aqueducts, crossed valleys by embankments, cut through hills when unavoidable (though few cuttings were needed), and followed contours to maintain a level course. The crossing of the Irwell by the Barton bridge,

200 yards long and 36 feet wide and of three large arches, was regarded as one of the wonders of the time: Arthur Young spoke of 'a scenery somewhat like enchantment . . . a view that must give you an idea of prodigious labour', when he stood beside the aqueduct 'looking *down* upon a large river with barges of great burthen sailing on it, and *up* to another river, being in the air, with barges towing upon it'. To the south the canal crossed the Mersey in a single arch of 70-foot span, and at Sale Moor 'a complete bed was made for the canal, raised at the bottom as well as at the sides, sufficient for conducting the water on a level. Great piles of deal were fixed as a mound to keep the earth in a proper position to form the banks; and when they were raised, the piles removed on . . . and the water brought forward by degrees'. This branch of the canal was steadily pushed forward through north Cheshire to join the tidal section of the Mersey at Runcorn gap by 1776; on the north side of the Mersey a branch was pushed westwards through the mining area around Leigh, and eventually joined to a branch of the Leeds and Liverpool Canal from Wigan.

The conveyance of goods to the Trent for shipment from Burton, noted above (p. 56) meant a long land haul and therefore the idea of a canal came relatively early, and the Trent–Mersey was opened in 1777 or 1778 (the date is uncertain). This canal runs through the Potteries to Middlewich: it was hoped that the Trent–Mersey Canal might join the Weaver, but instead it was led into the Bridgewater Canal at Preston Brook (p. 185); in 1793 a new basin was built at Anderton which came within 44 yards of the Weaver, but 50 feet higher. At first the salt was carried up the incline in carts, but later a 'railed' way similar to the railways of the eighteenth century collieries was made, ultimately to be replaced by a lift for boats from one level to another, much appreciated by juvenile—and other— visitors. The town of Runcorn in the eighteenth century had considerable significance as a canal centre, for the Bridgewater descends through it to the Mersey in a series of locks: in 1808 the connecting canal from Frodsham Bridge to Weston Point was constructed. Farther west, in Cheshire, the Chester Canal to Nantwich, completed in 1778, was reported by Holland in 1808 to have been unsuccessful in its early years though the construction of the Ellesmere Canal, sanctioned in 1793, gave hopes of new prosperity. Leaving the Mersey at Ellesmere Port, it crossed the Wirral peninsula to Chester and was linked with the Chester Canal to Ellesmere, Llangollen, and the Severn valley, and a branch was run off from Barbridge, near Nantwich, to join the Trent–Mersey Canal at Middlewich.

Towards the end of the eighteenth century, the problem of traversing the Pennines by canal was tackled, and Manchester acquired its intricate network of waterways, several of which are now derelict. The Manchester, Bolton, and Bury Canal, cut under an Act of 1791, ran from the Old Quay in Manchester through the Irwell valley to a point north of Prestolee, where a branch continued to Bury. Acts of 1792 and 1793 authorised the building of the Ashton-under-Lyne Canal, which with various branches gave an intricate system of waterways on the east side of Manchester, including those to the (former) Werneth colliery at Oldham, to the Bardsley collieries, and to Heaton Norris, over 100 feet higher than the valley of the Mersey at Stockport: a link was also made with the Huddersfield Canal along the Tame valley, and therefore with the waterways across Yorkshire to Goole and the Humber. Before the Huddersfield Canal was built under an Act of 1794 through Stalybridge and Saddleworth, goods were sent to Hull by wagons to Huddersfield, and thence by Sir John Ramsden's canal and the Calder–Hebble navigation: alternatively merchandise was taken by road through the Walsden spillway from Rochdale to Todmorden and Sowerby and forwarded on the Calder–Hebble navigation. This route was traversed by the Rochdale Canal, completed in 1804 (pp. 81–2). All these canals were helpful in giving connections between Lancashire and Yorkshire and the same objective inspired the building of the Leeds and Liverpool Canal, originally sanctioned in 1770 but not finally completed until 1816; although its influence on industrial location is particularly clear at Burnley and Blackburn, and most of all in Liverpool, much of its course is through a rural countryside. The Lancaster Canal, from Kendal to the course of the Leeds and Liverpool Canal near Chorley, also dates from the end of the eighteenth century, having been authorised in 1792. North of Lancaster the canal runs for long distances within a mile of the main railway line to Scotland, but its course is generally winding and involved; at Lancaster there is a viaduct admired ever since it was built. A branch was made to Glasson dock in 1825; but this dock, built in 1787, never had much success. Two other canals are of some interest: the Ulverston, less than 2 miles long, built in the 1790s with the object of making the town a port, and the Peak Forest, opened in 1800 (p. 68).

Industry

Industry already had a long tradition in Lancastria by the eighteenth century, and Redford has commented that by the middle of the sixteenth century Manchester was already an important centre of linen and woollen manufacture and a market for textile goods made elsewhere. In part its success as a trading centre was due to the lack of hampering restrictions on newcomers, who were received and even welcomed. The association of the textile trades with sixteenth-century Flemish immigrants is apparently mere inference lacking definite evidence. The textile trade developed wholly on a domestic basis, and by the eighteenth century some regional specialisation—later to acquire a most interesting but different form (pp. 99–101) —was seen. In the east from Colne and Burnley across the Rossendales to Bury and Rochdale, and in the numerous upland valleys around these towns, the early-eighteenth century trade was in wool, as in Yorkshire. Goods were carried along such pack-horse trails as the 'Long Causeway', from Burnley to Heptonstall (near Hebden Bridge) and Halifax, which passes through the Cliviger valley on the hill flanks high up above the gorge; there are many such old trails on high ground in the Pennines and Rossendales. Undoubtedly the domestic industry provided a useful supplement to the meagre resources on many high-lying farms in a difficult environment; in some places home working made possible an upward extension of settlement (p. 72). In west Lancashire, linen was made, with Preston, Ormskirk, and Warrington as market centres for its sale. Warrington was well known as a centre for sailcloth, and part at least of the flax (for which the heavy clays and damp climate were suitable) was grown locally though some was imported from Ireland, partly through Preston. In time this trade extended westwards to Wigan and even to Manchester, but fustian[1] was the main textile manufactured in central and southeast Lancashire. The fustian district extended from Blackburn, with a minor development at Clitheroe, to Bolton, and included the area westwards to Leigh and also the northern part of the Manchester lowland. Probably the trade grew here because imported cotton fibre, as well as flax, was available in Manchester, brought largely along the Mersey–Irwell navigation; eventually the cotton area bore a marked resemblance to the eighteenth century fustian area. The imports of raw cotton increased five times between 1700–10 and 1770–80.

Manchester merchants did so much to make the cotton industry successful that by 1774 some 30,000 people in and around the town were engaged in cotton manufacture. The merchants bought grey cloth from the weavers, arranged for its dyeing and finishing to meet the needs of customers, and dealt with export houses and wholesalers in London, Bristol, Liverpool, Hull, Norwich, and Newcastle. They gradually won the merchant trade of Bolton in the late eighteenth century, so that the town's warehouses were abandoned one by one. Some of the merchants carried goods to fairs, or hawked them about the country on pack-horses, or brought back sheep's wool for the manufacture of worsted yarn at Manchester, or for the clothiers of Rochdale, Saddleworth (Yorkshire), and much of the West Riding. The inventions generally associated with the Industrial Revolution did not result in an immediate cessation of handloom weaving, which in places lingered on well into the nineteenth century. The new mills were run first on water power, until the early nineteenth century, when the superiority of steam was clearly demonstrated; but the concentration on coalfields was developing before 1800. Even so, the steam-using cotton industry, though concentrated in Lancashire and adjacent areas of northeastern Cheshire, with some extensions into Yorkshire, was by no means confined to this area, for there were several mills in the Midlands around Derby and

---

[1] Fustian is a heavy fabric with a linen warp and a cotton weft, produced in various forms—often corded, but sometimes cut and raised. A. P. Wadsworth has written of the 'cotton-linens', which could be included as fustians, made in Manchester and district.

Nottingham, in the west of Scotland, in Durham, in London—and even in Bristol and various other places.

A number of towns sprang into vigorous life as a result of the factory development in textiles. Stalybridge in 1748 had 140 people supported mainly by the home spinning of worsted yarns for hosiers in Nottingham; but its first cotton mill was built in 1776, and run on water power, to be replaced by a steam engine twenty years later. Oldham, with about a hundred houses in 1761, had an old-established hat industry and a variety of fustian goods were made in the district; its first steam engine dates from 1796, when there were twelve mills employing several thousand people. At Stockport, where silk was well established early in the eighteenth century, there were some thirty 'manufacturers' by 1789, of whom two produced silk, three buttons, and the rest checks, calicoes, and cottons: some of these manufacturers, however, were buyers of domestic produce and suppliers of raw materials to the home workers, though a steam-power cotton mill was built in Stockport in 1790, and several of the old silk mills were converted for cotton spinning. Apart from the clear impetus to town growth of this new factory building, there were various efforts to establish rural industrial communities (on which, see also pp. 116–17). One of these was at Styal (Cheshire), where Quarry Bank Mill, now of great interest to industrial archaeologists, was built in 1784 by a member of the Greg family. The site was chosen regardless of every consideration except water power and communications, as the various pack-horse trails that crossed the valley here could be used for taking cotton yarn and finished cloth to and from Manchester, and also to handloom weavers in their crofts and villages. As the local labour supply was inadequate the Poor Law Unions were asked to supply apprentices who were boarded out or put in apprentice houses; in 1790 there were 183 free labourers and 80 apprentices, drawn from a wide radius. Samuel Oldknow, perhaps an even more famous industrialist than Greg, bought an estate at Mellor, near Marple in 1787, where he erected a spinning factory, diverted the river Goyt, and constructed dams and reservoirs for water power. Eventually he made lime-kilns and sank coalshafts. He encouraged the building of roads in the district and also of the Peak Forest Canal, by which some of his lime was carried to farms in upland areas as well as in lowland Cheshire. Unlike the Greg mill, however, Oldknow's has fallen into ruin.

Urban growth was to characterise the nineteenth century in Lancastria. There were numerous trading towns, many of which already had a strong industrial tradition by 1800: there was a growing textile industry becoming, gradually but surely, located in factories able to absorb the displaced home workers and many immigrants as well; there were roads that, though hardly adequate to their needs, made possible at least some circulation of commerce and people—no doubt in discomfort; there was a network of canals and river navigations, and more were planned. Above all,

Fig. 15 WATER POWER AND THE EARLY TEXTILE INDUSTRY. The upper diagram shows the location of mill-sites at breaks of profile along two minor Pennine streams. The lower map shows the site of Broadbottom, Cheshire, an early textile village with mills using the power available at two diversion gorges on the river Etherow.

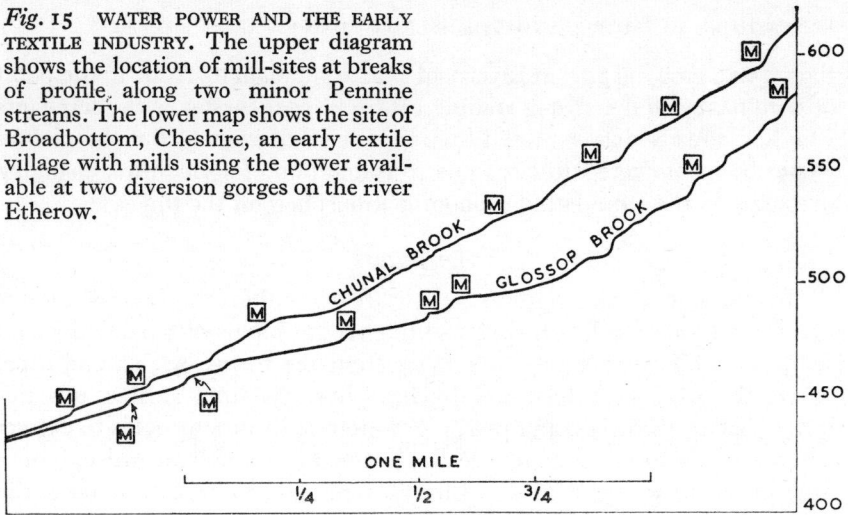

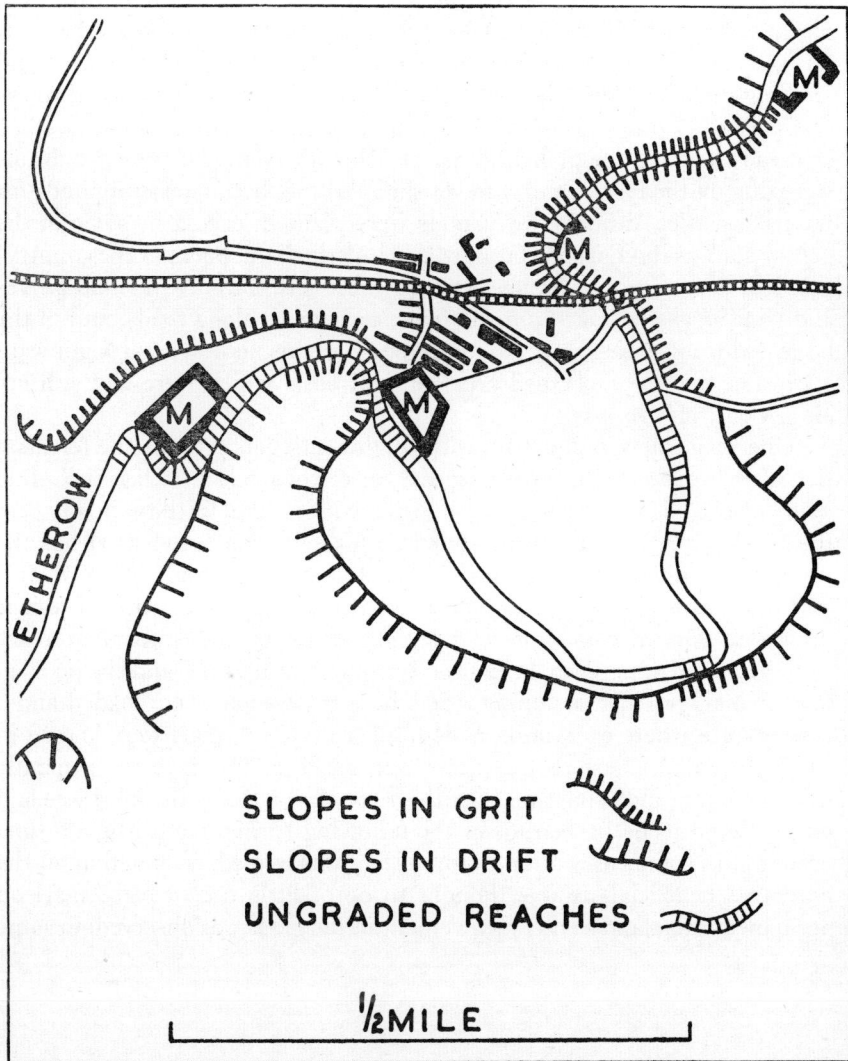

CHUNAL BROOK

GLOSSOP BROOK

ONE MILE

1/4   1/2   3/4

ETHEROW

SLOPES IN GRIT

SLOPES IN DRIFT

UNGRADED REACHES

1/2 MILE

there was a growing port in Liverpool able to supplant its rivals to the point of dominance, and a strong trading centre in Manchester with merchants who had already demonstrated their commercial acumen. But the picture would be incomplete without some consideration of agriculture, changing markedly in the stimulating economic atmosphere of the times.

Agriculture

By the end of the eighteenth century agriculture in Lancastria was becoming economically prosperous under the stimulus of a rising demand for farm produce. Manures were sent from the towns by cart and canal barge; the soils were fertilised by lime brought from various quarries in the distant Pennines, and marl pits were dug in various fields to extract a fertilising substance that, ideally but not invariably, consisted of a lime-impregnated clay or loam. Efforts were made to reclaim some of the peatmosses by drainage, so that in time they were transformed from the black wastes that depressed Defoe into areas that blossomed as the rose, but with crops and vegetables, though in a few areas also with flowers and seedling plants for suburban gardens. Much of Cheshire retained through this period its tradition of dairy farming, partly because many leases had clauses restricting the ploughing up of fields for crops. Ditches and drains were dug on the farms, and some of the marl pits became useful ponds for watering cattle. Although few woods were planted, except by some of the gentry such as the Earl of Stamford near Altrincham, much of the country-side had a bowery appearance, as trees were left not only in small groves and windbreaks but also in hedgerows, as avenues along roads, and in the large fields of areas given to dairying. To this, however, a significant exception was the reclaimed areas of peatmoss, which were and still are almost entirely treeless.

One major development from the eighteenth century was the fertilisa-tion of the soils, which, consisting of a variety of sands and clays including many of glacial origin, were not all gifted with natural fertility; in any case the fertility required renewal. Holt in 1795 said that 'good marl has the property of stiffening light land, and meliorating, and unbinding (if dry) stiff land. Stiff clay, it is true, for a long time resists the rain before it is saturated; but when made wet, it longer retains the moisture than a dry soil'. Marl had apparently been used from medieval times, and the pools in former marl pits had a sloping side where the wagons were loaded and a vertical face where excavation ended. Three types of marl were known in Lancashire and Cheshire, clay, slate, and shell; the first type was generally used for light sandy soils and the others for clay. Usually the marl was laid on grassland to be broken up in the following spring, from May or June onwards, in some cases after a crop of hay was reaped: frost action on the marl was beneficial. It was thought to be of little use to place marl on permanent grassland as no improvement in the grass was observed: in some places, however, marl was added as a crop grew, as well as on grassland and fallows, in anticipation of useful frost action and the spring ploughing. Not always was the right type of marl applied, for some farmers mistook a brown shining clay for loam and applied clay to clay. But the general effects were undoubtedly beneficial. Sea sludge was collected from the Ribble and Wyre rivers and some excellent fruit crops at Formby were ascribed to its use; similarly, at Weston (Cheshire) sea sludge from the Mersey was used. In some places on the Lancashire coast, a compost was made of lime, earth, dung, seaweed, and even shellfish. The finest of all fertilisers, however, was farmyard manure, generally mixed with earth from ditches or from the sides of lanes. Near the towns it was bought from stables, and fetched almost three times the price of nightsoil, available in large quantities from the towns. In some areas the lack of manure was a serious obstacle to the improvement, even the maintenance, of agriculture, as for example in the Fylde, where many farms had been ruined by long-continued cropping, though this area was well known for its fine cattle. Manures also included scrapings from the streets, mixed with lime, and liquid material from the farmyards.

Many other manures were used. In Cheshire there were numerous limekilns, especially on the east side, where lime was conveyed from Derbyshire, largely by road; a large area in the southeast of the county was supplied with lime from kilns at Astbury, south of Congleton. Much of the lime used in the central and western areas was brought from the Welsh coast and then along the Weaver, and some was also brought from the Leek district along the Trent–Mersey Canal and sold cheaply at the Acton Bridge Wharf, near Northwich. Lime was laid on fallow land, generally with scrapings of earth from gutters and ditches. In the Wirral, however, comparatively little was employed. Liming was widespread in Lancashire, and in some places manures of chemical origin were available such as soap ashes, which were reputed to be 'if put upon old lays . . . very advantageous, and very durable in pastures, but not so durable either on ploughed land or in meadow'. At Ashworth Hall near Rochdale the owner was experimenting with the use of bone dust, and the skimmings of sugar refineries mixed with soil made an extremely rich manure. Near Liverpool blubber from the whaling yards was used, and in places soot was collected for application in the spring on corn crops. In short, a wide variety of manuring was tried, not invariably with successful results, though there was clearly a wish for agricultural improvement and a willingness to experiment.

Similarly, there was a widespread interest in drainage at this time. Field drains were dug to varying depths according to the type of soil, and a channel was made for the water at the base of the trench, with slats of wood, stones, slates, broken bricks, or specially constructed bricks making a kind of inner pipe. In some areas of Lancashire hardened peat was used to construct the underground drain. The earth was replaced afterwards, and such was the demand for land that many marl pits were also covered in, though a large number of them still remain as ponds. Interest was growing in peat-moss reclamation, and two Liverpool men began the reclamation of Trafford Moss (now Trafford Park industrial estate beside the Manchester Ship Canal) in 1793. They made drains 6 yards apart, which opened into wider drains 100 yards apart carrying the water to the river Irwell; after experiments, the favoured practice was to make the initial drain only 1 foot deep, and gradually work down to a cut 3 feet deep and 18 inches wide. When the moss dried so that the base of the trench was dry, a cut 5 inches wide and 18 inches deep was dug and covered up as a permanent drain; by this time the general level of the peat was sinking through the loss of water. Before drainage, Trafford Moss had not been worth one shilling an acre, but afterwards it was valued at £3 an acre. Similar changes were noted on other mosses, such as Bootle near Liverpool, and Rainford, in southwestern Lancashire. Rainford had been improved from 1780 by making drains, and from 1787 potatoes, oats, and clover were grown. There was some division of opinion on the wisdom of paring and burning the surface of peat-mosses, but apparently it was widely practised, for example on Rainford moss and at Partington and Carrington—on Carrington moss, for potato growing—though technically burning was illegal, and it was also prohibited in many of the leases. The peatmosses were generally divided into narrow strips called Moss rooms, which ran from the edge to the centre of the bog, and as these were reclaimed they gave their shape to the new fields and farms.

The farms were of widely varied sizes. Both in Cheshire and Lancashire there were a few large farms, covering 350 acres or more—even in some cases 600 acres—having a residence called the 'Old Hall' or 'Manor House', of which some still survive, but almost invariably with a rebuilt house. Many of these in Cheshire were already famous for dairying and cheese making. Most of the farms were far smaller, and in Cheshire most of the land was in holdings of 50–100 acres, though there were numerous small farms of 20 acres or less. Holland gives a sample of 140 farms covering 5,689 acres (c.8½ square miles) and shows that only 2 were of more than 200 acres, and only 3 of 150–200 acres; 11 were of 100–150 acres, 30 of 50–100 acres, and 19 of 20–50 acres. But 75 were of 20 acres or less, and many of these could hardly rank as farms at all; their total area was only 253 acres. Holland notes that the holders were mainly employed as labourers on the larger farms or in other ways. In the Pennines, especially on the lower slopes, some of the enclosures of waste land were partly associated with industrial expansion: for example in Mellor hamlets were built having one or two farms and cottages with hatting shops, weaving sheds, and a small warehouse, on the road across Rowarth moor from Glossop to Marple. There are signs of similar developments around Rainow and Bredbury, and also Kerridge and Bollington. In Lancashire farms of 50 acres or less were most usual, and it was noted that many of the enclosures had resulted in small fields and farms, which had an unnecessary number of hedges, banks, and ditches that consumed a good deal of valuable land, harboured vermin, and impeded rather than facilitated the drainage of water. On the other hand, there were objections to large fields, as the cattle in them were exposed to the weather and could not stay out as long in the autumn, and near the sea some crops were injured by winds. Many of the banks were full of weeds that spread eagerly into the fields. In Cheshire and much of Lancashire the hedgerows were mainly of thorn, which was replacing the older field boundaries of hazel, alder, willow, holly, and other trees; but in the north of Lancashire there were some stone walls or even banks made of pebbles and earth, notably in the Furness district. By the end of the eighteenth century most of the open-field arable land had been enclosed, and farms were spreading over the 'waste' land and commons; for example Holland in 1808 thought that Delamere Forest offered little prospect for further enclosure, but much of it was enclosed between 1812 and 1820 (see also pp. 165, 167).

Leases in the Northwest were in many cases granted for the lifetime of three named persons, though others were for a period of seven years or more. In many cases there were stipulations on the amount of land that could be ploughed, which in Cheshire might be only one-quarter of the farm so that the amount of wheat and oats grown on the smaller holdings was sufficient only for the household and the stock. There were similar conditions on many Lancashire farms, with provisions that all the hay or straw was to be consumed on the premises, and that no wheat could be sown on bean stubble or any other stubble from which a crop had been taken in the same year. By the end of the century rents were high in Cheshire, with an average of 30s. an acre, but as much as 50s. to 55s. on some of the good soils in the south of the county and far more, £6 to £8, near the towns. Holland ascribes the high rent to four causes: firstly, the price of cheese and butter was high; secondly, extensive buildings were needed on a dairy farm; thirdly, the farmer's household was fed primarily from the farm; and fourthly, the demand from the towns for his produce was heavy and remunerative. Both by canal and road the farmer was able to reach his hungry markets cheaply. The farmhouses were substantial, mainly of brick with slates though some in Cheshire were timber-framed with brick or wattle and daub. Thatch had been largely replaced by slate, though many of the cottages still had thatch rising from eaves only some 6 feet above the ground. Many new cottages were built in the eighteenth century, generally of brick with four rooms and, at the gable end, a shippon on the ground floor with a barn above it. A favourite site for a cottage was a wide part of a lane or the border of a piece of common land where the occupier could keep his geese and pigs, or even a small cow. Over most of the Northwest the houses were spread irregularly over the countryside; but in the Wirral peninsula Holland notes: 'The farmhouses and buildings are all crowded together into villages, without any regard to the advantages of situation or to regularity of construction. The farmer may be two to three miles from his fields.'

Grass for the support of dairy cattle was regarded with some veneration over much of the Northwest, though the arable emphasis of north Cheshire and south Lancashire was already marked by the end of the eighteenth century. In the Nantwich area the grass was regarded as the finest in England, as it grew bountifully on the stiff clay soils, and in the southwest of the county (the Broxton Hundred) with the Wirral peninsula, grass flourished on a clayey loam or a strong clay. In Lancashire, much of the farming was mixed, and in the Fylde, traditionally the 'granary of Lancashire', there were some prime long-horned cattle which were sold widely. Milk was in great demand, and much of Manchester's supply was brought along the Bridgewater Canal: in Liverpool, however, it was carried as much as 10 miles along the roads, but several hundred milch cows were kept on rented fields on the edge of the city and fed on hay or brewery grains. There was some sowing of clover on grasslands, but generally the grass was left to regenerate itself after crops had been taken from the land for several years. When grass was sown on wet land, it was laid down on small ridges, though some farmers were making ridges 6 to 8 yards broad with a shallow trough between them. This was found easier to scythe if the grass was to be harvested as hay, and also easier for the cattle to graze, as the troughs, or 'internals', were shallow. Accounts of the time suggest that though the grasslands were so highly valued, and even manured or marled, more could be done to improve the quality of the herbage.

Crop rotations were varied. In Cheshire, on clay lands of no great strength, oats would be followed by a summer fallow, then by wheat (or oats again) and then by another crop of oats: alternatively wheat might be followed by oats for two years, and in either case the land would then be left in grass for several years. Sandy loams were sown to oats, followed by two crops of barley, though in some cases two crops of oats would be followed by two of barley; several years' use as grass came afterwards. Weak sands were used for oats in three consecutive years, with seven or eight years of grass, though on stronger sands oats were sown for two years, followed by turnips and, after marling, barley; on such soils, the period of use as grass was only four to five years. Everywhere in Cheshire the reverence for grass was seen. In some parts of Lancashire, however, a long succession of crops was taken from the same land: some fields in the Fylde were said to have been continuously cropped for more than a century. Marl was applied, followed by oats for two or three years, then alternate crops of beans and barley for about six years, when a summer fallow was given and some 'till' added (generally a mixture of earth and lime), followed

74

by wheat, then oats, beans, or barley for two years; after another fallow, this same sequence continued for twenty years or more. Such virtually continuous cropping was regarded as ruinous to the soil, and the Fylde was greatly in need of agricultural regeneration at the end of the eighteenth century.

Other rotations practised in the county included the sowing of oats or barley with dung, and then—if the soil were regarded as sufficiently rich—another sowing of barley, followed by a fallow to restore the land for wheat, then barley again, after which clover and seeds were set for hay. On some farms crops were taken for three consecutive years, first potatoes, then wheat, and finally barley with dung, after which the land was laid down to grass. In other cases early potatoes were followed by turnips, wheat, or barley, though in some instances early potatoes were followed by white clover and hay seeds, which were left to seed to produce a good grass crop. Although there is ample evidence that the rotation of crops was widespread there were indications that some farming practices were bad. Near Preston, for example, it was observed that oats was grown for as many years as a crop would appear, after which the land was fallowed for wheat followed by several years more of oats; eventually the land, left fallow, was covered with reeds and rushes until grass regenerated itself. Writers of the day were strongly in favour of replacing fallow periods by the raising of cabbages, beans, or turnips: Arthur Young had so overwhelming an affection for turnips that one suspects that he had one on his writing table as a source of inspiration.

The demand for all agricultural produce was growing steadily. Cheese, butter, and milk were selling firmly, and buttermilk was sold to poor people who consumed it with potatoes, or with oats as porridge, to which treacle was sometimes added. Poultry were reared both for eggs and table birds, notably in the Fylde, though hens were kept by the cottagers virtually everywhere; the Ormskirk market on Thursday was well known for its supplies, and patronised by poulterers who sold the fowl and eggs on Saturdays. In Cheshire also the markets were well supplied with eggs and table birds, and dealers bought them for later sale in the markets of the industrial towns. Few turkeys were kept, as they were regarded as a menace to crops, but geese were bred in large numbers by the cottagers, who kept them on commons or in lanes until midsummer, when they were sold to farmers who fed them on the stubble for sale in the autumn. One notable area for geese was Martin Mere, near Southport (see also p. 77), where large flocks were kept, happily feeding on grasses, aquatic plants, fishes, and insects, unaware of their destiny in the Michaelmas markets. But the local demand could not be met from the local supplies, for only the Fylde had any considerable surplus of poultry. The Liverpool markets drew supplies from Cheshire, Wales, the Isle of Man, and even Scotland and Ireland; and the Manchester markets acquired produce from Cheshire,

Derbyshire, Nottinghamshire, and Lincolnshire, and even from the markets of Kendal and Penrith.

In arable produce also it was clear that the local demand was far greater than the local supply, and it was said that Lancashire and Cheshire together could not provide the local needs for more than a few weeks each year. Large quantities of wheat and flour were brought in to Liverpool by sea, notably from Norfolk. Why not, therefore, sow more, and improve the output by better farming methods? Estimates given for Cheshire of the average yields per acre were wheat 24 bushels, barley 30 bushels, and oats 40 bushels: the estimates for Lancashire are rather lower, and it is certain that there were wide variations from one farm to another. Oats and wheat were ground at various local mills, and the former was a major foodstuff of the poorer classes, conspicuously in the north and east of Lancashire where oatcakes and porridge were favoured. Of other foodstuffs, the large quantities of potatoes sold in the markets of Manchester, Liverpool, and other towns were drawn largely from north Cheshire, including the Wirral, and south Lancashire. In places yields were as much as 10 tons to the acre and the plants were carefully protected against frost. Some market garden produce was grown, including carrots on the sandy loams north of Liverpool around Kirkby and towards Southport; similar soils in the Altrincham area were used for carrots and peas, and on some black loams at Timperley, near Altrincham, onions and other vegetables were grown for the Lancashire markets. In these areas nightsoil was a useful fertiliser and gardening belts of great productivity were developed; even asparagus was reported to be available in the Liverpool markets.

Half-starved mountain sheep were characteristic of Lancashire though on the Cheshire uplands a healthier type was reared. Many of the sheep on the open moorlands belonged to the innkeepers with premises beside the Pennine roads. Some sheep were kept on lowlands, having been brought by the Westmorland farmers at one year old, kept for three years, and then sold to Lancashire graziers for fattening, notably in Furness, where on the enclosed fields of Low Furness, seven or eight sheep could be kept to each acre, though on the moors of Seathwaite, in the Lake District, there were only three or four to the acre, and these were only half the weight of the Lowland flocks. Few were kept in the south of Lancashire, especially near the towns, as the fences were inadequate and dogs too numerous; the latter is still a complaint of farmers near the towns. Some of the open land available as rough grazing for sheep has since been forested, notably in Delamere Forest, where some land has also been reclaimed for fields since the eighteenth century. In its previous state before enclosure, Delamere Forest was a valued pasture, having a dry sandy loam lying thinly on red sandstones; the sheep were a small variety, giving good mutton and wool, which was mainly sold to Yorkshire manufacturers. The sheep, with some cattle, were grazed by farmers in the surrounding areas, but when the

Forest was enclosed their rights—in some cases imaginary—were withdrawn. Young and other travellers noted small flocks of sheep, 20 to 200 strong, on various commons but the farmlands were generally unsuitable as their soils were either natural clays or marled loams.

At the end of the eighteenth century, there were clear signs of agricultural intensification, due largely to the stimulus of urban demand. Much had been done to improve conditions by drainage, with fertilisation in various forms, though there were cases of ruinous crop rotations and bad cultivation. Some regretted the necessity of growing so demanding, and at times climatically precarious, a crop as wheat, and there were also criticisms of the prohibition on the export of wool. Tythes were regarded as a burden, and it was said that the glebe lands were badly cultivated. Short leases were deplored, and doubtless added to the difficulties of arranging farm improvements, especially those such as drainage schemes which commonly involved co-operation between neighbours. Near the towns there were too many dogs, and rats were numerous everywhere. Weeds grew too plentifully, and many farmers were apparently almost indifferent to them. But there were notable advances in land reclamation; of one of these, Martin Mere, R. Millward has given a fine description.[1]

> The rich dark soils, the huge rectangular fields that seem to stretch almost to the horizon, and the neat clumps of woodland, all lie on the site of Lancashire's largest lake. . . . Thomas Fleetwood . . . devised the plan for draining Martin Mere in 1692 . . . [but it] became a lake in 1755, when the flood gates that kept out the sea at high spring tides were broken through in a severe storm from the north-west that coincided with high water. It remained the home of wild birds until 1781 when Thomas Eccleston of Scarisbrick put up the capital for another attempt at reclamation. . . . A triple set of gates was built across the main sluice between the coast and the exit of the lake in 1783. In the following year several acres were put down to corn. Once again, in 1813, storms threatened the security of the new farms in the bed of Martin Mere, when the two outer gates were broken down by the sea. They were replaced by cast-iron cylinders equipped with valves, and with the help of pumping stations along the main sluice this area of rich, black soils, 10 feet below the high-water mark of spring tides, has become one of the most famous potato-growing regions in the county.

[1] In *Lancashire, an illustrated essay on the history of the landscape* (London, 1955), 50.

CHAPTER 5

Lancastria in the Middle of the Nineteenth Century

In 1851 the Census Commissioners learned with surprise that in Britain more people lived in towns than in the rural areas, and rightly recognised that this was a state of national living unique in history. It was an expression of the growing power of industry to support workers clustered in towns and industrial settlements called villages for want of a better word, many of which were destined in time to become towns. Lancashire with Cheshire as an industrial district had advanced markedly by the mid-nineteenth century, and it is therefore not surprising that in 1851, 68% of Lancashire's population and 48% of Cheshire's were in towns. These figures are only of limited value, for the basis of definition of a town was somewhat uncertain. But the statistical dominance of the town was seen in the Northwest twenty to thirty years before it was seen in the country as a whole, and many of the towns still show clear traces of the early nineteenth century, in old mills and factories and workers' houses built by the proprietors for their work-people.

Manchester and Liverpool were major towns of Britain by the mid-nineteenth century, and many more towns were growing rapidly under the stimulus of the two major industries, coalmining and cotton working, with which engineering was inevitably associated to supply machinery. And as the towns grew, some of the farmers became more prosperous and agricultural advancement was seen, though only, as shown on pages 103–9, in certain areas. But there was no clear and firmly drawn line between town and country, as both pits and mills spread themselves widely over the countryside. Coal was mined in numerous small pits, and miners' cottages were built in rows or formless huddles of dwellings. Cotton mills were placed beside streams, used for power and for washing processes, and in many places there were groups of cottages beside the mills, many of which have long since crumbled into ruin. Not all, however, for there are still some remote mill villages and hamlets in Lancashire and on the Pennine fringe of Cheshire (Plates 10–12, 14).

Steadily through the eighteenth century, turnpike roads, canals, and ports had opened up the Northwest to commerce, and not unnaturally some of the first railways were built here. Although some of the canals remained prosperous long after railways were built, for passenger traffic and the quick transport of goods, the railways had an undeniable competitive advantage. But for cargoes such as coal, grain, and other agricultural produce, the canals were still used considerably, and the hope that this would continue was expressed in 1856, soon after the Rochdale Canal Company had leased its line of navigation for over 20 miles to railway companies; it was reported that 'besides the import of raw materials and the export of manufactures over the German Ocean, Manchester has to import the food of its people, and in the cost of wheat, cattle, and potatoes from Yorkshire and Lincolnshire carriage forms an important item'. Even so, from the 1830s the Manchester Chamber of Commerce paid little attention to the canal system, though there was a continued interest in the navigation of the Mersey and the Irwell. Nevertheless, some of the canals, notably the Bridgewater and the Leeds–Liverpool, remained prosperous until the twentieth century (Plates 44–46).

Canals, roads, and railways

Canals. The network of canals achieved by the 1850s is shown in Figure 13 and described on pages 64–6. To a great extent the canals had contributed to the industrial growth of the Northwest, and had become favoured sites for industrial premises. Of these, two examples may be given: in Liverpool, a large number of factories and warehouses were built near the Leeds and Liverpool Canal; and in Manchester the Rochdale Canal, still surrounded by a number of fine early-nineteenth century warehouses close to the centre of the city, gradually acquired a line of factories between the city and Failsworth, where it turns northward. In Liverpool the canal-side industries became an extension of the dock-side belt and imparted a distinctly artisan character to the north-central areas of the city. The attraction of industry to the Rochdale Canal helped to join Manchester with Oldham, 7 miles away, by a continuous line of buildings; along the road parallel to the canal there was virtual continuity of settlement by 1848, according to the new 6 inch to 1 mile Ordnance map of the time. Manufactures requiring water, notably in the textile trades, for steam raising, processing, and other purposes, were allowed to draw it from the canals. Many other examples of the canal-side location of industries could be given; on the Leeds–Liverpool Canal it is marked at many places, notably at Blackburn and Burnley.

Passenger services on the canals had been successful before the railway age, but once accelerated transport was available they failed. On the Bridgewater Canal packet boats had gone daily from Manchester to Runcorn since 1807; but in 1850 there was a sharp reduction of fares to compete with the railway. One threat from the railways was their interest in leasing or buying up canals, finally made illegal in 1872. Some canals

79

were allowed to fall into disrepair, and in other cases the railways diverted traffic to their lines. In 1854, for example, the Rochdale Canal was leased by a group of railways including the Lancashire and Yorkshire, and not efficiently repaired, and the Manchester, Bolton, and Bury Canal lost much of its traffic once it was under railway control. The Bridgewater Canal, however, was vigorously maintained, and in 1840 the trustees attempted to widen and deepen their waterway so that it would take boats of 300 tons. This canal was merged with the Mersey and Irwell navigations in 1842, though there had been a working arrangement since 1810; like the Rochdale Canal, it had a fine group of warehouses in its dock area at Hulme, immediately south of the city centre of Manchester. Perhaps its greatest advantage was the link with other waterways, including in Manchester one with the Rochdale Canal, which still survives. At Worsley, running to the north of Chat Moss, there is a branch of the Bridgewater Canal to Leigh, which joins the Leigh and Wigan branch of the Leeds and Liverpool Canal; at Runcorn (p. 65) there was a link with the Trent–Mersey Canal and by the Runcorn and Weston Canal, with the Weaver navigation. Increasingly the Bridgewater Canal superseded the old Mersey–Irwell navigation, which through silting gradually became unnavigable in the 1880s. Always associated with coal transport, the Bridgewater Canal also had cargoes of cotton sent to Manchester in a single day, and when the idea of the Ship Canal was put forward the aim was to avoid transhipment of cotton cargoes at Liverpool and thus reduce transport costs and the profits of the Liverpool merchants (p. 186). The trustees of the Bridgewater Canal were prominent among the opponents of the Ship Canal.

To a considerable extent, the canals opened up the Lancashire coalfield. Coal was carried along the Leeds–Liverpool Canal to Liverpool, and figures for Manchester in 1834, 1836, and 1840 show that over three-fifths of the city's supply was carried by canal; by the 1840s, Manchester and district consumed over 26,000 tons a week, mainly from the Pendleton and Oldham districts, and Love in 1842 noted that one colliery alone sent out 40 boats every week, each with 20 tons of coal. One of the most vivid reminders of this is the colliery at Worsley, which is penetrated by waterways from the Bridgewater Canal. The colliery is entered by an archway 6 feet wide and 5 feet high through which special long flat-bottomed boats, carrying 7 to 8 tons of coal, were carried along by pulling on a handrail; in time, a vast ramifying system of waterways, in all over forty miles long, went forward to the coalfaces. Eventually coal was worked on four levels, two below and one above the main canal, and from 1795 two of these were connected by an inclined plane. Originally the Duke of Bridgewater owned only the collieries at Worsley, but he acquired others in the coalfield between Worsley, Bolton, and Bury, and in time many more pits were sunk, some of which were connected by tramways with the canal and its extension to Leigh.

Another expectation of the canal builders, largely realised, was that lime would be carried to fertilise the acid soils of Lancashire, and the Lancaster Canal, built under an Act of 1792, was designed to convey, among other cargoes, lime from the bare hills around Carnforth southwards and coal to the Fylde. The canal runs from a junction with the Leeds and Liverpool Canal, near Chorley, to Kendal. In 1833, Baines noted, a swift-sailing packet called the *Water Witch*, drawn by horses, covered the journey of 57 miles from Preston to Kendal in 7 hours; but the service failed after the railway was built in 1840. Lancaster's period of prosperity apparently lasted only for the second half of the eighteenth century; by the nineteenth century it had ceased to be a significant port. The decline was due in part to the commercial failure of a shipping house in 1799, but also—and this is far more relevant—to the accumulation of sand in the river so that only small ships could enter. The building of an outport, Glasson Dock, which was connected with Lancaster by a branch of the canal, was of only temporary significance. Another factor adverse to Lancaster was the rise of Liverpool to its position of dominance on the west coast. The only canal in Furness was the Ship Canal to Ulverston built in 1794–5 (65 feet wide at the top and 30 feet wide at the bottom depth of 16 feet, and 1¼ miles long), with the object of making the town a port.

The Pennines had for centuries been regarded as a major barrier in England; but in 1797 Aiken could comment on one of the marvels of the age:

> At the beginning of the century, it was thought a most arduous task to make a *highroad* practicable for carriages over the moors which separate Yorkshire from Lancashire; and now they are pierced through by *three navigable canals*! Long may it remain the centre of a trade capable of maintaining these mighty works!

The most northerly of these was the Leeds–Liverpool Canal which, having followed the Aire valley in Yorkshire, runs through Skipton and then traverses the drumlin-studded lowland of the Ribble–Aire gap, where its summit level near Foulridge is only 433 feet above sea level. The canal then follows the valleys of the Lancashire Calder and Darwen through Burnley and Blackburn, and then makes a wide sweep past Chorley and through Wigan to Liverpool; in its course round the western flanks of Rossendale it uses some of the glacial spillways of the Withnell series (p. 8). Its important connections with Leigh and with the Bridgewater Canal are discussed on page 65. Farther south, the Rochdale Canal from Sowerby Bridge through Todmorden was sanctioned by Parliament in 1794 though not formally opened until 1804: the town of Rochdale is connected to the main canal by a branch from Littleborough. This canal uses the easiest passage-way through the central Pennines, the Walsden Gorge, which carried glacial meltwaters from the glacial lake in the

81

Manchester lowland into the Calder valley; one attraction of this route was the low summit level, of c.600 feet. Many industries were attracted to the canal-side sites, particularly at Middleton Junction (Chadderton), Castleton, and Littleborough; those nearer Manchester have been noted on page 66. The third canal, the Huddersfield 'narrow', authorised by Acts of 1792 and 1793, climbs through the Tame valley from the Ashton Canal in Manchester and is a familiar sight to travellers on the main railway line from Manchester to Huddersfield. It runs beside Ashton, and thence through Stalybridge (Cheshire) and Saddleworth (Yorkshire) to the Standedge tunnel to connect with Sir John Ramsden's canal at Huddersfield.

In the early nineteenth century, Manchester was said to be as well provided with waterways as any city in the Netherlands (p. 79). The Bridgewater Canal is perhaps the most obvious in the city itself, but the Ashton Canal is well seen in the somewhat decayed eastern part of the city, for example in Ancoats. The Manchester, Bolton, and Bury Canal, now partly removed, was cut under an Act of 1791 (pp. 65–6). Finally, the Peak Forest Canal, authorised in 1794 and opened in 1800, begins at Ashton, where it joins the Ashton Canal, and runs south past Dukinfield, Hyde, and Romiley into the Goyt valley, which is followed to Whaley Bridge, with a tramroad extension to the limestone quarries near Dove Houses.

In Cheshire the canals were significant both for industrial and agricultural progress. The use of the Weaver navigation for conveying salt to the Mersey estuary led not only to the growth of the Cheshire salt industry but also to the establishment of a chemical industry on the coalfield at St Helens, served by the Sankey Canal (p. 64); later this industry developed at both Runcorn and Northwich. The canals west of the Weaver, completed before the end of the eighteenth century (p. 65), gave some stimulus to agriculture and, less prominently, to industry; and a further extension came after 1826, when the Birmingham and Liverpool Junction Canal was approved and constructed from its junction with the Ellesmere Canal at Hurleston, northwest of Nantwich, to Audlem in the extreme south of the county, where there is a fine flight of locks, and then continues towards the Black Country. Finally, in the east of the county, the Macclesfield Canal was authorised in 1827 and completed in 1831 from Talke, just inside the Staffordshire boundary, to Marple, where it joined the Peak Forest Canal, dating from 1794.

Figure 13 shows that Cheshire had a network of canals comparable with a modern railway system. Agricultural improvements were marked. The Peak Canal was built to convey lime from Derbyshire, beyond Whaley Bridge, to fertilise the acid soils on the Millstone Grit and other unpromising bases; and some lime was burned in kilns constructed by the famous industrialist, Samuel Oldknow, at Marple. Liming of the Cheshire soils was general from the mid-eighteenth century, and much of the lime was distributed by canal and taken on by carts. Manure from Chester, Warrington, Manchester, and other towns was widely distributed, and the nightsoil from Manchester was carried along the Bridgewater Canal to fertilise the areas between the city and Altrincham where two or even three crops a year of vegetables were produced for the markets of Manchester. Potatoes were sent in large quantities along the Bridgewater Canal, and also by the Weaver for the Lancashire towns, and in the 1830s and 1840s it was noted that tile drains were made at various places on the Ellesmere (and Chester) Canal and sold to farmers improving their land. In the rural areas near Nantwich potatoes were grown in large quantities, partly for sale in the Potteries and at Wolverhampton. In 1850, when the symptoms or at least the fears of a decline in the canal trade were apparent, a complaint was made that the stoppage of the packet from Northwich to Runcorn had brought hardship to the potato growers of the district.

The main effects of canal building in Cheshire were to stimulate agricultural production and to ease the transport of goods. In Macclesfield, for example, coal was brought from Poynton by canal, with stone from the quarries at Kerridge on the edge of the Pennines north of the town, hardware from Birmingham, and pottery from Stoke; beer was carried from Burton, and spirits were carried from London. But the canal gave no immediate stimulus to the silk industry, which long preceded it in time and endured a series of booms and slumps due to causes other than the lack or abundance of good transport. During the 1840s, however, it was prosperous, and in 1848 it was observed that the land between the canal and the town had been built over with houses, mills, warehouses, and workshops. Although some of the canals ceased to be profitable after the railways were built, they did not lose all significance; indeed, materials for the Potteries are still taken by barge along the Trent–Mersey Canal, and some later industrial developments, such as that at Broadheath, Altrincham, were at least initially associated with canals—in this case the Bridgewater.

Roads. Only to a slight extent were the highroads competitive with the river navigations and canals in the early nineteenth century: to a great extent each contributed to the general growth of trade and industry in Lancashire and Cheshire. Until the latter part of the eighteenth century carriage on horseback both of people and goods was general, but the increasing use of wheeled vehicles and the covering of longer distances made unpaved highways and bridlepaths inadequate. In some areas these seventeenth century ways may still be seen, particularly in rural areas as quiet lanes and also in the Pennines, where slabs of hard sandstone were laid down across difficult ground; but the road system in its present form was largely the creation of the turnpike trusts, though it was only during the last great period of road building, 1789–1830, that virtually every place that could be deemed a town acquired such roads. Yet there were curious inequalities. Most of Cheshire was well served by turnpikes by 1820, and its towns, notably Chester, Nantwich, Congleton, and Macclesfield, were significant route centres, though the Wirral beyond Birkenhead and Parkgate was badly served until the 1830s when the first suburban movement across the Mersey from Liverpool was noticed. In southeast Lancashire, with the adjacent industrial area of northeast Cheshire, there was an early and thorough development of turnpike roads, many of which were used partly to carry coal from the then numerous small collieries and also to serve the widespread textile mills; but the west and north of Lancashire were badly served. A dozen turnpike roads converged on Manchester, but only two on Liverpool, connecting the port with Preston and Warrington. And there were no turnpikes at all in the Fylde west of the road from Warrington to Lancaster; similarly, the Forest of Bowland, still a surprisingly remote area of the Northwest, had no turnpike. But the Rossendale upland was well served, probably because its textile industry and coalmining were already growing.

Not all the turnpike roads were well kept up, and the main improvement came after 1810 when Macadam and Telford made remarkable improvements on British roads. By 1848 there were 744 miles of turnpike roads in Lancashire of which most were metalled roads. Indeed, only a fairly strongly constructed road could stand up to the demands made on it. In the neighbourhood of Manchester, Liverpool, and Wigan, pavements of large stones and boulders were laid down, usually down the middle of the highway, with a gravelled way on either side, though on the Bury New Road, which dates from 1826, the middle track was gravelled to a width of 4 yards with stone pavements 3 yards wide on each side. The number of carriers was large, and in 1804 it was said that there were more wagons and carts in Lancashire than in any other part of the kingdom: this is a natural expression of the relatively advanced industrial and commercial life of the Northwest. This affected rural Cheshire as well as the manufacturing districts, for the roads carried not only industrial raw materials and goods but agricultural produce to the towns and fertilisers to the farms. Partly based on a previously existing system of roads and lanes, the turnpikes also included some new roads such as those to Bury, Ashton, and Eccles from Manchester. Only completed as an integrated system by the beginning of the railway age, the turnpikes faced an immediate crisis. When the Liverpool–Manchester railway was opened in 1830 the road tolls fell to one-fifth of their former value within four years. Some roads remained prosperous, such as that from Rochdale to Edenfield, which was not competitive with any railway but able to profit from the extension of trade brought by the new lines. One coach service which prospered was that from Lancaster to Ulverston across the sands of Morecambe Bay, but this was abandoned after the Carnforth to Ulverston branch of the

Furness railway was opened in 1857. Many stretches of road were transferred to the care of the improvement commissioners which were the fore-
runners of modern municipal councils. From the 1860s the tolls were
gradually abolished, though the last, on the Blackburn and Preston New
Road, survived until 1890: in 1888 the new county councils became the
main authority for the care of the roads.

Railways. The railway pattern of industrial Lancashire is of immense
complexity, but in its origin showed four main aims: to provide routes
from Liverpool and Manchester to London; to cross the Pennines to the
industrial towns of Yorkshire; to establish a strong south–north line of
communication known as the 'west coast route', though in fact it touches
the coast only on the shores of Morecambe Bay; and to connect the
towns with one another, especially Liverpool with Manchester and the
growing textile towns. No universal plan of railways was made but the
system grew up through the floating of a vast number of railway companies, soon to be amalgamated into a few, notably the Lancashire and
Yorkshire and the London and North Western (Fig. 16).

In September 1830 the historic Liverpool and Manchester line was
opened, having been built at far less than the estimated cost, at least in its
crossing of Chat Moss. Still a major line between the two cities, this
railway originally went to a station in Liverpool Road, Manchester, which
still survives; but later, in 1844, a connection was made to a new station
at Hunts' Bank, which ultimately became by extensions the adjoining
stations of Exchange and Victoria. In Liverpool, the original station was
at Crown Street, with a link to the docks at Wapping—one of many goods
lines eventually made—but in 1836 it was led through tunnels to Lime
Street. In 1831 a branch was run off from Newton-le-Willows to Warrington, which was originally planned as a feeder to the Liverpool–Manchester
line but which became part of the west-coast route between Warrington
and Winwick Junction. Steadily the railway was pushed northwards, for
in 1832 the Wigan branch railway was opened from a junction at Parkside
on the Liverpool–Manchester line, nearly two miles south of Golborne,
to Wigan, and in 1834 the line from Wigan to Preston was opened. The
west-coast route was finished to Lancaster in 1840 and to Carlisle in 1846.
Meanwhile the line from Birmingham to Warrington was opened through
Crewe in 1837, so that both Liverpool and Manchester acquired their first
London connections through Warrington, though the new Manchester–
Stockport line was opened in 1840 and two years later continued on through
Sandbach to Crewe.

An early railway of special interest was the line from St Helens to
Runcorn gap, that is, to the north side of the Mersey opposite Runcorn
in Widnes. There was a connection to the Liverpool–Manchester line at
St Helens Junction, and the whole length of railway was 12 miles. Opened
in 1833 (though the section from the Junction to the town may have been

4

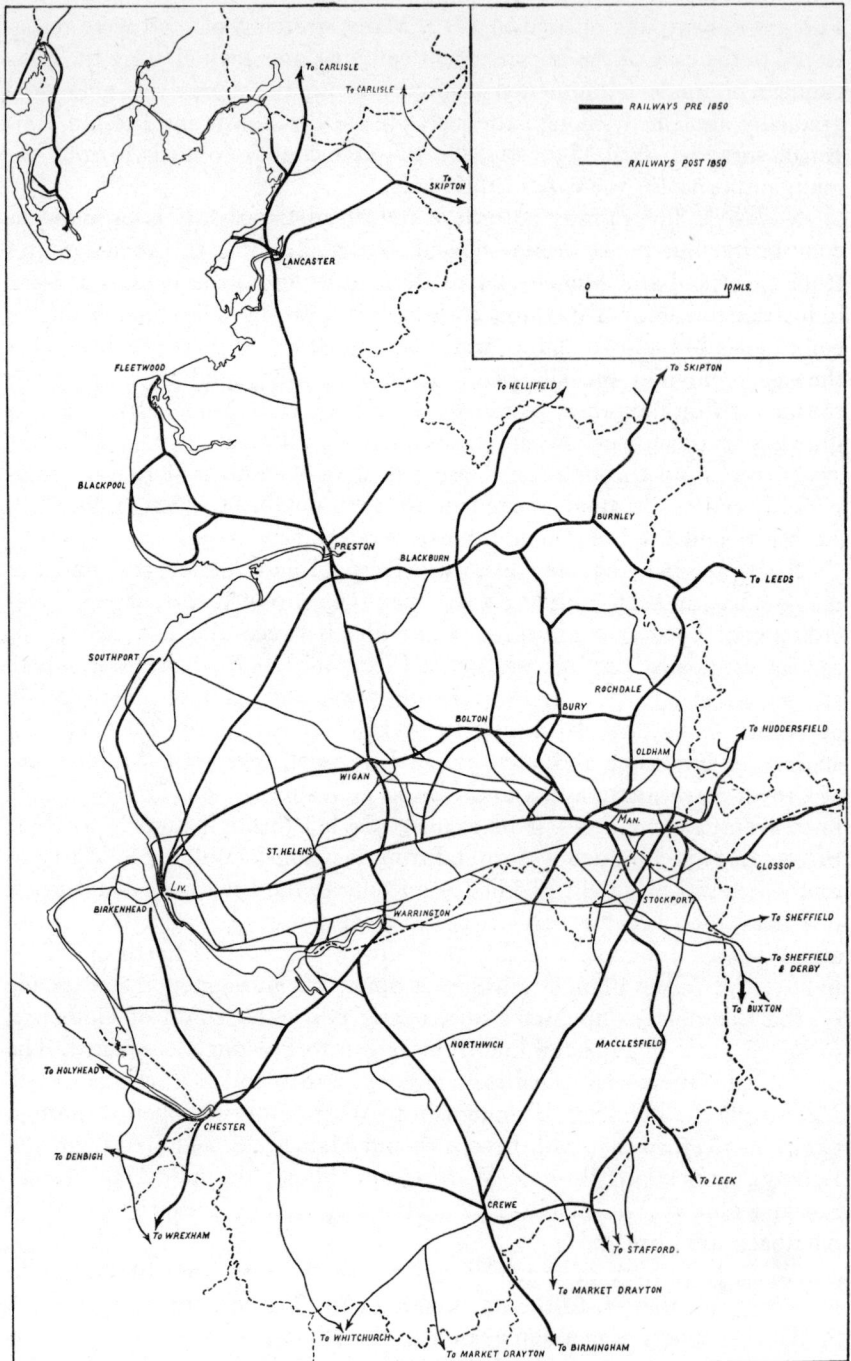

Within the map:

RAILWAYS PRE 1850

RAILWAYS POST 1850

0 — 10 MLS.

To CARLISLE
To CARLISLE
To SKIPTON
LANCASTER
FLEETWOOD
BLACKPOOL
To HELLIFIELD
To SKIPTON
BURNLEY
PRESTON
BLACKBURN
To LEEDS
SOUTHPORT
ROCHDALE
BOLTON
BURY
OLDHAM
To HUDDERSFIELD
WIGAN
MAN.
ST. HELENS
GLOSSOP
LIV.
BIRKENHEAD
WARRINGTON
STOCKPORT
To SHEFFIELD
To SHEFFIELD & DERBY
To BUXTON
To HOLYHEAD
NORTHWICH
MACCLESFIELD
CHESTER
To LEEK
To DENBIGH
CREWE
To WREXHAM
To STAFFORD.
To MARKET DRAYTON
To WHITCHURCH
To MARKET DRAYTON
To BIRMINGHAM

Fig. 16   THE RAILWAY SYSTEM OF LANCASHIRE AND CHESHIRE.

86

available from 1832), it was united in 1845 with the Sankey Brook navigation (p. 64) as the St Helens Canal and railway. This railway was a stimulus to the growth of St Helens and also of Widnes, though the famous Runcorn railway bridge was not built until 1869 as part of the scheme which gave a direct rail link to Liverpool without using Warrington. Widnes owed its existence to the railway; and so too did Fleetwood, which was connected with Preston by the Preston and Wyre line, opened in 1840. Fleetwood was named after Sir Peter Hesketh-Fleetwood, who designed a classical town of which some traces survive; it was to be both a resort and a port and for a few years had a boat service to Ardrossan which gave, until the west-coast route was complete, the quickest service to Scotland. In 1846, however, branch lines were opened to Blackpool and to Lytham, already known as holiday centres, and Fleetwood's future seemed uncertain.

Crossing the Pennines gave the railway engineers problems similar to those faced earlier by the canal builders. The easiest route, followed by the pioneer Manchester and Leeds railway, was that through Rochdale and Littleborough, and then along the Calder valley to Hebden Bridge, Brighouse, and Wakefield to an easy passage to the Aire valley at Leeds. From Manchester the line which, like the Rochdale Canal (p. 66), uses a glacial spillway, was completed to Littleborough by 1839 and the whole route was opened in 1841. Also in 1841, a branch was opened from Castleton (now part of Rochdale) to Heywood, which in 1848 was continued as a through line to Bury, Bolton, Wigan, and Liverpool. But the main route from Manchester to Leeds was that through Huddersfield; in effect this was made up of one independent line, the Huddersfield–Manchester, and parts of two others, the Sheffield, Ashton-under-Lyne, and Manchester railway and the Manchester–Leeds railway. From Manchester the Sheffield line was opened to Godley in 1841 and for the whole distance in 1845, when the 3-mile-long Woodhead tunnel was finished; at Stalybridge, the Huddersfield line, opened in 1847, follows the Tame valley and runs through the Standedge tunnel, also 3 miles long, to Huddersfield, whence it continues northwards to join the Manchester and Leeds railway at Kirkheaton.

In Cheshire as in Lancashire, the network of railways gradually became closer. The initial enterprise of building the line from Warrington to Birmingham in 1837 (p. 85) was followed in 1840 by the line to Chester and also by the line from Chester to Birkenhead, which did not, however, reach the Mersey owing to a clause in the Act of Incorporation that branch lines must be built to all the ferries if to any at all, which was clearly impossible. The extension to Woodside station, beside the ferry to Liverpool, was not built until 1878. Chester gradually became a significant railway junction with the opening of the line along the North Wales coast from 1846 and the line to Warrington in 1850. From Crewe, unlike

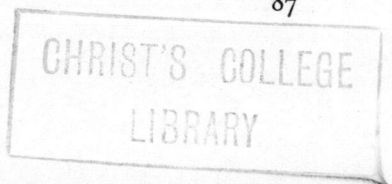

Chester a new town of the railway period, a railway was built to Stoke-upon-Trent in 1848 with a connecting line from Harecastle to Congleton, and the famous six-point star of lines was completed in 1858 by the route through Nantwich to Whitchurch and Shrewsbury. Meanwhile in east Cheshire various additions were made, notably that from a junction at Cheadle Hulme, on the Manchester–Crewe line, to Macclesfield in 1845, which in 1849 was joined to the new line from Congleton to Harecastle, and so to Stoke. In the industrial northeast of the county the railway network became more complicated as an increasing number of lines were built in the growing industrial areas; for example, in 1845 a line was constructed from Guide Bridge station on the Sheffield, Ashton, and Manchester railway to Stalybridge on the Huddersfield line, and later, in the 1860s, railways were added in Hyde and district with a line from Marple to Macclesfield in 1869. One important suburban line, of considerable influence in the growth of the Manchester conurbation, was that to Altrincham in 1849.

Lancashire, to as great an extent as northeast Cheshire, or even greater, acquired a network of railways that connected virtually all the growing industrial towns with one another by the 1850s. On the north side of Manchester much of this enterprise was associated with the East Lancashire railway which, having absorbed other lines, was itself absorbed in 1859 by the Lancashire and Yorkshire railway, a line developed mainly from the Manchester and Leeds railway. In 1838 a line was opened from Salford to Bolton, with which the Bury–Liverpool line of 1848 (p. 87) was connected later. Gradually the East Lancashire company pushed northwards into Rossendale, and beyond it to Blackburn, which became a strong railway centre of north Lancashire, and also to Burnley. In 1846 the company opened a railway from Clifton Junction (at Pendlebury) on the Salford–Bolton line, to Bury, Ramsbottom, and Rawtenstall along the Irwell valley. This began the penetration of Rossendale, which was continued by extensions from Rawtenstall to Newchurch in 1848 and to Bacup in 1852. Another important addition, in 1848, was the construction of a line from Stubbins, less than a mile north of Ramsbottom, to Haslingden, Accrington, and Burnley in 1848, with Colne in 1849, where a connection was made with the line from Skipton to Colne, opened in 1848. From Burnley a link was made through the Cliviger gorge, a glacial overflow channel (p. 15), to Todmorden in 1849. These lines strengthened the local specialisation in the cotton trade since, for example, yarn could easily be transported from the spinning area around Manchester to the weaving area around Burnley and Blackburn.

Blackburn acquired in 1847 a railway to Darwen which was extended by Bury in the following year; in 1850 the line northwards through Clitheroe was completed to Chatburn. In 1848 a connection had been made with Burnley, and there was already a link with the main line from

Wigan to Preston at Farington dating from 1846. In 1850 a line was made to give a quicker approach to Preston through Bamber Bridge, which brought the Blackburn line to a point just south of the Ribble. Preston acquired increasing importance as a railway centre, for in addition to the main arterial west-coast route it had the lines from Blackburn, Accrington, and the other cotton towns to the east, the Fylde railways that were to carry millions of holidaymakers and others for generations, and feeder lines from Liverpool and Manchester. The first of these, opened in 1849, ran from Walton Junction in Liverpool, on the Wigan to Bury line (p. 87), through Ormskirk to a junction at Lostock (near Preston) on the west-coast route; the second, of much earlier date, was completed from Bolton to Chorley in 1841 and to Euxton Junction in 1843. In addition Preston had a line to Longridge from 1840, but this was not connected to the main station until 1885.

Although the Merseyside conurbation was growing rapidly in population in the middle of the nineteenth century, it acquired far fewer railways than the larger conurbation focused on Manchester. The line to Southport from Waterloo was constructed in 1848; and additional lines gave access to Liverpool Exchange station in 1850 and to the central (Chapel Street) station in Southport in 1851. These new railways stimulated suburban growth in Waterloo and Crosby, but the initial outward movement to the Wirral peninsula depended on the ferry services since the surburban railways, later to be so important, were not opened until the 1880s. For goods traffic, however, Liverpool had an extremely complicated system of lines, some in tunnels under the city. Southport, visited from the eighteenth century for sea bathing, grew mainly from the 1850s, strengthened in 1855 by the railway line from Wigan, which provides a quick Manchester connection. Farther north, a railway known as the 'Little North Western' to distinguish it from the L.N.W.R., was opened from Morecambe to Lancaster in 1848 and extended to Clapham (Yorkshire) on the main line from Leeds to Carlisle in 1850. As in Blackpool and Southport, the railway was an asset to the growing, if always much smaller, seaside town of Morecambe, but the extension to Heysham harbour came far later, in 1904, with the opening of the new sea route to Belfast. 'Across the Sands', in the Furness district, the Furness railway was first opened from Barrow to Dalton, extended to Ulverston in 1854, and finally to Carnforth in 1857.

By the 1850s the four main features of the railway system in Lancastria noted on page 85 were a reality on the landscape; clearly the progress made in twenty years had been rapid. It is beyond the scope of this book to detail the many absorptions of one company by another that took place (but see, for a brief note, p. 88); without such absorptions the system would have been even more complicated than it became. Various lines were added after 1850, not all of which remained permanently successful. The main effect of the railways was to open up much of Lancastria to a far wider market than had been known before and especially to stimulate the growth of Liverpool as a centre of both overseas and local trade. Having a long tradition of textile working, Lancastria was now ready to advance to the position of the greatest cotton-manufacturing area in the world, which, in spite of shocks such as the American Civil War, it retained until the First World War. It had also the advantage of coal supplies to supplement the water power of its hard-worked rivers. Under the stimulus of rapid town growth, so vividly expressed in the Victorian character of the towns in the Northwest, agriculture had improved, though in varying measure from one place to another. Many of the canals, but by no means all, ceased to be remunerative; and the roads, losing through traffic such as stage coaches and packet services, became mere service routes for each locality until the motor age.

The mining industry

Cheap transport was the first of the main needs of Lancashire's growing industries. Coal at low cost was the other, and by 1859 a mining industry with an annual output of some 10 million tons had grown to supply it. Mining was still primitive in technique, though the pits made up in numbers what they lacked in size and efficiency. Almost every patch of truly exposed Coal Measures, free from any considerable thickness of drift, was worked by a rash of tiny undertakings. They extended from Cronton, now a Liverpool suburb, to the Pennine valleys near Glossop, from Colne almost to Macclesfield, and in the upland of Rossendale to heights of 1,400 feet. A technical revolution was coming to the industry. Though small, shallow pits, typically employing about a hundred men and sunk to a depth of a few hundred feet, were still the most numerous, a few larger and deeper mines were being constructed: at Pendleton a depth of 1,500 feet had been reached. Though primitive, the industry was by no means unproductive: its average output of roughly one ton per man-day is comparable with the modern average. Industrial grades of coal were priced at c.4s. per ton at the pit-head; but each 40,000 tons of output raised cost the life of one miner, possibly a woman or a child.

Though mining was much more widespread in the coalfield than now, the bulk of the industry's output in 1850 was supplied by three districts of intensive exploitation. All three were located where the demand was greatest, where communications to supply more distant markets were best developed, and where the seams themselves were most easily accessible. All three conditions were met in the middle Douglas valley near Wigan, from which about one-third of the field's output was raised. The Douglas here is deeply incised into rich Middle Coal Measures, so that coal-crops were closely packed along the drift-free valley sides. From the rash of pits working these shallow seams complex webs of gravity-tramways led down the slopes to the Leeds–Liverpool Canal (which had now replaced the old

Douglas navigation) on the valley floor. This took coal westwards to Liverpool, which derived half of its supply from Wigan. Preston to the north was supplied by two alternative routes, the lower Douglas branch of the Leeds and Liverpool Canal and the Lancaster Canal with its tramway

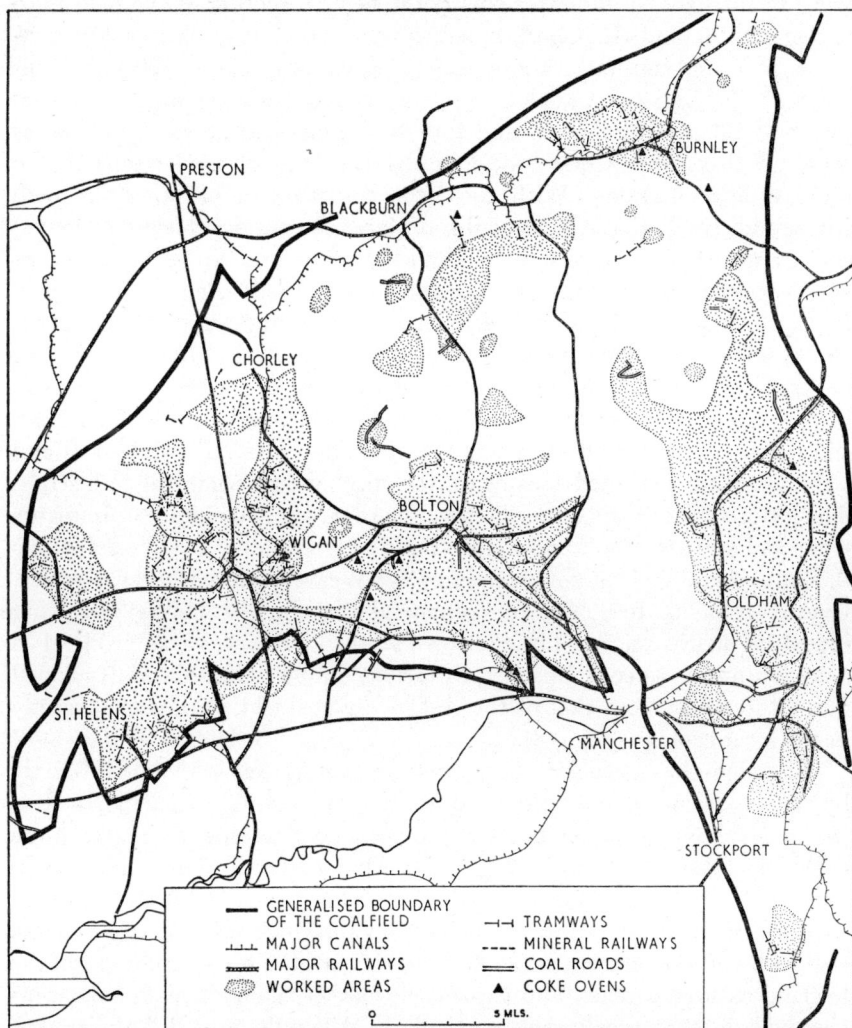

Fig. 17 THE DISTRIBUTION OF MINING AND THE PATTERN OF COMMUNICATIONS IN THE LANCASHIRE COALFIELD IN 1850.

extension (Fig. 17). Clearly, Wigan's status as Lancashire's greatest mining town was the outcome of its superb water communications; but now railways to Liverpool and Bolton, Preston and Warrington, and from Southport to Manchester were carrying part of the output. And local demand for fuel was rising, for cotton firms were attracted by the cheap coal and surplus female labour of the mining communities. By 1840 the mills employed 6,000 persons, and thus the foundations of the coal-and-cotton economy of central Lancashire were laid.

The southwest angle of the coalfield, near St Helens, was another focus of intensive mining, for this is the nearest section of the field both to Merseyside and the Cheshire salt towns. Here, as at Wigan, the provision of water communications was the great stimulus to the growth of mining. The Sankey Canal of 1757 gave a connection to the Mersey estuary west of Warrington, and thus St Helens had access by all-water routes both to the Merseyside and (by the Weaver navigation) to the mid-Cheshire markets. With the later construction of rail links with Merseyside (by both the Liverpool and Manchester and St Helens railways) coal transport costs were reduced, and there was even an attempt—never very successful except for the bunker traffic—to develop a coal export trade from Liverpool. At St Helens, as at Wigan, industries grew quickly and absorbed an increasing volume of the local output. Glass making, an old trade here, was revolutionised by the building of the first large factory in 1773. No better site for the industry exists in Great Britain. The pure, silica-rich Shirdley Hill sand was the chief raw material, while coal and soda ash were provided locally by the mining and chemical industries. The latter was introduced to the town in 1828. Its two chief requirements were coal and salt: the former was abundantly available at low cost, while the latter could be brought cheaply by the Weaver and Sankey waterways. Copper refining, too, had an ephemeral place in St Helens' evolving industrial structure, and like the town's other industries was prodigal in its consumption of coal. In short, St Helens' industrial tradition developed quite differently from that of the rest of the coalfield, with roots directly in the local geology (Fig. 18).

Elsewhere in Lancashire the growth of mining was stimulated directly by the expansion of the textile industries, and this was particularly clear in the development of the third of the great concentrations of pits, in the coalfield of the north and east of the Manchester lowland. The radial system of canals reaching outwards from Manchester, with the tributary network of mineral tramways, opened up this southeastern angle of the coalfield, and the concentration of two-thirds of the textile industry in the lowland assured a ready and expanding market. Unlike Liverpool, Manchester had its own collieries, particularly at Pendleton and Ardwick, but these faced competition from more distant pits. The collieries of the Bolton–Worsley area had access to the city by the Bridgewater and Bolton Canals (Fig. 19); part of the output of the Pennine fringes of the coalfield was gathered by tramways and brought to Manchester by the Ashton and Rochdale Canals. Almost every other cotton town of the area had its local collieries; indeed some mills had pits in their own yards. Stockport was not on the coalfield, though the collieries of Bredbury and Poynton kept it

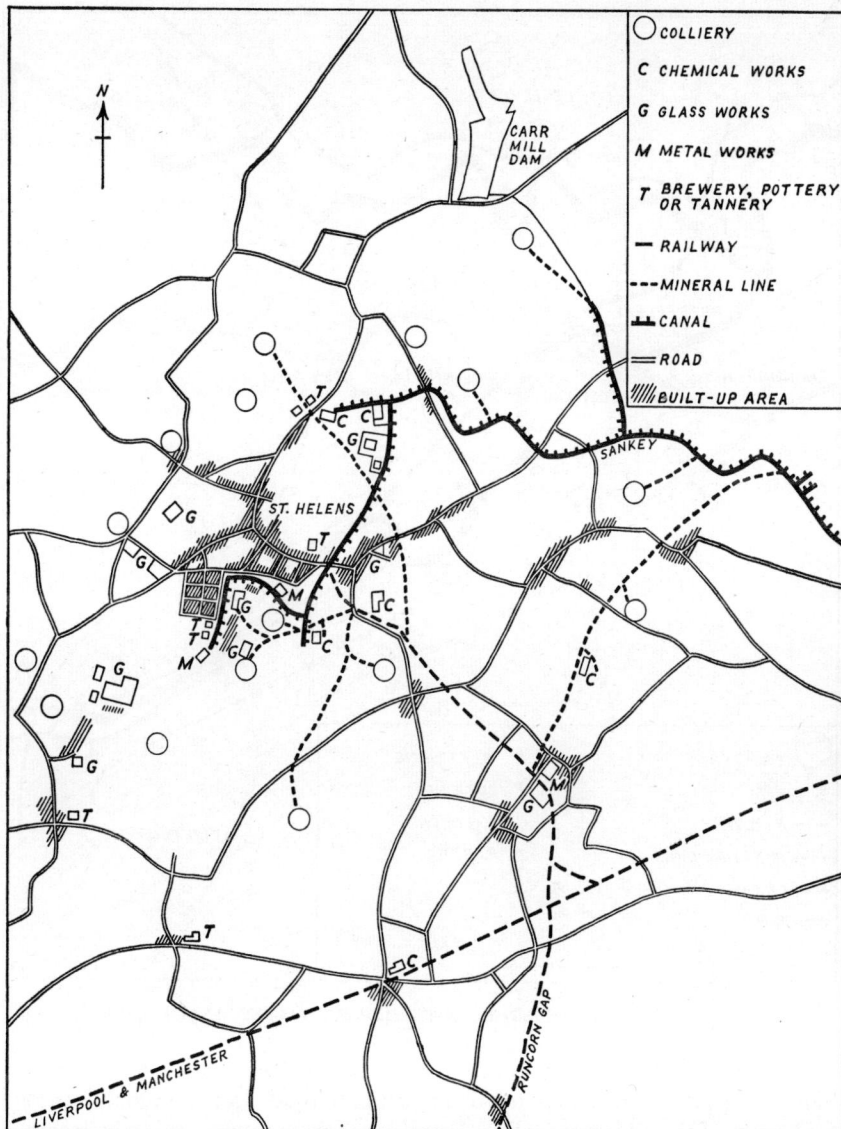

Fig. 18   ST HELENS IN 1845.

amply supplied. Unlike the Wigan and St Helens districts, the Manchester coalfield had no interest in external markets, for local urban and industrial demand grew so quickly that the local fuel supply was ultimately to prove inadequate.

Elsewhere in the coalfield mining was on a smaller scale, as Figure 17 shows. The towns of Rossendale were supplied from pits on the bleak hillsides, which sent their output along short tramways which led downhill

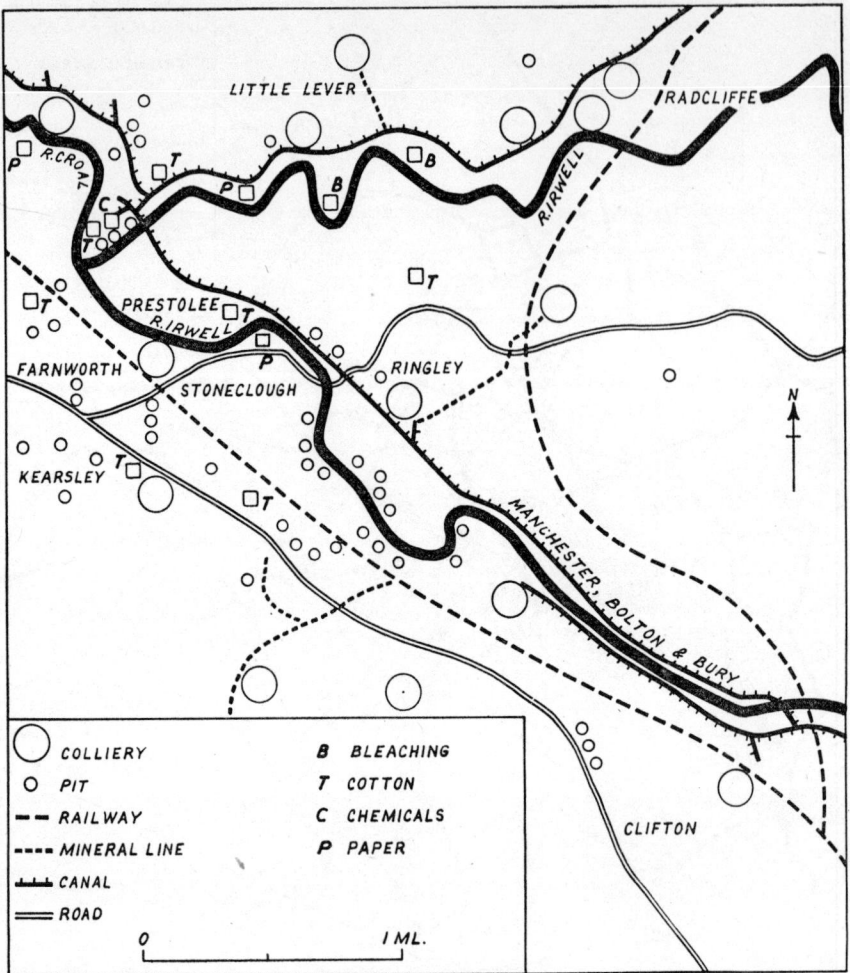

Fig. 19   INDUSTRY IN THE IRWELL VALLEY, 1845.

to the turnpikes, or along 'coal-lanes', that is, moorland lanes from the high-lying pits to the valley towns or turnpike road. In the almost detached coal basin of the Blackburn–Burnley syncline mining was still in its infancy. Some of the pits served the growing weaving communities directly by road or tramway, but many stood beside or were linked with the Leeds and Liverpool Canal, which was the chief artery of coal movement in this district.

The textile industries in 1850

By 1850 the cotton industry had achieved the stature of a great modern manufacture, complex in its structure and characterised by an intricate system of regional specialisation. It had passed through several revolutions in technique. The earliest spinning machinery was more commonly worked by water power than steam, and consequently the earliest mills were located at natural power sites, particularly on the glacially disturbed streams of the Rossendale and Pennine flanks of the Manchester lowland. The towns of the plain were at a significant disadvantage, except where ungraded lowland rivers could give useful power, as at Manchester and Stockport. But from the early nineteenth century the waterwheel became progressively outmoded by the quick development of the steam engine, so that by 1840 only 16% of the industry's energy came from the rivers. This change in the source of power induced a shift in distribution, for now sites on or near the worked coalfield had an overwhelming advantage. But even when an almost modern type of steam-powered spinning mill began to appear the industry's technical revolution remained incomplete, for weaving was still largely a handicraft, practised in the cottage and on the farm. Not until the 1820s was a fully efficient power loom perfected, and as late as 1835 there were only 61,000 power looms in Lancashire cotton mills. At first power weaving was carried on chiefly by established spinning firms, whose mills thus became integrated units; and at this stage the Manchester lowland still had the bulk of the looms, which were concentrated especially in the north Cheshire towns. From 1840 a partial but increasing geographical separation of the two developed. Weaving became, progressively, the concern of specialist firms which grew most quickly in the young textile towns of the Blackburn–Burnley lowland, while spinning remained dominant in the southeast (Figs. 21, 22).

The geography of the Lancashire cotton industry in the mid-nineteenth century had two main features: its tightly restricted location within Lancastria, and a developing pattern of sub-regional specialisation in particular branches of the trade. The concentration of so large a proportion of the British cotton industry into Lancashire was due not to physical but to historical and economic causes, for the county had no unique range of physical advantages for the growth of the manufacture. Its cheap fuel and humid atmosphere, its fast-flowing streams and soft, clean water could have been found as easily in north or south Wales, in west Cumberland or Lanarkshire. Several of these areas, as well as the north Midlands and West Riding, had cotton industries of greater or smaller size. Lancashire's critical advantages lay rather in its early interest in the fustian trade (by which it served an apprenticeship in the cotton industry), in the adaptability and inventiveness of its textile craftsmen, in the initiative and ability of its businessmen, and, not least, in the closeness of its American links through its great port on Merseyside.

Nevertheless the distribution of the cotton industry within Lancastria was a response to geographical factors. Figure 20 shows that already by 1840 the manufacture was tightly concentrated into the area of eastern

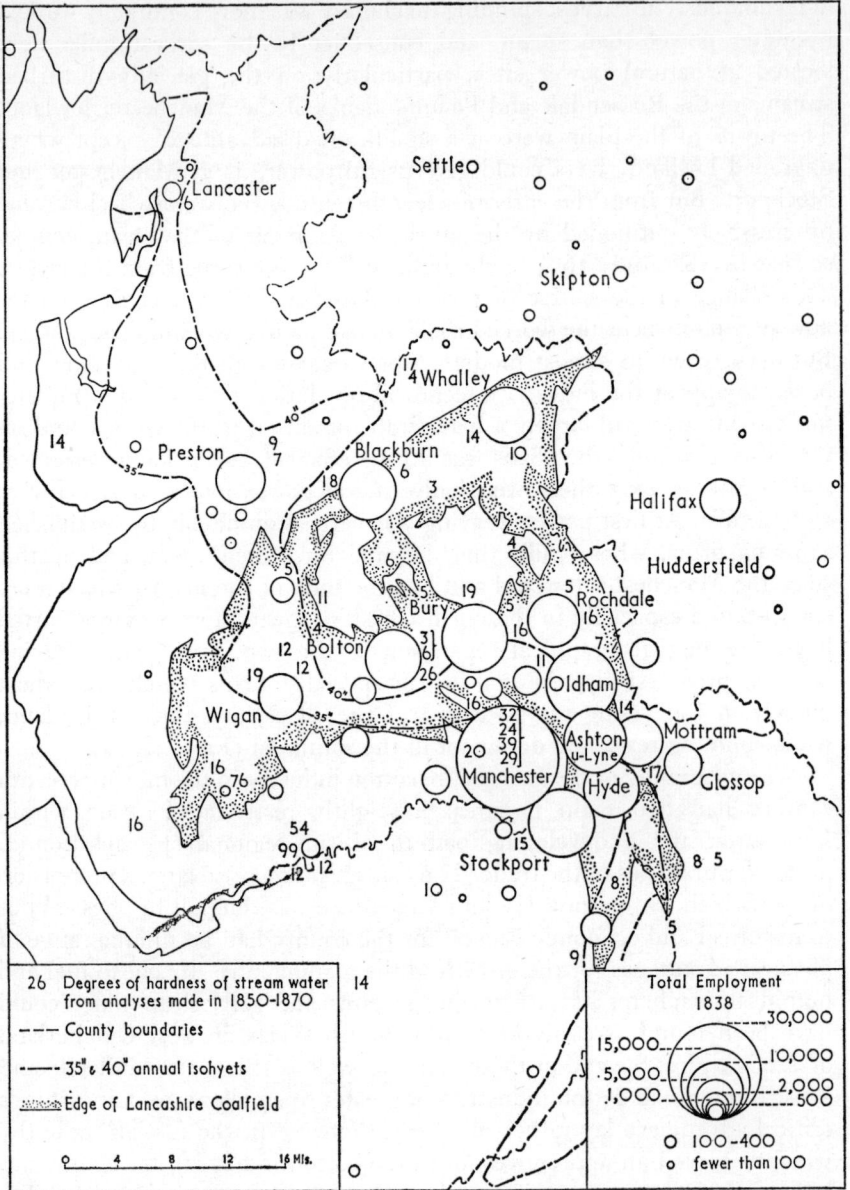

On the map:

Settle○

Lancaster 3 9 6

Skipton ○

14

Preston ○ 9 7

17 Whalley 4

14 10

Blackburn 6 18 3

Halifax ○

Huddersfield ○

5 11

Bury 5 19 5

Rochdale 5 16

12 Bolton 3 6J 26

16 7

Oldham

Wigan 19 12 40" 35"

11

16 32 24 39 29

Ashton-u-Lyne 14

Mottram

16 76 20 Manchester Hyde 17 Glossop

16

54 99 12 12

15

Stockport 10 ○ ○ 8 8 5

8

5

9

26 Degrees of hardness of stream water
    from analyses made in 1850–1870   14

- - - County boundaries

-·-·- 35" & 40" annual isohyets

▨▨▨ Edge of Lancashire Coalfield

0   4   8   12   16 Mls.

Total Employment
1838
                    ___ 30,000
15,000 ___   ___ 10,000
·5,000 ___   ___ 2,000
1,000 ___   ___ 500

○ 100–400
o fewer than 100

Fig. 20 THE LOCATION OF THE COTTON INDUSTRY IN 1838. Compiled from the Factory Inspectors' Returns of 1838, this map was first published in *Trans. Inst. Brit. Geogr.* **28** (1960), 141.

96

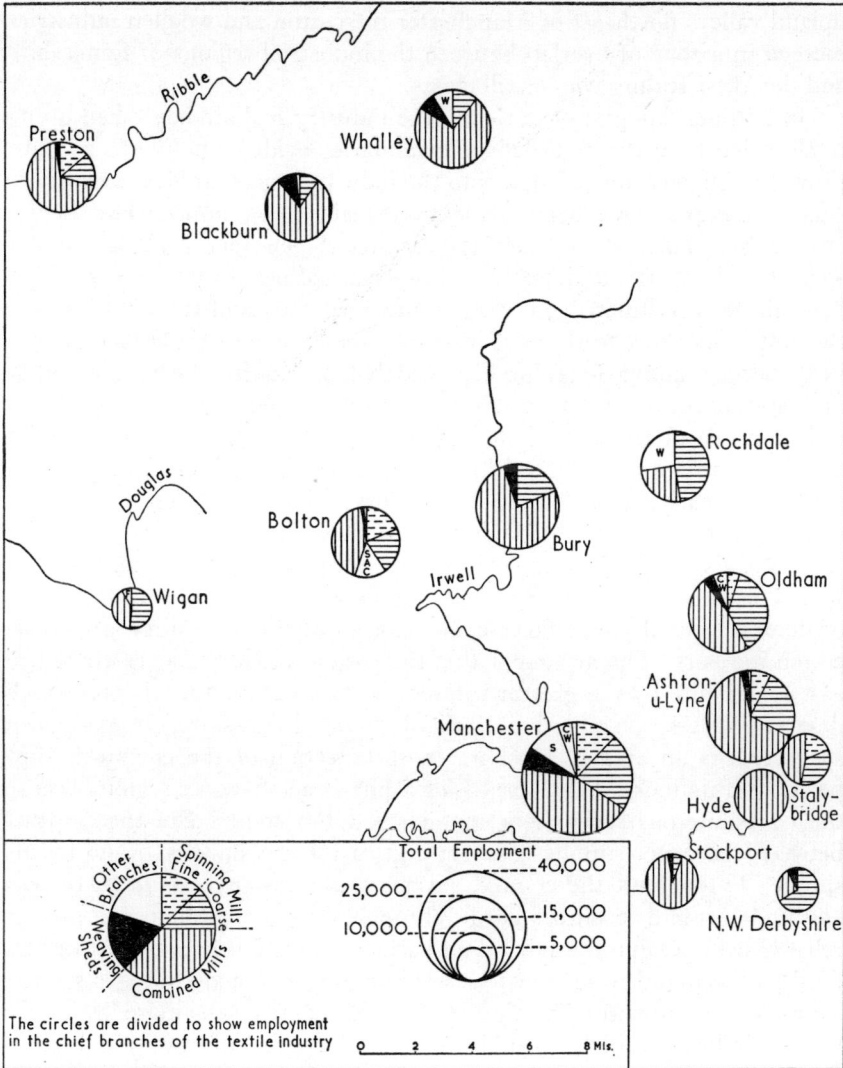

Fig. 21 THE STRUCTURE OF THE TEXTILE INDUSTRIES IN LANCASHIRE, 1840. The combined mills both spun and wove cotton. The 'other branches' are distinguished by a letter key: S=Silk, W=Woollens, F=Flax, CW=Cotton waste, SAC= Spinning of all counts of cotton yarn, fine and coarse. First published in *Trans. Inst. Brit. Geogr.* **28** (1960), 144.

Lancastria which has contained the great bulk of the trade to the present day. The towns of the Burnley–Blackburn coal basin were then, as now, the northern margin of the textile province: Preston was a northwestern outlier, and the western boundary through central Lancashire ran near Chorley, Wigan, and Leigh, as it does still. A salient of cotton manufacturing lay along the flank of the Pennines to Bollington, while in the upland valleys northeast of Manchester the cotton and woollen industries merged in a zone of overlap between the industrial regions of Lancashire and the West Riding which still exists.

In outline, though not in detail, the industry had already taken up its modern location: the well-defined boundaries evident in Figure 20 have proved to be permanent barriers to the industry's geographical expansion. Many attempts have been made to explain these limits. The higher atmospheric humidity of east Lancashire, its cheaper coal, its greater agricultural poverty, and, lastly, the superior softness of its water supplies have all been postulated, in turn, as the chief causes of the restriction of the cotton industry to the east of the county. Some of these factors may be dismissed summarily: it has been widely believed that the high humidity of east Lancashire is favourable for cotton, yet climatic statistics show little contrast in atmospheric humidity between east and west Lancashire and crude attempts to control humidity, especially in fine-spinning mills, were made early in the nineteenth century. Though agricultural poverty certainly drove the smallholders of Rossendale into domestic textile work, by no means the whole of the cotton province was an area of poor farming. In any case, scarcely a village in Lancashire was without some tradition of domestic textile manufacture, but not all of them acquired a modern cotton industry. The argument that the cotton industry was restricted to east Lancashire by the greater softness of its water supplies is one which deserves closer examination. Triassic west Lancashire, it has been suggested, is an area of hard water—a reflection of the chemical composition of its rocks—while east Lancashire is a soft-water region because the Carboniferous series here contains few limestones. But the contrast between the water supplies of west and east Lancashire is by no means simple. Throughout the county, surface water resources tend to be soft and underground resources hard. Through its higher rainfall and greater relief east Lancashire has abundant surface water, but in west Lancashire hard underground water must be used to supplement the meagre surface supplies. Not unnaturally, the east of the county was more attractive to any industry which needed enormous supplies of water, though it was the quantity rather than the quality of the supply which was most important.

Soft and pure though the rivers of east Lancashire were in their natural condition, they were no longer so by the period of the quickest growth of the cotton industry. Pollution had converted them into industrial sewers in their middle and lower courses and had greatly increased their hardness, so that when the Royal Commission on River Pollution of 1870 gathered its evidence it found that the river supply over much of east Lancashire was harder than the underground water of the west. Effectively, east Lancashire ceased to be a soft-water region when industry began to grow strongly here, but cotton manufacture remained, and the 1870 Commission found that spinners and weavers were almost indifferent to the quality of their water supply: only the finishing firms reported that soft and pure water was necessary to their operations. In short, the advantage of east Lancashire lay less in the quality of its water than in the abundance of the supply and also in the river power so widely available here in the early and formative years of the cotton industry (Fig. 23).

The cost of fuel was a much more significant factor to early millowners than the supply of water. The early steam engine consumed vast quantities of coal, of which the price varied emphatically with distance from the mines. As the fuel bill was one of the most important factors in the total cost of production, a mill sited more than a few miles beyond the edge of the worked coalfield was penalised unless it was worked by water power, as many of the outlying mills were. The advantages of coalfield location to the industry are obvious in Figure 20: the great bulk of the manufacture lay on the coalfield, almost every part of which had its mills by 1840. Almost everywhere the edge of the Coal Measure outcrop was the limit of the cotton-working district. To this general rule there were only two exceptions. Preston had mills though it lay 10 miles from the nearest pits, but its fuel was carried cheaply both by rail and water from Wigan. Conversely, St Helens, an important mining district, failed to develop a permanent interest in the cotton industry, for the single mill at work in the middle of the nineteenth century was closed later. The competition of the established glass, chemical, and copper industries for canal-side sites and for the limited water resources of the area may have excluded the cotton industry from the town.

Not only had the cotton industry taken up essentially its modern location by 1850, but it was also beginning to reveal, in outline, the present pattern of regional specialisation. The separation of spinning from weaving was still incipient, but the complex pattern of both regional and local specialisation in particular branches and qualities of cotton manufacture was already forming. Manchester was then, as now, the least specialised of the cotton towns. It had both looms and spindles, usually housed together in large integrated mills; it made both fine and coarse goods. Nor were its mills wholly concerned with cotton, for in 1837 it was second only to Derby as a silk-manufacturing centre of the country. Textile finishing, too, was strongly established on the streams flowing down to the city, and bleaches and dyes were produced at many small chemical factories. The infant engineering industry was already outgrowing its association with the textile trades. Looms and mules were among its earliest products, but steam engines, railway equipment, and a wide range of foundry products were already made.

Each of the other towns of the Manchester embayment not only depended almost entirely on cotton, but also concentrated on a single branch of this industry. Bolton, already the chief centre of the fine-spinning

99

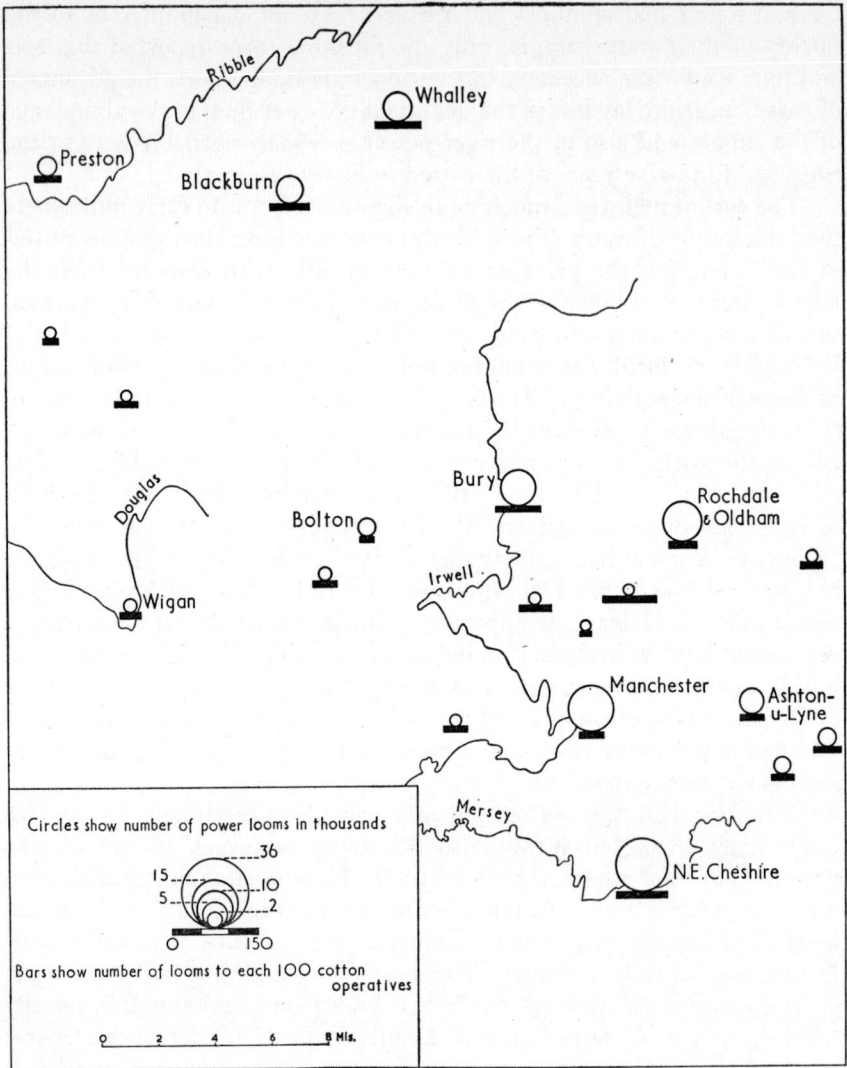

Fig. 22 THE GROWTH OF POWERED WEAVING IN THE COTTON INDUSTRY TO 1840.
First published in *Trans. Inst. Brit. Geogr.* **28** (1960), 147.

industry, had few looms and little interest in coarse-spinning. Oldham,
in contrast, was already associated with the coarse-spinning branch, but
it was less narrowly specialised than Bolton, for its largest mills were
integrated and the town was one of the largest centres of the new power
weaving. Rochdale was already a member of the coarse-spinning group of
towns, but unlike Oldham it had not adopted the power loom. Never a
town quick to change, Rochdale clung tenaciously to its old woollen

industry, now transferred from the home to the factory. Bury, another centre of coarse work, was as progressive in adopting power weaving as Rochdale was slow. But the highest degree of local specialisation in weaving in the entire cotton province was in the towns of northeast Cheshire, where Stockport and Hyde formed the heart of the contemporary weaving belt.

Elsewhere in Lancashire, too, the textile industry had a marked local individuality: indeed, in 1850, as at the present day, no two cotton towns were alike in their industrial structure. Rossendale had an archaic industry. Water power lasted late in these valleys where every stream can turn a millwheel. Tiny coarse-spinning watermills were spaced along every valley, and woollen mills were almost as numerous here as cotton factories. Neither industry had yet grown to the point of stimulating much town growth: villages, hamlets, and the smallholdings of the overpopulated hills provided the labour for the mills of the valleys. In total contrast, in central Lancashire the typical mill was large, new, steam-powered, and, in most cases, combined weaving with spinning. Both the cheap coal and the surplus female labour strongly attracted the industry to this area, where it grew late but very quickly converted loosely knit mining villages into true towns.

The towns of the extreme north of the textile province, particularly Blackburn, Burnley, and their smaller neighbours, were in 1850 entering their period of most rapid growth. They owed more to the extension of the railway net—which now joined them to both Liverpool and Manchester— than to the slow and roundabout Leeds and Liverpool Canal. Their growth came at a time when weaving was passing through its delayed technical revolution and growing more strongly than spinning, so that they inevitably developed a special concern with the production of cloth. Though in 1850 this specialisation was in its infancy, already the combined mills of these towns probably had many more weavers than spinners, and cottage weavers were still very numerous. During the 1840s most of the new enterprises established here were small specialised weaving firms of the type which was to multiply with great speed later in the century and to dominate the area until the present time.

By the mid-nineteenth century Lancashire had acquired a dominant share, some 63%, of an industry which then yielded more than half of the total value of the nation's exports. The manufacture provided about 170,000 jobs directly and an enormous number indirectly through the stimulus it gave to transport, commerce, and the growth of ancillary trades such as engineering, chemicals, and coalmining. New towns had been created and old ones enormously enlarged throughout the textile zone, and a great port had grown on Merseyside largely to serve the needs of this wonderfully productive hinterland. Even the agriculture of Lancastria had been remodelled to supply the demands of the cotton and mining

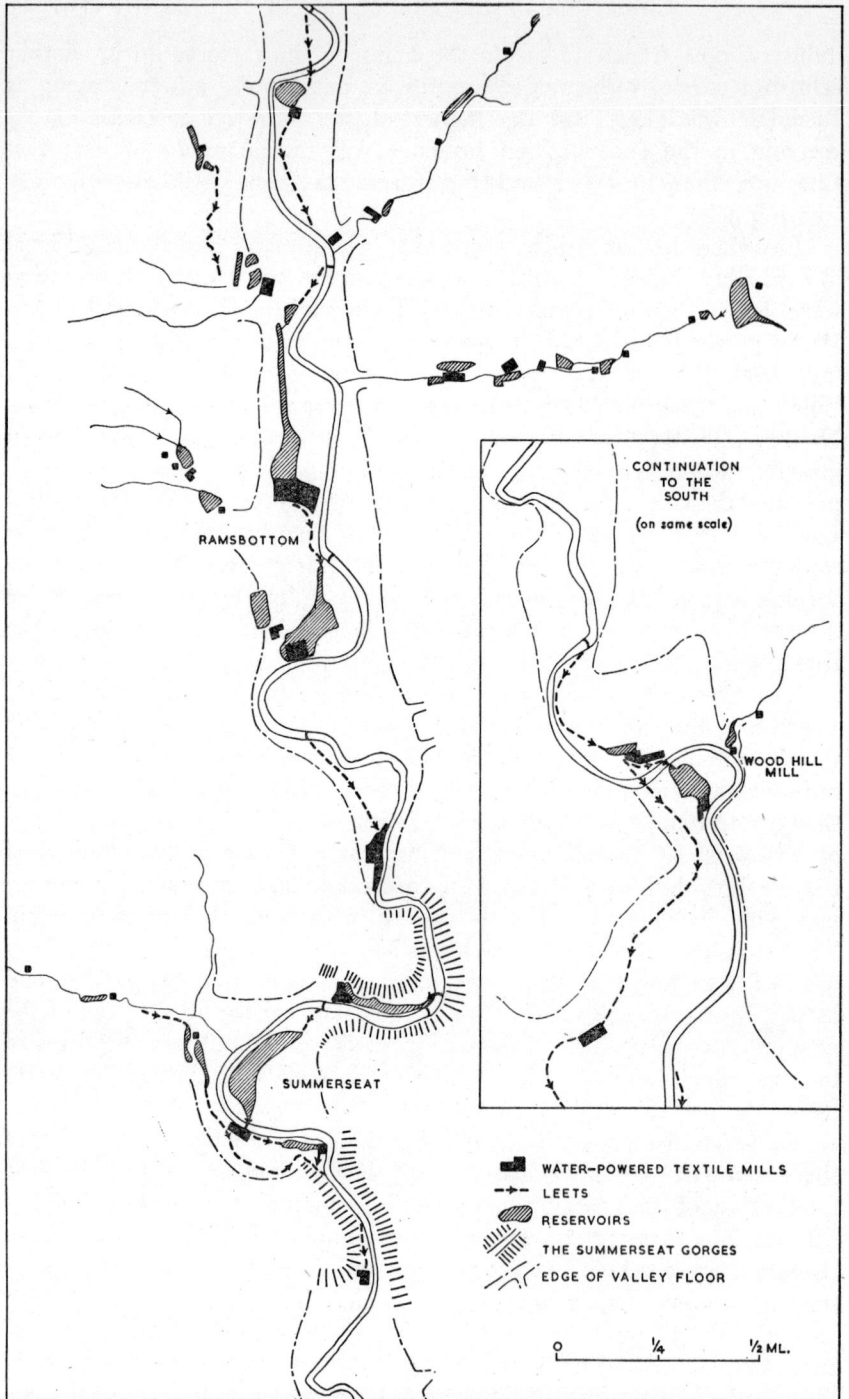

Fig. 23 WATER ENGINEERING IN THE MIDDLE IRWELL VALLEY, 1845. As explained in the text, p. 95, there is a clear relation between the water-power mill sites and the glacial diversions of rivers in the Rossendale upland and the Pennines.

communities. Clearly the growth of this single great staple industry had reshaped both the economy and the landscape of Lancashire at a speed unmatched in any other region of Great Britain.

Agricultural geography c.1850

Late though it was in reaching Lancastria, the agrarian revolution continued to transform the rural economy of the region in the mid-nineteenth century. But it was making varying progress. The great stimulus to agricultural change was the growth of insatiable urban markets, and thus the new and more intensive types of farming were confined to the areas near the great industrial concentrations or with direct access to them by rail and water. In general these economic factors had a more powerful effect than purely physical influences on the progress of agricultural improvement in Lancastria.

Though the old contrasts between fell and plain were as sharp as ever, differences within the uplands were now appearing. Where local urban demand justified the effort moorland agriculture was experiencing quick improvement, but elsewhere farming remained backward. It was realised that the 'weeping climate' of the moors was an almost insuperable obstacle to arable farming and grain production, for slopes which were not too steep for the plough were almost invariably too wet. Drainage was seen as the spearhead of improvement, and tile-drain systems were being laid by many improving landlords, some of whom had established tile factories for the purpose. The Peel family, for example, were attempting to upgrade moorland slopes near Oswaldtwistle by drainage followed by heavy liming. But not even such radical treatment could make land like this fit for the plough, for the climate would always make grain cultivation a gambler's risk. The obvious destiny of the lower slopes of Rossendale was to supply the milk which the growing towns of the valleys were demanding in increasing quantities. Dairying was already dominant in southern Rossendale. Little attempt was made to raise arable fodder crops, but carefully managed meadows, heavily limed and manured, supplied the winter feed. Improvement of this type was common up to 1,000 feet, and under favourable conditions it reached 1,300 feet.

Farther from the industrial towns there was less incentive to improve the moorlands. The remoter parts of Rossendale were little changed; here a subsistence agriculture was closely linked with domestic industry. Land was undrained and chiefly pasture of poor quality. Tiny acreages were planted to oats and potatoes, sheep were grazed on the unenclosed moor; and a few cattle were kept for the family's own needs. In Bowland a system of comparable simplicity prevailed, but with little domestic industry to provide a cash income, so that cheese was made and cattle were raised for sale to the fattening districts of the lowland. In Bowland much of the upper moor was in purely seasonal use, as rented summer grazing for lowland cattle and sheep. Some measure of the carrying capacity is given by the local rule that '2 acres of fell and lowland together will keep 3 sheep'. In this wild and remote country, which neither invited improvement nor provided landlords with the income to effect it, life retained an almost medieval simplicity, and the traditional diet of oatcakes, whey, and salted meat survived. Where cropping was attempted a system of shifting cultivation was employed, while on some of the sheepland the landlord owned the flock and the tenant was entitled only to the natural increase; this was a very old practice.

The lowlands of Lancastria were much further advanced in agricultural technique than the uplands; but they too had now developed marked regional contrasts adjusted not only to the physical but also to the economic environment. The influence of town growth on the intensity of lowland land use was obvious and striking. Two concentric agricultural zones surrounded Liverpool. The inner, reaching from 3 to 4 miles from the town's edge, was a band of intensive market gardening to which the light soils of the Triassic platforms were well suited once they had been manured by the use of urban waste. Beyond the market gardens lay dairy farms, in a zone which extended some 10 miles from the city. Here much old, unproductive pasture had been ploughed for fodder crops and even for grain cultivation. Potatoes, too, were grown in rotation. So great had been the improvement brought by immediate access to a great urban market that some of this land—along the Preston road—was described as the finest land in England.

But the construction of canal and rail communications made possible the penetration of Liverpool's influence far beyond its immediate hinterland. Its 'milkshed' extended almost to Preston, and the parishes along the Leeds and Liverpool Canal were specialising in vegetable crops for the urban market. Rufford was noted for onions, Scarisbrick for carrots, and Ormskirk for potatoes: west Lancashire soils were well suited to this last crop. The light loams of the Shirdley Hill and glacial sands are free warming and ideal for early potatoes, while the drained peats gave magnificent yields of the later 'maincrop' varieties. The canal not only took these crops to market but also brought in return the town's waste which was in universal demand as a fertiliser.

If contemporary writers are to be believed, southeast Lancashire was by no means as advanced as the southwest: though it had an even greater urban market to supply, its soils and climate are much less conducive to intense cultivation. The sticky boulder clay of much of the Manchester lowland lay 'in old grass of inferior quality' according to J. Binns, and when this was ploughed it was often left as summer fallow, an old practice considered barbarous by the better farmers. But the better land of the Mersey valley was obviously more productive. The rich water meadows of the valley floor fed large herds of dairy cattle, and the light soils of the terraces produced wheat, hay, and early potatoes. By far the richest land in the Manchester region lay along the Bridgewater Canal, where mixed arable cultivation of a market garden type had reached a stage of great intensity. Oats, potatoes, carrots, and the green vegetables were grown in a zone which closely resembled the similar belt along the Leeds and Liverpool Canal. Like Liverpool, too, Manchester was drawing on the milk supplies of distant areas, for the Preston railway brought milk to the city from places as far north as Chorley.

Throughout the lowlands of Lancashire, the mid-nineteenth century was a period of great progress in peatmoss reclamation (Fig. 24). About one-third of Chat Moss had now been brought into cultivation through the digging of drainage ditches and the heavy applications of lime and town waste. Trafford Moss, too, and smaller patches of peat like Ashton Moss were being brought under the plough, but progress was slower in the large Carrington–Warburton group of mosses in north Cheshire. On all the reclaimed peatland farming was almost wholly arable: little stock was kept, and the pattern of cropping was directed towards feeding both the human and the horse populations of the great towns. Oats and potatoes were grown widely on the mossland. In southwest Lancashire many mosslands were being reclaimed, and an almost identical cropping system was being established. Rainford Moss was being reclaimed by the Derby family, and in the coastal peat-belt broad zones of reclaimed land surrounded the wet unimproved cores.

Central Lancashire, within the limits of the coalfield, had a much poorer and less advanced agriculture than either the southwest or the southeast. The rougher, higher surface and the greater rainfall of this area of sticky clay-drift soils were physical hindrances to intensive cultivation, but its distance from the great cities was at least as great a disadvantage. As early as 1850 farmland had been seriously damaged both by pitwaste accumulation and—far more widespread—by mining subsidence. A traditional system of farming survived in this unpromising district. The land lay largely in old pastures, in which ploughing was not only physically difficult but also, on many farms, prohibited by the terms of lease. Little drainage had been attempted, and the old system of summer fallowing was particularly wasteful in an area which contained so little arable land. The single sign of progress was an increasing interest in dairying, but as yet little use was made of root fodder crops.

This reluctance to plough old pastures was also common among the farmers of north Lancashire, an area too remote from the towns of the south to have been influenced strongly by their growth. One contemporary observer, Binns, had never seen 'such execrable old blue-grass pastures' as those of the Fylde. The low state of farming here was the product of the soil exhaustion which followed an earlier period of overcropping, when the southern Fylde has been termed the 'granary of Lancashire'. Without

Fig. 24 PEAT MOSSLANDS, PARTLY RECLAIMED, IN THE MERSEY VALLEY EAST OF WARRINGTON, 1848. Much peat remained open, unenclosed and undrained in 1850, but the progress of reclamation over the previous 70 years is marked by the large fields of regular shape round the edge of the moss.

drainage, refertilisation, or a balanced rotation, successive croppings of oats in time ruined these once-rich soils, and they were allowed to revert to poor pasture grazed by herds of inferior cattle. Since the Fylde was too far from the cotton towns to sell milk in its liquid form, cheese was the chief cash product, and this was sent southwards through the great Preston market. In general, there was almost as great a task of improvement to be faced in the boulder clay country of the Fylde as in its peatmosses.

Mossland reclamation here was progressing vigorously, under the direction of landowning families like the Cliftons, who were transforming the landscape of the south Fylde. Marton Moss was becoming rich crop-land: 6,000 acres were already productive and a force of 160 men was at work on the rest (cf. p. 77). Beyond the Wyre the largest mosses in the county, the Pilling–Rawcliffe group, were being reduced both by large-scale and piecemeal drainage. From 1840 the Fylde had a railway con-nection with south Lancashire, so that the potatoes, turnips, and other arable crops of the reclaimed peat could find a large, non-local market.

The farmers of Lonsdale are given more unstinted praise than those of any other part of Lancastria in the accounts of the mid-nineteenth century. A traditional system survived here—the rearing of both beef stock and sheep on the 'sweet' limestone and rich lowland pastures for sale in the south of the county. Dairying for cheese making was a sub-sidiary interest, but cropping was limited both by strong relief and high rainfall. That even limestone pastures were heavily limed is eloquent of the acidity of these wet soils. Along the coast there were pockets of intensive arable farming, located chiefly on drained peat or reclaimed alluvium strengthened by the application of fish manure. In the mild climate of the coastlands vegetables, early potatoes, and grains were profitable crops. Fruit was grown at Silverdale, and there was intensive market gardening in the Morecambe district. The completion of the railway to Preston and the south had now brought Lonsdale within the economic orbit of industrial Lancashire.

It was generally agreed by contemporary authorities that Cheshire had made much slighter progress than Lancashire in adapting its agriculture to the new opportunities of the industrial era. The double stimuli of town-growth and improved communications had not been so strongly felt in this county which, in a physical sense, is better suited to intensive and profitable agriculture than Lancashire. Reports of improving landlords are less frequent from Cheshire, and it is clear that its farmers were still com-mitted to an old and now obsolete system. Over most of Cheshire the traditional dairy specialisation survived with little change. On the heavy drift lands of the central basin, in the lowlands of the Dee and Gowy valleys and on the wet flanks of the Pennines practically all the land was in permanent pasture. In the Northwich and Nantwich Hundreds it was estimated that only one-eighth of the land was cropped and in the Broxton

Hundred only one-sixteenth. Certainly the ploughing of these heavy clays was not easy, but in Lancashire even wetter pastures were being broken, after drainage, with great profit to farmers. The reverence that the Cheshire man felt for his pasture, the widespread insertion of restrictive clauses into leases, and the lack of drainage systems—in part due to insecurity of tenure—all limited ploughing in the Cheshire grasslands. Yet much of Cheshire is better suited to arable use than Lancashire. Over a considerable area the rainfall is below 30 inches and though soils are generally heavy they were rarely so wet as to be either marsh or moss.

That cropping was possible even on the heavy drift of central Cheshire was obvious, for half a century earlier much more land had been under the plough. Land was reverting to pasture from arable use over most of the cheese-making area. This was associated with a loss of rural population to the growing industrial towns of the north; indeed, parts of the dairy region lost half their farm population during the first four decades of the century. Paradoxically, the chief effect of the Industrial Revolution on farming in the heart of Cheshire was to intensify the traditional specialisation. Most farmers here lived mainly from the sale of cheese at Nantwich and other smaller markets; they grazed a 'mongrel stock' on old, undrained, undisturbed pastures and grew little except small quantities of wheat and potatoes, with oats for the working horses.

Change and progress were most evident in the parts of Cheshire closest to Manchester and Liverpool and with the easiest access to these great markets. In north Cheshire, near the Bridgewater Canal and the new railways from Manchester, the farming system was now based on the supply of produce to the city. The light soils and level surface of the Mersey high terrace made excellent cropland when fertilised by the large quantities of urban waste transported by canal boats. Potatoes, wheat, and vegetables were raised for the Manchester market, together with great quantities of oats and hay for the enormous horse population of Manchester and district. Market gardening was becoming established in this canal-side belt: Sale was known for its onions, while the sandy 'downs' of Altrincham produced early potatoes. Two-thirds of the area in these parishes immediately south of the Mersey was cropped and here dairying was of minor significance though farther south the proportion fell to between one-third and one-fifth of the acreage in a zone from which liquid milk was supplied to the Manchester market. Beyond a line joining Mobberley, High Legh, and Runcorn cheese making became dominant, for this was the maximum distance from which milk could be carried by barge and train to the city. Even the construction of the railways from Crewe to Manchester and Warrington led to little extension of the 'milkshed', for dairying was replaced by potato farming in some localities along their tracks. In Wirral, as in north Cheshire, proximity to a great urban market brought new life to agriculture. On the light loams of the sandstone platforms one-third of the acreage was cropped with a rotation based on wheat and potatoes. A sunny climate and low rainfall were influences as important as the demand of the local market in establishing an intensive half-arable, half-dairy system here.

From this outline of Lancastrian farming in the mid-nineteenth century—a period when the foundations of the modern pattern of agricultural specialisation were being laid—a number of conclusions may be drawn. Lancashire farmers caught the spirit of enterprise and experiment which was the feature of the times. Backed by improving landlords, many of whom could draw on industrial fortunes, they were adapting their farming to the opportunities which town growth presented. In Cheshire the impact of economic change was felt only locally and tradition rather than experiment guided farming practice. Improvements were fewer and reclamation slower. Communications were the chief key to these major regional contrasts in the rate of agrarian change: they not only encouraged local specialisation but also permitted the great intensification of land use by transporting from the cities the sewage which was the only cheap fertiliser available to an arable farmer. This unsavoury traffic was a most important element in the mutual interdependence of a Victorian town and its countryside.

Town growth

Exact recognition of the towns of 1801 is not easy, for many of the industrial settlements had not acquired either the size or the appearance of towns but like many modern mining settlements were more akin to a workers' camp around a number of mills and factories, in some cases having no previous existence as a village. The remotely placed industrial village beside a mill is characteristic of the whole Pennine textile area. Many such mills and even, though not invariably, the workers' houses associated with them have perished, as, for example, in some of the Rossendale valleys, but villages and even towns, surviving to the present, developed around small hamlets having a domestic industry. Of Stalybridge, Baines wrote in 1825: 'The scenery here is bold and impressive, but those enemies of the picturesque, pit-coal and steam engines, have diminished its natural beauties, and substituted in their place beneficial employment for the poor and increased opulence for the wealthy.' In 1748 Stalybridge had 140 people; but it grew rapidly when the first cotton mill run by water power was opened in 1776 and the first steam engine was set up in 1796. By 1828 it acquired by law twenty-one town commissioners chosen by the wealthier inhabitants, who in 1832 opened a town hall and market house. Similar commissioners were appointed elsewhere; for example Ashton-under-Lyne acquired them in 1827, before which date the town was managed by agents and officers of Lord Stamford's court-leet with the parish churchwardens and officers. Originally consisting of narrow streets, Ashton grew from the mid-eighteenth century as a cotton town having a gridiron pattern of wide streets and squares, with a market house dating from 1827 and a town hall from 1840. The authorities of these towns provided water, gas, sewerage (in time), and even baths, libraries, and other amenities, and the public buildings also included numerous churches and an inadequate number of schools. Even so, much of the growth was haphazard, not unnaturally since the rate of industrial expansion was so swift.

In 1801, out of the 865,791 living in Lancashire and Cheshire, 414,769, or 48%, were in towns. Fifty years later, the population had increased almost threefold, to 2,486,961, of whom 1,603,775, or 65%, were in defined towns. This is, however, an understatement, as the industrial population was spreading beyond the areas defined as urban at each census. During the 1840s England and Wales as a whole passed the vital stage in its economy at which more people were congregated in towns than in rural areas; but this stage was reached in Lancastria more than twenty years earlier. In spite of the present slum-clearance schemes and plans to provide new town centres, the imprint of the early-nineteenth century industry is still clear in many towns of Lancashire and Cheshire, notably in the older mills such as those of Stockport, Stalybridge, Macclesfield, or Congleton. Equally it is seen in the surviving houses of the time, of which many artisan types are now far below acceptable standards though they are not undignified in appearance, whether built of stone as in Stalybridge or of brick as in Macclesfield. Church architecture includes Gothic Anglican buildings of varying success and, from the earlier years of the nineteenth century, some Nonconformist chapels of good plain design, especially in brickwork, provided that they have escaped later modernisation.

At the beginning of the nineteenth century Liverpool (82,295) and Manchester (75,281), with its immediate neighbour Salford (18,088) across the Irwell, were rivals of Birmingham for the status of the largest provincial town. All three grew rapidly to the mid-nineteenth century and in fact multiplied their populations fourfold, so that in 1851 the populations were Liverpool 375,955, Manchester 303,382, with Salford 85,108— far more than Birmingham's 232,841 at the same date. At the time of writing large areas covered with early-nineteenth century houses are being demolished, and the ground used either for modern flats, for industries, or for public buildings. This is, however, merely a continuing stage in a long process, for as early as the 1840s the inner areas of these towns were losing population as town houses were transformed into shops, warehouses, offices, and even small factories; many houses were pulled down to clear sites for the new railways, widened and new roads, factories, warehouses, and public buildings (Fig. 25). Although there are still relics of the 'West

End' quarters of Manchester in the streets between Deansgate and the river and in Liverpool around the university and the Anglican cathedral, now almost entirely non-residential in use, everything combined to send people farther from town centres (Fig. 26). Land became too precious for housing as commerce grew, and the increasing pollution of the air from

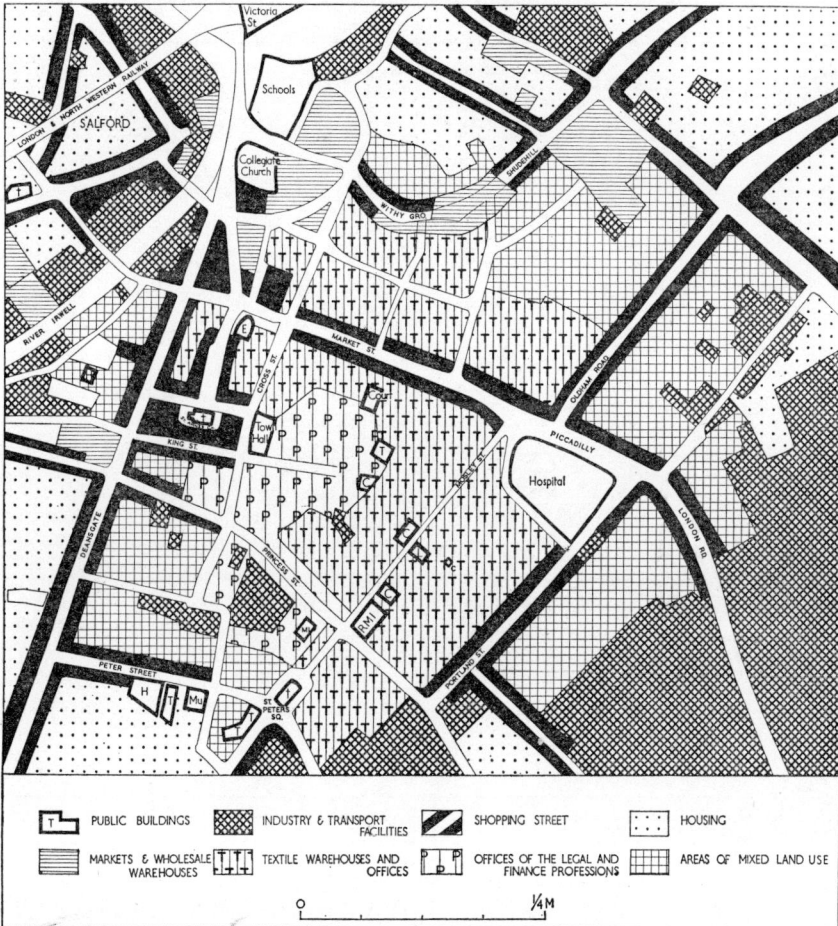

Fig. 25 CENTRAL MANCHESTER IN 1845. Based mainly on directory material. E, Exchange; T, Theatre; C, Club; L, Library; RMI, Royal Manchester Institution; MI, Mechanics Institute; Mu, Museum; H, Hotel.

factories reduced the amenities of the central areas (Plate 51). Both aspects were noted by Cooke-Taylor in 1842. Commenting that Manchester was becoming a great commercial centre and the mart of the cotton trade, he wrote that in the Exchange 'transactions of immense extent are conducted by nods, winks, shrugs, or brief phrases'. And on the suburban movement he wrote that 'the forest of chimneys pouring forth volumes of steam and smoke forming an inky canopy which seemed to embrace and involve the whole place ... drives everyone from the township ... who can possibly find means of renting a house elsewhere'; the wealthy settled in what were then the 'open spaces of Cheetham, Broughton and Chorlton'. Gradually the vacant ground of the inner suburbs was filled by factories and artisan houses and the wealthy moved out farther, in Manchester to suburbs

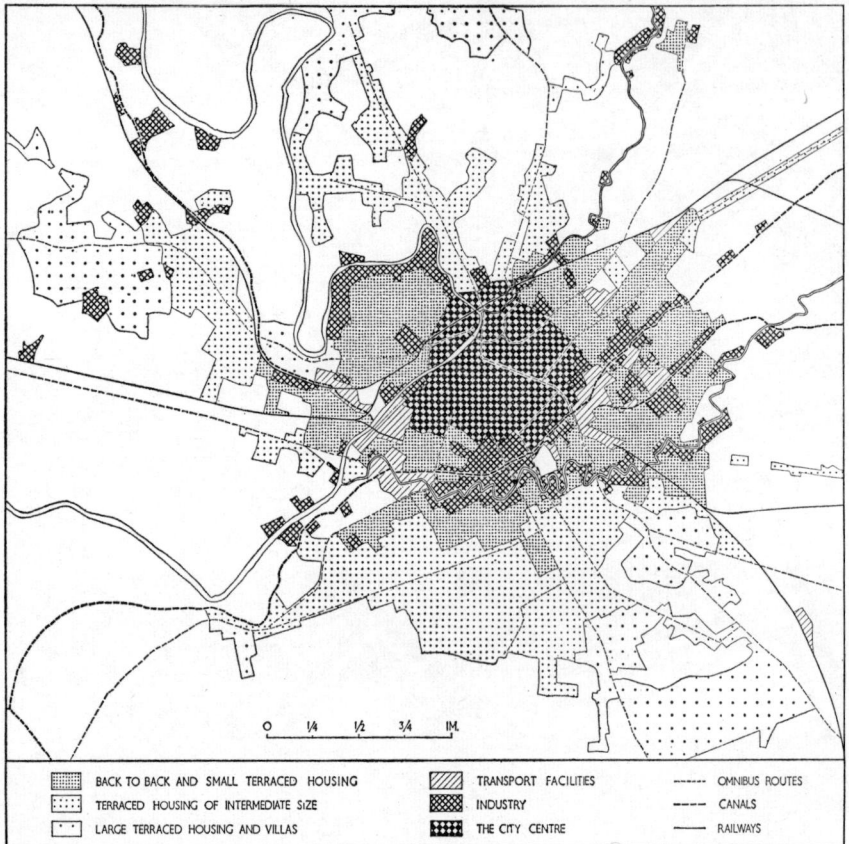

Fig. 26   URBAN LAND USE IN MANCHESTER, 1845. From the first 60-inch to one-mile Ordnance Survey map.

such as Didsbury, Northenden, and even Altrincham and Bowdon once it was reached by the railway in 1849 (Fig. 26). Merseyside had a similar outward movement, and when regular ferries were provided the suburbanisation of the Wirral peninsula began. In Birkenhead, the population increased from 319 in 1821 to 2,793 in 1831, 8,463 in 1841, and 24,999 in 1851. Mr Laird of Greenock had founded a boiler-making and shipbuilding yard at Wallasey in 1824, and the first Birkenhead docks were built in 1851; gradually Birkenhead shared in the general trading and industrial expansion of Merseyside, and the slow but inevitable trans-formation of the Wirral peninsula into a residential and commercial segment of the Merseyside conurbation continued (Fig. 27, Plate 50).

Of the Cheshire towns, the largest in the early nineteenth century were Chester and Stockport. In 1801, their population was almost equal, with 15,174 in Chester and 14,830 in Stockport, but by 1851 the popula-tions were 27,766 and 53,835 respectively. Chester was then, as now, the epitome of a strong market town, having failed to maintain its position as a port through the silting of the Dee and the increase in the size of ships. Well served by communications, based initially on the Roman road system and on the use of the Dee but in the early nineteenth century on a number of turnpike roads and the canal which traverses the town just outside the walls, where it cuts through the fine sandstone bluff which provides the town site, it has had a variety of industries, none of which, until recent times, was of considerable size. Stockport has an even finer site than Chester, with its market and church on a sandstone bluff sloping steeply to the Mersey; but in its industrial growth many factories and houses were built beside the river and in tributary valleys. A town on two levels, its main east–west road runs beside the river and above it runs the north–south road, constructed from Heaton Norris on the north in 1824–6 with a bridge 40 feet above the water level and an embankment to reach the upper surface on the south. As an engineering wonder, however, this road is overshadowed by the railway viaduct of the line from Manchester to Crewe (p. 182). By the middle of the nineteenth century Stockport was a considerable industrial town, with cotton, hat making, and engineering as its main trades, but it maintained its function as a strong market centre.

Both Macclesfield and Congleton retain something of the atmosphere of the early-nineteenth century town. From the early seventeenth century their inhabitants and those in neighbouring villages had made silk in cottages or small workshops with tools or hand-driven machinery, and there are still weavers' garret houses with three floors in Macclesfield: the top floor has a long row of windows to admit as much light as possible. In some cases a master weaver lived on two floors and used the top floor as a workshop for the labours of his family but in others the garret ran along a whole row of cottages and was approached by outside stairs—here small manufacturers had work-people as weavers. By the beginning of the nineteenth century the silk industry was located largely in mills, mostly of considerable size, of which many still survive. In 1801 Macclesfield had 8,743 people and Congleton 3,861, but by 1851 the numbers had grown to 39,048 and 10,520. Since then there has been little growth in Macclesfield, where house building outstripped demand from the 1830s to such an extent that by 1861 so many were vacant that few were added in the last forty years of the century. Apart therefore from modern suburban houses

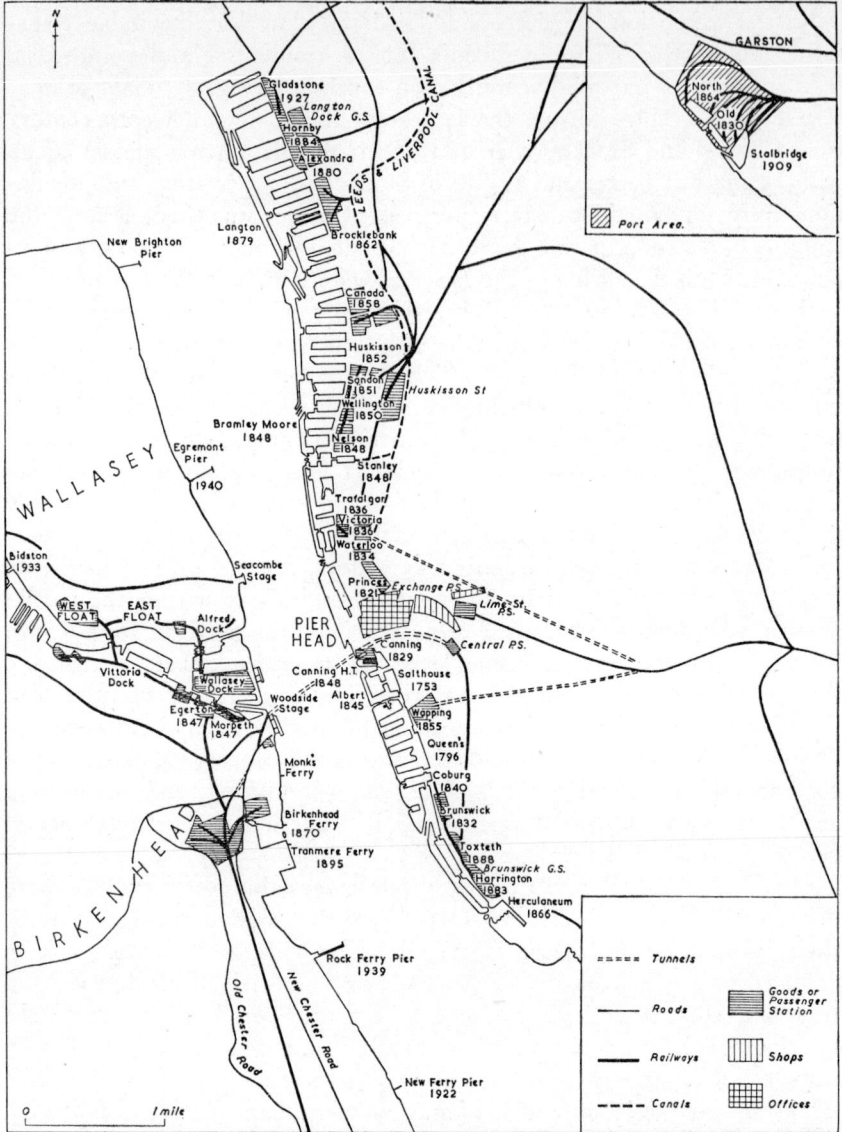

Fig. 27 THE MERSEY ESTUARY AND ITS DOCKS. The dock system was steadily developed from the eighteenth century, and from 1893 to 1956 was served by an overhead railway. On the Cheshire side the growth came with the railway, shown here: also shown are the passenger and goods lines of Liverpool. All the ferries have been closed except for that to Woodside, though there is a summer service to New Brighton. The main office and shopping areas of Liverpool are indicated. See Allison, J. E., *The Mersey Estuary* (Liverpool 1949). Previously published in Freeman, T. W., *The conurbations of Great Britain* (Manchester 1966), 107.

and the modernisation of the central area, Macclesfield has virtually the appearance of a mid-nineteenth century town, and indeed much the same population. Both in Macclesfield and in Congleton there are some interesting Nonconformist chapels of the early nineteenth century; but the best example in Congleton, dating from 1808, has been ruined in appearance by modern 'improvement'. Like Macclesfield, Stalybridge grew rapidly in the early nineteenth century but very little since then: by 1842 it had 32 cotton mills with over 9,000 employees and its population increased from 3,596 in 1801 to 23,387 in 1851 (see also pp. 174–5).

The remaining towns of Cheshire in the early nineteenth century were much smaller. They include several market towns such as Altrincham, which increased in population from 1,692 in 1801 to 4,488 in 1851, Frodsham from 1,250 to 2,099, and Knutsford from about 1,600 to 3,127. Hyde differed from these, for it was primarily industrial, and its growth rate was swift through the success of the cotton trade: it had 1,063 people in 1801 and 10,051 in 1851. At Runcorn the increase from 1,379 to 8,049 was ascribed to the growth of trade along the Bridgewater Canal and to the quarrying of the excellent local stone, and for a time it was also a favoured bathing place. The three wych towns, Nantwich, Middlewich, and Northwich, were all small. In Nantwich the salt working was declining to its final extinction in 1856 though there were other industries, such as the making of glass, shoes, and even cotton.[1] The town increased slowly in population from 3,463 in 1801 to 5,426 in 1851 though it failed to acquire the new railway junction of central Cheshire which gave impetus to the growth of Crewe, a new town of the 1840s. To this day, however, Nantwich is a major road junction. At Northwich, Winsford, and to a lesser extent at Middlewich, the salt trade was prosperous: Northwich grew in population from 2,969 in 1801 to 4,870 and Winsford (with Over) from 1,634 to 4,942. Sandbach also ranked as a market town, but remained small and had less than 3,000 people in 1851; and two smaller places, Tarporley and Audlem, though possessing charters for markets dating back to the thirteenth century, remained villages in appearance through the nineteenth century to the present time.

In Lancashire the town population increased fourfold between 1801 and 1851, from approximately 300,000 to 1,200,000. As noted on page 78, the census commissioners did not always find it easy to say which places were towns in a county of many somewhat amorphous mining and industrial settlements: in fact, few new industrial towns arose in Lancashire during the first half of the nineteenth century (but cf. Widnes, pp. 87, 185) as most were mining and cotton centres already established by 1800; except Oldham, all the main cotton towns were markets of considerable

---

[1] All of these ceased: gloves in 1863, cotton in 1874, and shoes, following the burning of a factory in 1925. Like many other old towns, Nantwich has had a variety of industries. See p. 173 and E. A. Johnson and R. Russel, *A Short History of Nantwich and Neighbourhood* (Nantwich, 1902).

antiquity. By 1851 Manchester and Liverpool were major provincial cities (pp. 110–12); the growth of Manchester was associated not only with its factories for cotton and engineering, but also with its increasing dominance as the central mart of the cotton trade. Baines noted that in Bolton merchants built warehouses during the late eighteenth century, but gradually all were closed as goods were more readily sold in Manchester. Liverpool profited as a port not, as is often said, by the decline of Chester but with the expansion of industry in Lancashire, aided by its new railways as well as by canal communications. By 1851 places like Preston (69,542), Bolton (61,171), Blackburn (46,536), Burnley (24,745), Rochdale (41,513), and Oldham (72,357) were all strong manufacturing centres, associated largely with cotton though at Rochdale there was also a considerable woollen industry with some engineering, and at Oldham, as in some neighbouring districts, there was hat manufacture. In and around the towns listed above, except for Preston, coalmining was prevalent and the resources seemed almost unlimited. Wigan (31,941) was particularly significant as a mining centre, having a canal-borne trade to Liverpool and other parts of Lancashire, and a growing metallurgical industry as well as cotton mills. At Preston, as at Lancaster, efforts were made to develop the Ribble as a port, especially after 1837 when the channel was deepened, quays built, and—in 1841—a dock made at Lytham: but no great profit came of this venture, though Preston was revived as a port at the end of the century (Plates 47, 48).

Many of the towns had little apparent planning, though there were exceptions such as Ashton-under-Lyne (pp. 109–10), under the influence of the Earls of Stamford. But there were many examples of manufacturers who built mills, houses, and not unusually a church also for their workers: Millward has mentioned the association of the Grant brothers with Ramsbottom, where they built mills, cottages for the workers (of whom many were immigrants), a large hall, and a Presbyterian church. In Preston, the Horrocks family, first established in 1791, built a spinning mill, handloom sheds, and rows of cottages. Some such places were industrial villages, such as Brooksbottom, with a mill, cottages, and a Methodist chapel, built by J. R. Kay from 1829 and described as 'a thriving and happy colony of workpeople', though the evidence is not invariably so favourable. Cooke-Taylor in 1842 regarded with favour such mills as those of Turton, with the owner's residence above it, or at Egerton where there was a mill and neat cottages for the workers, both of which were owned by the Ashworths. A similarly favourable view was taken of the Greg settlement at Styal (p. 68), by Cooke-Taylor, who wrote: 'A healthy spirit of emulation has long since existed among the proprietors of rural mills and print-works; they were not less proud of the comfort and respectable appearance of their operatives than a nobleman is of his palace or demesne. . . . In everything that tends to promote intellectual acquisition

116

the operatives in a well-managed country mill are fully on an equality with their brethren in Manchester; in the means for preserving healthy cleanliness and morality, they are decidedly superior.' Some of the rural mills— by no means all—were eventually surrounded by towns, and though some writers saw the growth of towns with dismay, others rejoiced in the indications of prosperity. 'Thank God,' said Cooke-Taylor of Bolton's chimneys, 'smoke is rising from . . . most of them! The smoke creates no nuisance here—the chimneys are too far apart; and it produces variations in the atmosphere and sky which . . . have a pleasant and picturesque effect.' But he was shocked by the squalor of the growing slums of Bolton and other towns; having visited the huts and hovels of Ireland, the cellars of Liverpool, the wynds and vennels of Glasgow, nowhere had he seen 'misery which so agonized my very soul as that . . . in the manufacturing districts of Lancashire'. Another aspect of the general problem of town growth is given by the comment of Baines on Blackburn in 1825: 'The streets are irregularly built, partly owing to the intermixture of glebe and other lands, and partly due to that eccentricity of taste and variety of convenience which generally prevail in manufacturing places.'

Oldham (Plate 49) is one of the most typical Lancashire towns of the Pennine fringe. Already, with 21,677 people, a considerable town by 1801, it had been a mere village of a hundred houses forty years earlier; but by 1851, with 72,356 people, it was smaller only than the cities of Liverpool, Manchester, and Salford. Piece by piece, its moors were sold for industrial development and covered with mills, mill dams, and workers' houses. At this stage its trade was carried by road and two canals, the Rochdale and the Oldham–Ashton, though in 1846 an Act authorised the first branch-line railway to Oldham. Bolton had increased its population from 17,966 in 1801 to 61,171 in 1851; having a long tradition of textile working, it had numerous bleaching grounds around the town, and had developed the fine spinning for which it became famed. Though cotton spinning was the main trade by 1851, Bolton also had ironworks and coalmining. Of other towns famed for cotton, Bury grew in population to 25,484 in 1851, and numbered among its industries calico printing, established by Robert Peel, father of the Prime Minister, with cotton and woollen manufacture; far into the nineteenth century many of its mills were run on water power. In time these towns were to be joined to others by continuous building to form part of the Manchester conurbation (pp. 198–9); but they have long-established traditions of independence. Even within the conurbation there are still some industrial villages of the type previously described, such as Rhodes, near Middleton, where a small works was taken over by Silas Schwabe in 1832 and developed into a vast bleachworks for which water was acquired from thirteen reservoirs in local streams; a chimney 321 feet high, long a landmark in the district, was built in 1846.

5

In time houses were built around the works, but to this day it is recognisable as an expression of its time (cf. Plates 15–17).

Many other towns of Lancashire were growing steadily during the first half of the nineteenth century; but apart from those already mentioned only a few had acquired a population of even 10,000 by 1851. Excluding West Derby (10,971), then growing as a suburb of Liverpool and later incorporated within it, these towns of more than 10,000 were Accrington (10,374) and Darwen (11,702), both predominantly textile centres, and two towns of a more varied industry, Warrington (22,894) and St Helens (25,403). Warrington (p. 44) has for many centuries been a major trading town; in the early nineteenth century it had cotton weaving but also various metallurgical industries including wiredrawing and the making of pins, files, and hardware, as well as glass making and soap manufacture. At St Helens, in a prosperous coalmining district, the main industries were glass making and chemicals, of which the latter, abandoned later, has left vast mounds of refuse now being quarried for road metal. The main growth of the smaller towns was due to the cotton trade. At Chorley (8,907), for example, the chief products were muslins and calicoes, and there were large printing and bleaching works on streams in the district; at Haslingden (6,154), a town built largely from local stone, there were several cotton mills on the local stream, the Swinnel. Nearer to Manchester, Eccles (4,108) had a cotton mill and factories for various types of textiles, including silk and linen; and at Middleton (5,740), though the main industry was cotton spinning and weaving, there were also bleaching, printing, and dyeing, with some manufacture of silk. On the coast, Blackpool had 2,180 inhabitants by 1851 and Southport 4,765; although people had gone to the coast for sea-bathing for more than a century, Southport was at first the more favoured of the two places. Both grew rapidly when reached by railways in the 1840s.

As the railway system became intricate, so the great Victorian expansion began. Much was altered in their central areas with new town halls, old crumbling churches restored or entirely rebuilt, new churches of Gothic design added, and Nonconformist chapels built in large numbers. Suburbs expanded with the rising wealth of the mercantile and professional classes, particularly near to railway stations or along roads served by horse omnibuses or accessible for private carriages. Artisan quarters increased also, generally nearer to the mills and works. Already in the forefront for industrial power, the Northwest made its position far stronger in the first half of the nineteenth century, and the builders of railways were attracted to the areas as surely as the builders of canals came before them. Rivers were harnessed to such an extent that the Irwell was said to be the most hard-worked in the world. Local government agencies were set up to meet the increasing problems of such large numbers of people crowded together in small areas, with rivers made foul by sewerage and industrial effluents. Another problem was the spoliation of areas by industry, in flashes due to mining subsidence, mining spoilheaps, or the mounting chemical waste of St Helens. But agriculture prospered as the town demand increased and the way was opened for increasing specialisation of farming characteristic of our own time.

CHAPTER 6

The New Industrial Revolution

A distinction has been made between two groups of British industrial regions, the 'fortunate' and the 'unfortunate'. The former, which lie in midland, metropolitan, and southern England, are regions of quick and continuing economic growth; they are attracting the bulk of both Britain's industrial and social investment, and they contain an increasing proportion of its total population. The latter, the 'unfortunate' industrial regions of Wales, of Scotland, and of northern England, have failed to repeat, in the twentieth century, their quick economic progress of the nineteenth. They have lost, or are losing, their traditional staple industries; and continuing migration from them has affected their rate of population increase, which is far below the national average. To these areas the industrial revolution of the twentieth century has brought little but industrial decline and intermittent social distress.

Considered as a whole, Lancastria must be described as an unfortunate area. In the first Industrial Revolution it made spectacular economic progress through the immense but ephemeral success of its cotton textile industry. Until the closing decades of the nineteenth century it was increasing its share of the nation's population and wealth. In the decade of the 1890s this region's rate of population increase (12%) was almost exactly equal to that of England and Wales (12·2%); but since then the population of Lancastria has grown more slowly than that of England and Wales and at progressively lower rates. The region's rate of population growth fell to 2·9% during the period 1921–31, and was only 1·9% between 1951 and 1961, in comparison with a national rate of 5·3%. That Lancastria has lost its economic momentum is shown even more clearly by its falling share of the country's employment: between 1952 and 1958 the number of workers grew by only 1%, while the increase for England and Wales was 7%.

There is little mystery about the causes of Lancastria's present economic debility. It is hardly surprising that a region which contains the bulk of Great Britain's most quickly contracting industry—a cotton manufacture based upon a half-exhausted coalfield—should be in decline. During the late 1920s and throughout the 1930s unemployment persisted widely in the textile towns, and it has broken out more briefly and locally in the post-war years. Unemployment provoked heavy and sustained migration southwards to more prosperous areas. This has continued—indeed, it has accelerated—in the years since 1945, despite the absence of persistent unemployment. Migration is almost always age-selective: it involves the age ranges from 20 to 45, and thus reduces the reproductive population. Birth rates have fallen throughout the areas of migratory loss, and death rates have increased, for the average age of the population of a typical textile town has risen through the loss of so many young people. Today a natural decrease of population is occurring over most of the textile area of eastern Lancastria.

The decline of Lancastria's traditionally dominant industries, cotton manufacture and coalmining, is clearly the prime but not the only cause of the region's present difficulties. Its failure to attract enough employment in 'replacement' industries is at least as significant. All the evidence of the post-war period is that 'footloose' industry tends to avoid the textile districts of eastern Lancastria. Certainly, new trades have been attracted to districts which formerly enjoyed Development Area status, and old cotton mills have been converted for a variety of new industries; but in general the coalfield and the cotton towns have failed to attract enough new employment to balance the decline of their older industries. Throughout the textile zone the volume of work available is declining quickly, in some of the most seriously affected towns by rates which exceed 10% per decade. But it would be misleading to characterise the whole of Lancastria as a region of economic decline. Over most of west and southwest Lancashire and in the industrial areas of central and north Cheshire vigorous expansion is taking place. These areas—many of them non-industrial in Victorian times—are now attracting most of the new manufactures of the region. In short, the replacement industries are avoiding the towns which need new employment desperately: consequently the general distribution of employment in Lancastria is changing fast, and, inevitably, a redistribution of the region's population is taking place. Lancastria, like Great Britain as a whole, has its 'fortunate' and its 'unfortunate' areas.

The decline of the staple industries

Though in Victorian Manchester it seemed that Lancashire monopolised the world's cotton industry almost by divine dispensation, it is now clear that some contraction of the region's textile industry was, from the first, inevitable. Lancashire had no unique range of advantages for the cotton industry, which it acquired almost by historical accident. In its more rudimentary forms this is a simple manufacture which has naturally become the spearhead of industrialisation in many parts of the tropical world, and perhaps the most widely dispersed of the world's great industries. Countries which were Lancashire's customers in the nineteenth century now have their own mills, and some have become successful exporters of cheap cloth.

The graphs in Figure 28 give a statistical summary of the industry's atrophy over the past twenty years. Its decline began in the 1920s, after the brief boom which immediately followed the First World War; for the growth of infant cotton industries in countries which had formerly imported their cloth led to a quick decrease in the total volume of world trade. Lancashire's markets shrank still further with the general depression of the 1930s, when Japan, a powerful, low-cost rival, quickly captured much of the remaining trade. The mills enjoyed an ephemeral recovery in the late 1930s, due to larger sales in the home market, but soon after the outbreak of war in 1939 the industry was concentrated to free both premises and labour for the production of armaments. Only a remnant of the cotton

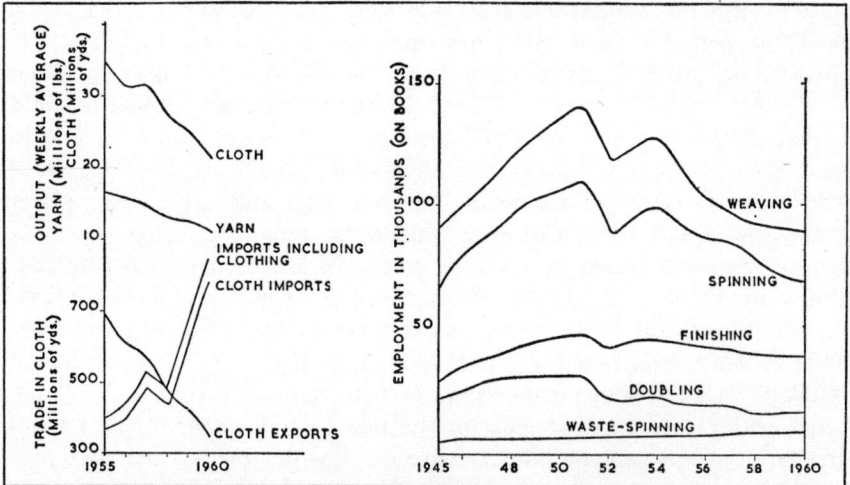

Fig. 28 RECENT TRENDS IN THE COTTON INDUSTRY. The left-hand diagram shows the crisis in import–export trends 1955–60, the right-hand graph the post-war contraction of employment in the industry.

manufacture, its skilled labour irretrievably dispersed, survived to face the difficult problems of a competitive post-war world. A slow and short-lived recovery followed the Second World War; but the sharp recession of 1952 heralded a worsening crisis which halved the labour force of the industry during the following decade. By the late 1950s Lancashire's mills seemed threatened by total extinction: while exports continued to fall, imports of cheap cloth from Asian countries of the Commonwealth grew so rapidly that by 1958–9 they exceeded the yardage (but not the value) of exports.

As even the once-secure home market slipped from its grasp, it became clear that the cotton industry could not save itself unaided. Masses of redundant and obsolete machinery filled the half-idle mills; investment in modernisation was at a standstill, and the unemployed or underemployed operatives were being lost permanently by migration to more fortunate areas or by transfer to more stable industries. These were the circumstances which inspired the Cotton Industry Act of 1960, essentially a plan for radical reorganisation through the scrapping of surplus machinery and the closure of redundant mills in return for compensatory payments. The aims of the Act were twofold: firstly, to reduce the industry to a size more in keeping with its present commercial prospects; secondly, to stimulate a sadly belated technical modernisation by the offer of re-equipment subsidies. The first of these aims was achieved with spectacular success: the industry made such indecorous haste to liquidate itself that 49% of the spindles and 40% of the looms were abandoned. It is more difficult to measure the progress of modernisation; but by 1961 three-quarters of the spinning capacity was in ring mills, and the old, obsolete mules that had survived in astonishingly large numbers are now rapidly disappearing. But in 1961 only 29% of the looms were automatic, and the industry was still worse equipped than its rivals overseas. Paradoxically, by then a labour shortage was troubling this shrinking industry. It continued to lose workers to other trades, and it proved difficult to find sufficient labour for the double or treble shift operation necessary for new machinery to be economic.

Figures 29 and 30 show that there have been strong local contrasts in the rate of the cotton industry's decline. The first of these maps shows the decline of the industry between 1931 and 1951, and the second illustrates the much quicker and more radical reorganisation of the industry under government sponsorship in 1960. The strongly marked contrasts in rate of decline which stand out so clearly in Figure 29 are associated with the pattern of intense regional specialisation in particular branches of the trade which was for so long the distinctive feature of the geography of the cotton industry. The coarse-weaving towns of the Blackburn group, which once lived by the production of coarse, grey cloth for tropical markets, lost two-thirds of their textile employment; but the fine-weaving centres from Burnley to Colne were shielded against the shock of Asian competition by their specialisation in high-quality cloths for 'advanced' markets, and they suffered far fewer mill closures. Similarly, the Bolton group of fine-spinning towns lost much less mill employment than the Oldham coarse-spinning district. The finishing section of the cotton industry has proved much more resilient than the manufacturing branches, and towns with a strong interest in bleaching and dyeing—for example, Manchester and Ramsbottom—lost little of their textile employment. And other factors, unconnected with specialisation, are involved in the pattern of decline revealed by the map. As some of the remoter and least accessible centres suffered badly, there was some peripheral contraction of the textile province. But in one marginal district there was little decline: in the mill-and-pit towns of central Lancashire few closures occurred, for many of the mills here are comparatively new, large, and easily modernised, and there was little competition from

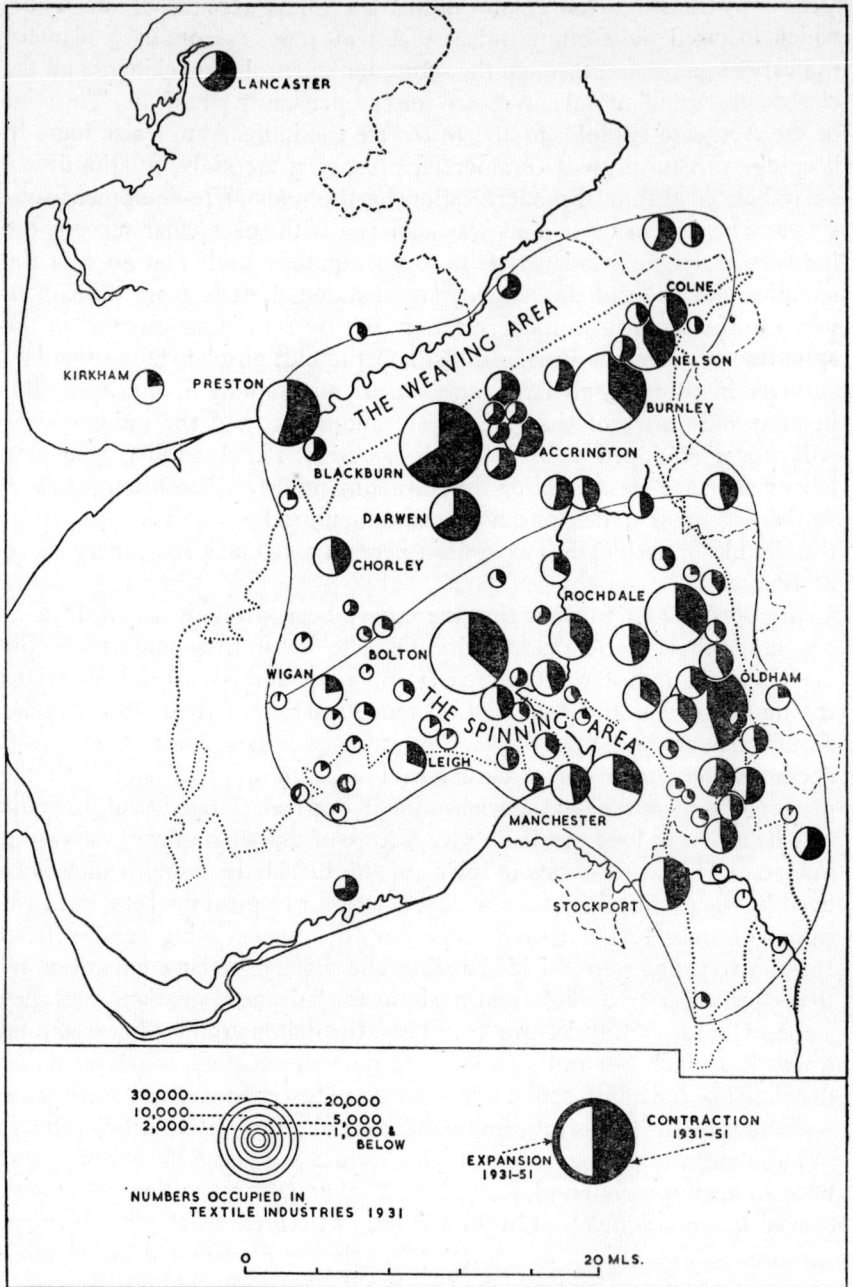

Fig. 29 THE CONTRACTION OF THE COTTON INDUSTRY 1931–51. First published in *Econ. Geogr.* **38** (1962), 302. The only expansion is in the extreme southwest of the Coalfield.

other industries for the abundant local supply of female textile labour. In contrast, the industry declined especially quickly in some towns of great industrial breadth, such as Stockport, where competition for labour has been intense since 1945.

In the much quicker contraction of the cotton industry during the single year of reorganisation (Fig. 30) some of the trends of the earlier period were repeated. There was further peripheral contraction as some of the outliers of the industry disappeared, and, again, the towns of greatest diversity of employment have experienced very many mill closures. But some new and significant features may be observed in the pattern of decline shown in Figure 30. Specialisation in fine qualities of work no longer assures survival. The traditional centres of fine spinning and weaving—Bolton and northeast Lancashire respectively—have lost more of their looms and spindles than the heavy-textile districts of Rossendale and the Rochdale area (Area 3 of Fig. 30), where much of the output is of cloth for industrial uses like tyre fabric and belting. Another feature of the changes shown in Figure 30 is that the traditional weaving belt of the north from Blackburn to Colne (Area 1) has lost a very high proportion of its looms by scrapping; it now contains scarcely half of the industry's weaving equipment, though at one time it had almost three-quarters. Much lower proportions of the working looms have been scrapped in the southeast of the cotton province and along its western margins. The weaving branch has experienced a distinct shift to the south and west and has again become partly integrated with the spinning branch, as it was in the early nineteenth century. As part of the same trend, there is now an increasing tendency for vertical integration to replace the old 'horizontal' organisation of the industry, in which most firms specialised in a single process. Many of the most successful firms, which have survived the recent difficulties most easily, have fully integrated vertical structures; and many of the districts which have experienced the slightest recent contraction (Fig. 30) are those in which the degree of specialisation is lowest, for example Wigan and Rossendale.

The changes which are remodelling the cotton industry are complex, but they may be summarised in simple, regional terms. Today a fourfold division of the Lancashire textile province has greater significance than the old, twofold distinction between the spinning and the weaving belts.

1 *From Blackburn to Colne.* In the old weaving belt of the north, there is still intense specialisation in the weaving branch, though the area has a much smaller proportion of the industry's looms (51%) than formerly. Spinning is still feebly developed here, despite a recent small increase, and except near Accrington there is little employment in the finishing trades. The social impact of the decline of the cotton industry has been greater here than in any other part of Lancastria: between 1952 and 1958 the volume of mill employment in the Burnley area fell by 24% and in the Blackburn area by 21%. In the former, the mills still provide one-third of all the work

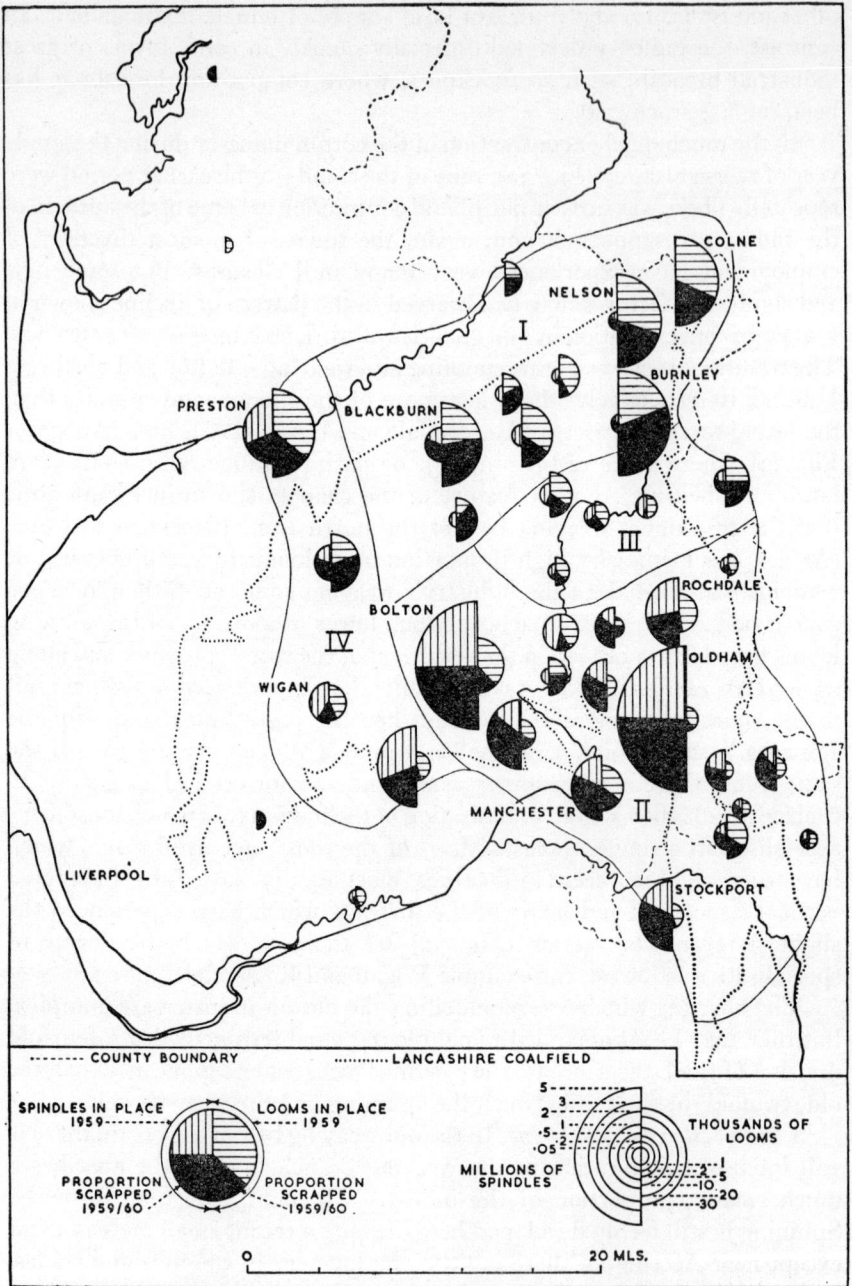

COLNE
NELSON
BURNLEY
PRESTON
BLACKBURN
I
III
ROCHDALE
BOLTON
OLDHAM
IV
WIGAN
II
MANCHESTER
LIVERPOOL
STOCKPORT

-------- COUNTY BOUNDARY   .... LANCASHIRE COALFIELD

SPINDLES IN PLACE   LOOMS IN PLACE
1959 ----   ---- 1959

PROPORTION   PROPORTION
SCRAPPED   SCRAPPED
1959/60 ·   · 1959/60

5
3
2
·5 1
·2
·05   THOUSANDS OF
                 LOOMS
MILLIONS OF   1
SPINDLES   2 ·5
                     10
                     20
                     30

0   20 MLS.

Fig. 30 THE GEOGRAPHICAL EFFECTS OF THE COTTON INDUSTRY REORGANISATION
ACT, 1960.

126

available, and the decline of the industry has caused some periods of sharp but fortunately ephemeral unemployment.

2 *The Manchester conurbation.* This, the core of the traditional 'spinning area', has been less seriously affected by the decline of the last decade. Although more than half its spindles were scrapped during the process of rationalisation, it still retains three-quarters of the industry's spinning capacity, now overwhelmingly in 'ring' mills. But there has been little abandonment of looms in the spinning towns, which now have about 30% of the weaving capacity. There were always exceptional districts here, such as Hyde and Radcliffe, in which weaving was the dominant branch; but the spinning zone as a whole has markedly increased its share of the cloth output. Many of its towns are now best described as having a balanced cotton industry, with looms and spindles in roughly equivalent numbers. Only Bolton and Oldham remain strongly specialised spinning centres. The Manchester embayment and its hill flanks have long had most of the textile finishing, the most progressive branch of the industry, which has survived strongly except in Manchester itself. Strung along the valleys of the streams from which they draw their process water, the dyeing and bleaching plants are important employers of male labour, particularly near Bury and Rochdale and in the Pennine valleys east of Manchester.

3 *Rossendale and the Rochdale area.* In the deep valleys of this area a distinctive textile industry characterised by the close integration of spinning and weaving has shown a great capacity for survival. Employment in the mills fell by only 5% during the critical period 1952–8. Among the reasons for this unusual stability are the slighter competition here for mill labour from other industries, the local specialisation in heavy textiles for industrial uses, and the strength of the finishing industry, which has actually increased its employment since 1952.

4 *The western margins of the cotton province.* The towns from Preston to Leigh rival Rossendale both in the strong survival of their cotton industries and in the absence of extreme specialisation in either spinning or weaving. In Wigan and Leigh there were falls of only 6% and 9% respectively in mill employment between 1952 and 1958. Neither spindles nor looms have been scrapped in large numbers, and the area now has 12% of the industry's spinning capacity and 4% of the weaving—in each case a greater share than in 1950.

Many changes besides these distributional shifts have come to the Lancashire cotton industry during its years of decline. It is no longer true to call it simply a 'cotton' industry, for almost one-half of its cloth output is now composed wholly or partly of the man-made fibres. Rayon, nylon, and terylene can be woven on cotton looms, and their widespread adoption has saved the weaving branch from even worse disaster. Cut rayon 'staple' is also used as a substitute for raw cotton in the production of heavy yarns for furnishing and other fabrics. But the introduction of man-made fibres has had a disastrous effect on the fine-spinning industry of the Bolton district, for they have largely replaced poplins made of doubled yarns in high quality clothing. Close links now exist with the chemical industry.

Technical changes, too, have made some progress in recent years. In 1959 half the spinning machinery 'in place' in mills consisted of aged and obsolete 'mules'; after rationalisation the more modern and productive ring spindles accounted for 76% of the surviving capacity. Since most 'mule' operatives are men but 'ring' spinners are women this slaughter of the ancient mules has posed serious social problems. Slower progress has been made towards the modernisation of weaving: even after reorganisation only 30% of the looms were automatic. There is no doubt that labour supply holds the key to the further progress of technical modernisation, without which the industry can scarcely hope to survive. Re-equipment is uneconomic except when coupled with multishift working; but the dwindling and ageing labour force in the mills has prevented the widespread adoption of shiftwork, except for the short, evening 'housewives' shift. Only about one-quarter of the industry's equipment is worked more than a single shift each day, though there are signs that shift-working is increasing, if only slowly. Roughly two-thirds of the mill labour is female, and the married women particularly object to shiftwork. Nor will they travel more than a mile or two to work, so that cotton firms which had hoped to recruit the experienced labour of mills closed under the reorganisation scheme have often failed to do so, even when they have provided special transport. Indeed, the cotton manufacturers may not be able to retain enough workers even for single-shift operation; wastage by retirement is heavy, for almost two-thirds of the labour force is over forty years of age and there is virtually no recruitment of school leavers. This loss of labour is at least as great a threat to the future of the industry as its loss of markets.

The Lancashire coalfield and the mining industry

The coalfield of Lancashire is by no means the largest in Great Britain, but it was one of the richest in its initial endowment of resources. The productive Middle Coal Measures series reaches a thickness of 6,000 feet, the greatest in the country, and the poorer Lower Coal Measures are over 1,000 feet thick. In all, thirty seams of workable thickness were available, and the most recent estimates suggest that almost 1,500 million tons of coal still await exploitation in seams of more than 2-foot thickness down to a depth of 3,600 feet. This is clearly not an exhausted coalfield, but it is a quickly declining one. Production has fallen to roughly 12 million tons yearly, less than half the peak output of 26·5 million tons in 1907.

During the nineteenth century this was, for its size, the most energetically worked coalfield in Great Britain; indeed, its output was for a time greater than that of the much larger Yorkshire field. Today the Lancashire mining industry must pay for this over-vigorous and often wasteful exploitation of the past, for it is working a seriously diminished resource from which the best, shallowest, and most profitable coal has already been won. Moreover, the Lancashire field was always known for its structural complexity and technical difficulties in the form of steep dips, intricate faulting, and 'washouts'. For many years this was a 'high-cost', loss-making field in which the National Coal Board closed many pits not only

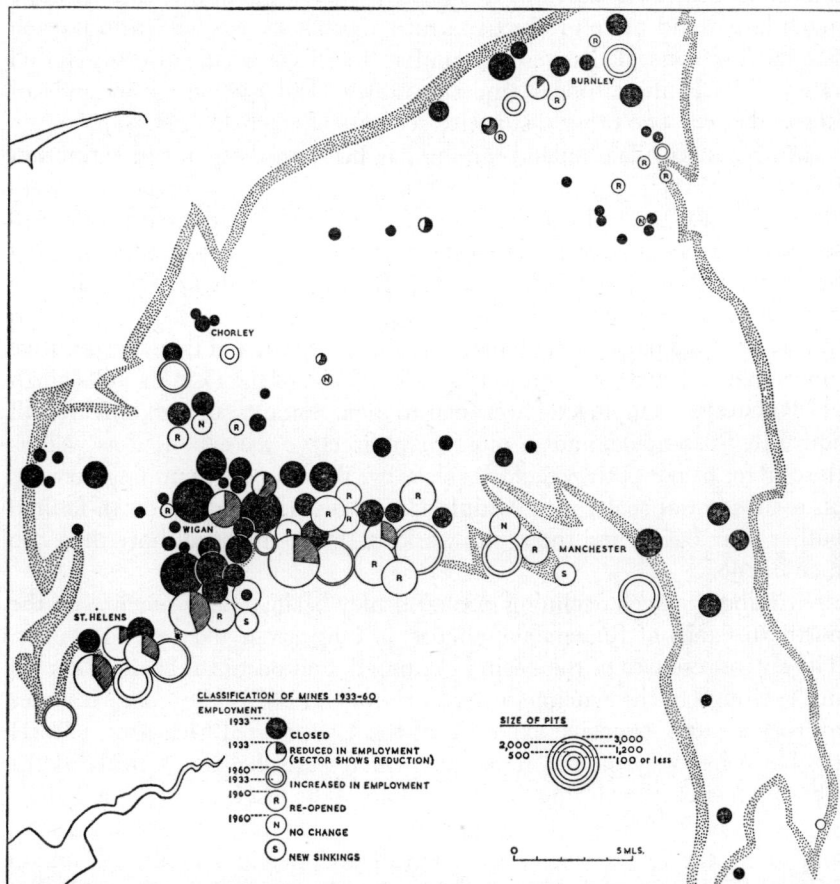

Fig. 31   THE CHANGING DISTRIBUTION OF THE LANCASHIRE COALMINING INDUSTRY 1933–60.

because of the local exhaustion of the seams but also because of their competitive inefficiency. Recently there has been a marked rise in the field's profitability.

In consequence of its complex structure the Lancashire coalfield is divided into a number of segments, and these provide a convenient framework for an account of the industry's decline. The field is roughly triangular in shape, with a long narrow salient reaching southwards along the Pennine flank almost to north Staffordshire. The broad base of the triangle lies east–west from Manchester to the suburbs of Liverpool, while the northern apex is to the northeast of Burnley. Lower or Middle Coal Measures are exposed throughout the whole of this area, except where the transverse anticline of the Rossendale uplift has raised Millstone Grits to form the high plateaux at the heart of this moorland block. The almost detached Burnley coal basin lies to the north of this barren core, while to the south lies the much larger and more productive south Lancashire coalfield with its rich but narrow concealed extension under the Trias of the Mersey–Irwell valley. The Pennine 'finger' and the Lower Coal Measure moorlands of Rossendale are two other distinctive sections of the field (Fig. 31).

In the Rossendale upland mining has been on the point of extinction for half a century, but it still survives weakly. The resources here were never rich, for the upland seams are few and thin; but the intricate dissection of the landscape rendered them easily accessible to simple working by horizontal adits or shallow shafts. In 1850 a rash of tiny collieries covered these hillsides, and coal was carried to local markets over rough tracks. By 1900 most of these had long disappeared, and the few primitive mines that still survived were very small in scale: of the 14 in the hills north of Manchester 8 employed fewer than 30 men. Some small workings are still active in Rossendale, and in most cases fireclays are exploited as well as the coal for heavy-pottery factories close by. But in one area mining survives on a substantial scale: rich Middle Coal Measures form a down-faulted outlier near Bacup and the 4 pits working them employed more than 500 men in 1964.

Mining has been declining in the Burnley basin, a deep syncline on the northern flanks of Rossendale, almost as long as in the upland proper. The entire resource of the basin is 'exposed' and occurs at shallow depths in the trough of the syncline, where a thin band of Middle Coal Measures overlies a more extensive exposure of the Lower Coal Measures. Clearly the basin has very limited resources, which were depleted quickly as the weaving towns grew during the second half of the last century. The shallow seams of the Middle Coal Measures were largely exhausted by the 1930s, and today the lower seams, especially the Upper and Lower Mountain Mines, yield most of the output. Though only about $2\frac{1}{2}$ feet in thickness, these seams contain coal of excellent coking quality. The quality of the coal has given this field an extended life, for working conditions in thin and steeply tilted seams are so difficult that most of its pits are loss makers. Indeed the slow decline of mining near Burnley has recently accelerated: of the 20 pits at work here in 1913 most survived until the later 1950s, but by 1964 only 6 were still producing coal. The loss of roughly one-quarter in the mining employment of the Burnley area during the last few years is serious, for the large pits of south Lancashire are beyond daily travelling range.

In the long narrow salient of Coal Measures which can be traced along the foot of the Pennines from Rochdale almost to the Potteries mining is now virtually extinct. Scarcely a mile wide in places, this mere strip of coal-bearing strata contains seams which dip extremely steeply westwards off the Pennine monocline and are thrown to unworkable depths beneath the Triassic beds by the Red Rock fault. Well served by early communications, this part of the field was grossly overworked during the nineteenth century. In 1911 there were 24 pits at work here, about half of which were of sub-stantial size, with between 100 and 500 men underground. By 1938 only 9 pits survived, and 4 of these were tiny undertakings with fewer than 30 men. All closed during the war and post-war years, though the last sur-vivor, the Ashton Moss colliery, remained until 1961. Few employment problems have been caused by the disappearance of the mining industry of the Pennine flank, for the great growth of the reconstructed Bradford pit in eastern Manchester has made it possible for redundant miners to find work comparatively close to their homes.

Throughout the history of the Lancashire field the great bulk of both output and employment has been concentrated upon the broad strip of Middle Coal Measures which stretches across south Lancashire from suburban Liverpool to central Manchester. The whole of this section of the field dips southwards from the axis of the Rossendale anticline; its western limit is the Boundary Fault beyond which the seams, if present at all, are downthrown beneath the Trias too deeply to be workable. At one time the Irwell valley fault was thought to set a similarly distinct eastern limit to the south Lancashire field, but productive seams have now been proved, under the Trias, and are coming into use to the east of it. Though geologically the most favourable section of the entire field, south Lancashire has serious technical problems. Close to the Rossendale scarps the seams are com-paratively shallow and dips are slight; but here the reserves were never great, for they have little depth and consist partly of Lower Coal Measures. Southwards the thickness of the series increases, but dips steepen towards the cover of Trias, beneath which the seams plunge to unworkable depths at dips as much as 20°.

Intense structural disturbance is one of the continuing problems of the mining industry in south Lancashire. A closely spaced series of major faults trending from NNW to SSE traverses the field, and minor faulting at right angles breaks the seams into a system of panels. Profitable seams dis-appear against faults, or are interrupted by 'wash-outs', the sand-filled channels of rivers in the Carboniferous period which removed the peat from which the coal was formed. Faulting reaches its greatest intensity in the Wigan trough of shattered Coal Measures which crosses the field from Chorley to Golborne. So broken and disturbed are the seams here that modern mining engineers have expressed their surprise that the coal could ever have been won profitably; yet until the inter-war period this was one of the most productive districts of the field.

Figure 31 shows the great changes which have taken place during the last thirty years in the distribution of the mining industry of south Lancashire. Almost all the pits which, until the 1930s, worked the shallow Coal Measures towards the foot of the Rossendale upland in a broad belt from Chorley to Bury have been closed. The only survival is at Chorley, where a small group of pits is still producing coal from workable pockets at the northern end of the Wigan fault trough; but there was a sharp fall in employment here in the later 1950s. In south Lancashire, as in so many other fields, there has been a 'down-the-dip' shift of production to deeper resources less affected by piecemeal nineteenth century operation. By 1960 the output came mainly from a line of large pits spaced along the southern margin of the field from Bradford, in east Manchester, to Cronton on the outskirts of Liverpool. But this southward movement of the industry has been guided in a complex manner by the faulting of the field. The broken seams of the Wigan area have now been almost completely abandoned, for their exploitation is totally uneconomic under modern circumstances. As Figure 31 shows, this was by far the part of the field most seriously affected by the contraction of the industry between 1930 and 1960; and the quick decline of mining near Wigan has not been balanced by any growth of employment farther south on the deeper coalfield (except for the new Parkside pit); for the complex faulting continues into the concealed extension and renders it largely unworkable. Farther west, along the margin of the coalfield, a simpler and clearer southwards shift has taken place. The few small pits working the limited resources of the Skelmersdale basin until the 1930s have all closed, but most of the large pits along the southern rim of the field near St Helens have escaped closure or contraction. But in general the eastern half of the south Lancashire field has had a much more fortunate recent history than the western.

In the Manchester area a number of exhausted mines have closed, but three of the surviving collieries are modernised giants, like Mosley Common and Astley Green, employing between 2,000 and 3,000 men each, and a new pit, at Agecroft, is now working the newly discovered seams concealed beneath Trias east of the Irwell valley fault. Both the Agecroft and the Bradford collieries supply coal directly by conveyor to adjacent power stations. Closures have been roughly balanced by expansion; in fact the Manchester area is short of mining labour, and there is a very large daily 'import' from the abandoned coalfield to the north and west. Near Leigh, too, the industry has survived strongly, but here the pits have attracted much less investment in modernisation than those closer to Manchester, and their future seems less secure. About one-seventh of the mining employment in the Leigh area has been lost since 1952, which is a serious decline in a town still supported by an undiversified 'mill-and-pit' economy.

In essence, two great changes have remodelled the Lancashire mining industry during the period since the inter-war depression: it has become concentrated into a very few large units, and it has been redistributed so that the great bulk of employment now lies in a narrow belt along the southern margin, straddling the deeper 'exposed' Coal Measures and the narrow concealed extension under Trias to the south. By 1961 the ten largest collieries, all in this zone, employed some 19,000 men, almost 60% of the total for the entire field; and the two new pits—at Agecroft and at Parkside, south of Wigan—are both on the southern margin. There is little doubt that the concentration into a small number of large pits will continue, for many of the smaller units have an uncertain future; but it is unlikely that this will be associated with a further extension of mining southwards. The tragedy of the Lancashire field is that its concealed extension is so narrow and so difficult to work. The seams dip so steeply to the south that within three or four miles of the Triassic overlap they have plunged below the 4,000-foot level which is the present maximum depth of operations. In places, faulting adds further problems by downthrowing panels of the concealed field to unworkable depths.

Since the First World War the Lancashire coalfield has struggled under a mounting burden of technical and commercial difficulties. Steep dips and minor folds, complex faulting, 'wash-outs', and the risks of penetrating old, unmapped workings full of gas and water have all made it an expensive field to work. During the inter-war depression, Lancashire mines were increasingly affected by Yorkshire competition, for the pits of the east Pennine field are worked at much lower cost and with higher outputs per man-shift. Yorkshire coal was able to undersell Lancashire despite the cost of the rail transport. Coal still crosses the Pennines in very great quantity, for the Northwest now produces only about half its coal consumption. This increasing import of coal from outside the region was one of the primary causes of the very quick contraction of the Lancashire mining industry during the 1930s; but it also brought some progress towards reorganisation and rationalisation by the formation of amalgamations of mining companies which made possible the closure of the least efficient pits and the concentration of output on the most profitable units, a process continued under nationalisation (Plates 19, 20).

Other problems affect coalmining in the Northwest. Much of the worked field is intensively urbanised, and damage by subsidence is a greater problem than in most other fields. For example the rich resources in east Manchester worked by the Bradford pit underlie densely built-up industrial and residential areas, in which subsidence damage is frequent and serious; and the Agecroft pit is now extending its workings under the northern suburbs of Manchester. The payment of subsidence compensation adds surprisingly little to the costs of coal production; but a continuing problem to the industry is the need to preserve pockets of coal which could otherwise be mined profitably, such as those underlying roads or railways.

Perhaps the most serious human problem which the industry faces is

133

the increase in the length of the miner's journey to work through the southward shift of mining. Many of the towns and villages of the abandoned coalfield still contain large communities of miners. Wigan, for example, is still a miners' town, though no longer a mining town. Conversely, the districts in which mining is now most active have comparatively small numbers of resident miners. Worsley, for example, has one of the largest clusters of pits within or near its boundaries, but it is partly suburban in character. As Figure 32 shows, there is now a considerable disharmony

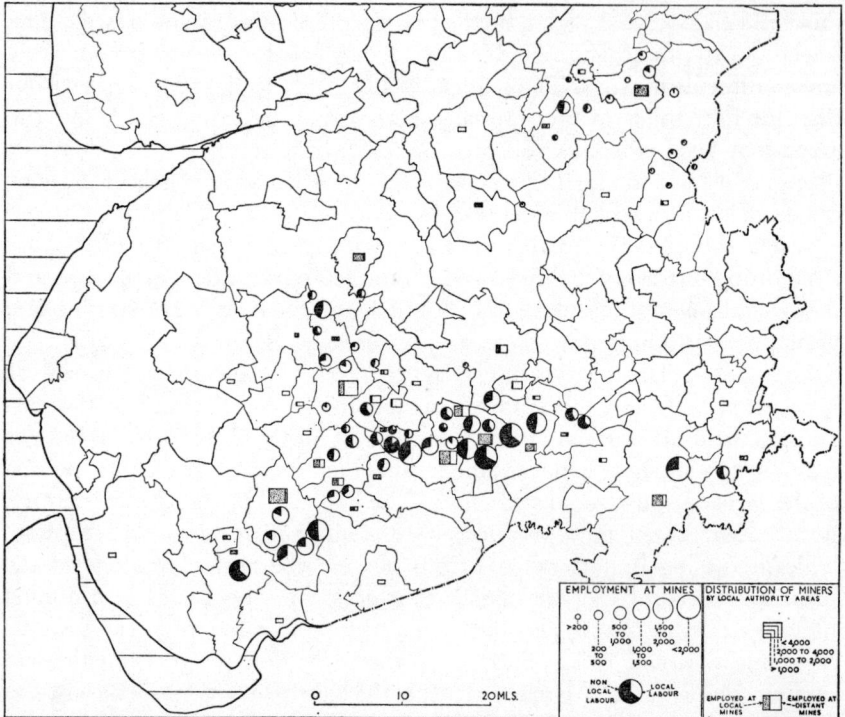

Fig. 32   THE LANCASHIRE COALFIELD: DISTRIBUTION OF MINES AND THE MINING LABOUR FORCE, 1957.

between the distribution of miners and the location of collieries; and Figure 33 shows that substantial numbers of miners must travel 10 miles or more to their employment. Some of the movements shown are comparatively short-range. The Bradford pit employs miners from the towns of the exhausted Pennine flank coalfield, and the pits near Worsley draw labour from Bolton, only 5 miles away. Thousands of miners in the Wigan area travel much farther to their work, though the opening of the new Parkside pit south of the town has provided some local employment. Wigan men travel chiefly eastwards, to the line of pits in the southern edge of the field from Leigh to the western outskirts of Manchester. The St Helens pits, too, draw workers from distant sources, particularly from Merseyside and from the long-dead Upholland–Skelmersdale section of the field. This long daily journey is a technical as well as a human problem, for absenteeism is high among men who travel considerable distances. Some of the pits of the south which rely most heavily on the long-distance import of labour have been seriously affected by chronic absenteeism.

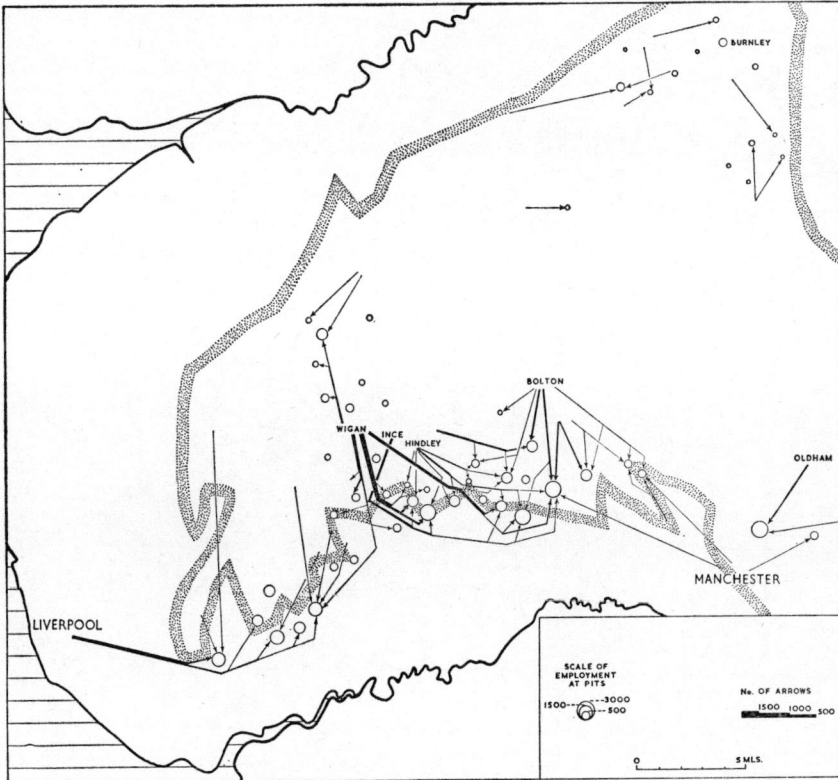

Fig. 33 THE LANCASHIRE COALFIELD: JOURNEY TO WORK OF MINERS, 1957. Information kindly provided by the National Coal Board.

The replacement and alternative industries

As late as the 1920s coal and cotton provided more than one-quarter of all employment in Lancashire as a whole and almost two-thirds in the textile zone of the east of the region. Today these two traditional industries provide only 15% of the county's employment, though there are still areas, especially in central Lancashire, in which more than half the work available is in the mills and pits. But in general the Northwest now has a broadly based industrial structure in which the metal-working and engineering group is by far the strongest single element. Four other industrial groups—

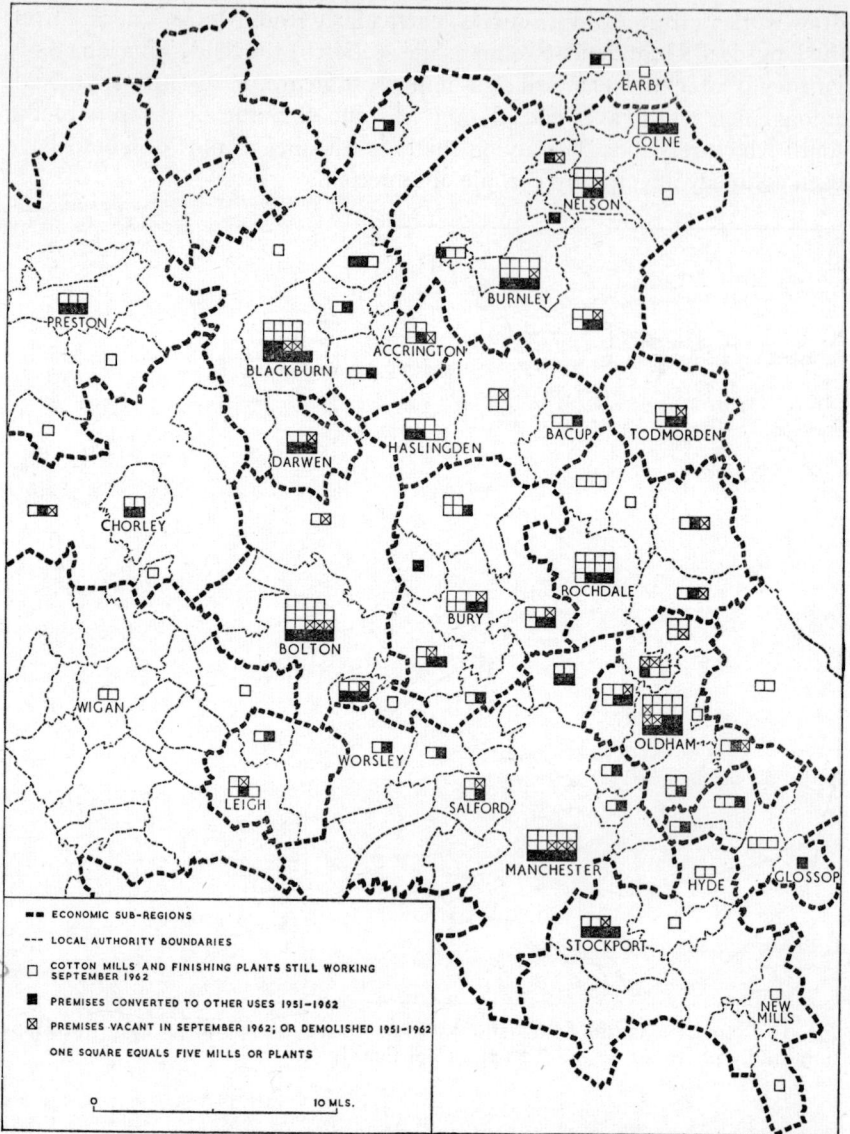

Fig. 34 THE ABANDONMENT AND CONVERSION OF COTTON MILLS, 1951–62. This map and Fig. 35 have been kindly provided by Mr R. L. Holt, M.A.

chemicals, clothing, food, and paper—have grown to very considerable size: each provides at least 100,000 jobs, and their expansion has done much to replace the employment lost by the decline of the traditional trades. Some of these manufactures, for example paper making and chemicals, are in no sense new to the region, for they are established 'alternative' industries which have long provided some diversity of employment in the cotton towns. Others, for example electrical engineering and vehicles, are more strictly 'replacement' industries of recent growth. A third group, particularly the alkali industry of the mid-Mersey basin and the shipbuilding of Furness, have long sustained the growth of industrial regions away from the coalfield and the textile towns.

Table 1 summarises the industrial changes which have taken place in Lancashire over a period of almost thirty years. The coefficients of specialisation were calculated by comparing the industrial structure of the county with that of the country as a whole. In effect they show whether Lancashire had more than its fair share (coefficients above unity) or less than its fair share of the major industrial groups listed. The decline of the old, traditional trades is clear: cotton's contribution to employment has been virtually halved since 1931, but coalmining has declined very much less quickly.

TABLE 1

INDUSTRIAL TRENDS IN (LANCASHIRE) 1931–1959

	1931		1959	
	Percentage of insured employed	Coefficient of specialisation	Percentage of insured employed	Coefficient of specialisation
Agriculture	2·3	0·37	0·7	0·23
Mining and allied industries	4·9	0·69	4·2	0·79
Chemicals	1·7	1·54	3·6	1·5
Metal and engineering group	9·8	0·9	18·6	0·9
Textiles	19·6	3·3	11·2	2·87
Clothing	5·1	1·16	3·6	1·38
Food and drink	3·9	1·15	4·4	1·22
Paper and printing	2·4	0·96	2·8	1·28
Service industries	47·2	0·87	46·7	0·88

Mining has contracted more slowly in Lancashire than in the country as a whole, and in consequence, perhaps surprisingly, its index of specialisation in the county has risen. Clothing, too, is shown to be an industry of declining importance, both in the county and in the country, but again it has survived better in Lancashire than elsewhere for the county now has

137

distinctly more than its fair share of this rather weak industry. By far the brightest element in these industrial changes is the vigorous growth of the engineering group, which almost doubled its share of total employment over the period. But this expansion is much less impressive when viewed against national trends. Engineering grew at almost exactly the same pace in Great Britain as a whole as in Lancashire. Thus its index of specialisation has not changed and still indicates that the county has less than its average share of this prosperous trade. The chemical group made quick progress, having more than doubled its share of employment in the county, but in this case its expansion was quicker outside Lancashire, and its index of specialisation has weakened slightly. The food and paper groups have made slighter but valuable progress. In the former, a quickly growing trade, Lancashire now has a distinctly greater than average share, while paper making has expanded quickly enough to convert a negative index of specialisation into a positive one.

Metal-working and engineering industries have made much the largest contribution to the creation of new employment to replace the losses in the older industries. Yet by no means the whole of Lancastria's engineering industry is expanding, for there are large contracting sections in weak and sensitive branches of the trade. The manufacture of textile machinery, in particular, has declined rapidly in sympathy with the decay of the industry which it served. Once the most important branch of engineering in many of the cotton towns of east Lancashire, its weakness explains the sharp fall in engineering employment in towns like Bury and Oldham during the 1950s. Railway engineering, too, is an important but quickly contracting industry in many towns of eastern Lancastria. The large plants include the two at Gorton (east Manchester) and the Crewe, Horwich, Earlestown, and Newton-le-Willows works. Several of the British Rail workshops are to be closed partly or wholly (e.g. Gorton); some smaller plants have already been closed.

Fortunately other branches of engineering have grown considerably. The steam-engine building and general mechanical engineering which was so strongly developed in nineteenth century Manchester has declined, the victim of technological progress, but it has left behind it a legacy of specialised engineering in many forms. Pumping and air-conditioning equipment, flour milling and coking machinery, printing equipment, valves, and handling devices are a few almost random samples from a very wide range of products. Adaptability is the dominant characteristic of the Manchester engineering industry; for example, the old boiler-making trade is now chiefly concerned with the manufacture of tanks and pressure vessels, particularly for use in oil refining and the chemical industry. This flexibility has been less marked in most of the smaller towns, where the old forms of engineering have lingered with slower change; for example, in Accrington five-sixths of the engineering employment was in textile machinery in 1951, though it has since become more varied through mill conversion for light engineering. But there are notable exceptions; for example, a Rochdale company whose trade was once chiefly with the textile industry now makes casting and gears for a very wide range of customers. The tradition of technical training and apprenticeship which is so strong in the southeast Lancashire engineering area has materially assisted the development of these new, specialised manufactures. Indeed, a high standard of technical skill is one of the features of the engineering industries of the area. Branches like machine-tool manufacture, particularly strongly developed at Altrincham and Stockport, depend heavily on the reservoir of skill and experience which the local labour force possesses.

By far the most important and quickly growing branch of the engineering industries of the region is one which has no nineteenth century roots, the electrical engineering trade. This is concentrated chiefly in south Lancashire with Manchester as its oldest and still its largest centre, though light electrical engineering has grown quickly in Merseyside since the Second World War. The development of the Trafford Park industrial estate beside the Ship Canal was one of the primary reasons for Manchester's quick growth as a manufacturer of electrical equipment, for this attractive site became available just as the foundations of this industry were being laid. Today more than 20,000 workers are engaged in electrical engineering in Trafford Park alone, and the total for the Manchester conurbation was roughly 50,000 in 1951. Electrical engineering takes varied forms in Lancastria. One of the two largest firms in the Manchester conurbation makes electronic devices, while the other is concerned rather with heavier products such as power-station equipment. Cables are made in Trafford Park, Helsby, and Prescot; the recent growth of electrical engineering in northeast Lancashire has been chiefly for the production of vehicle components, while television equipment is made in a group of factories centred on Blackburn.

The greatest recent change in the structure of the engineering group of industries in the Northwest has been the quick expansion of vehicle manufacture. This industry is not new to the region: cars were made in Manchester in the inter-war period by both the Ford and Crossley companies, and the manufacture of diesel engines (an outgrowth from the old gas-engine industry) is still important in the eastern part of the Manchester conurbation. But until the early 1960s the vehicle industry of the Northwest was concerned primarily with the production of trucks and buses, chiefly at Sandbach and Leyland. The latter is now the greatest focus of the British heavy-vehicle industry. Sited beside the main London–Glasgow railway and skirted by the new M6 motorway, the Leyland group of plants has superb communications with the industrial complex of the Midlands, and the ports of Merseyside are within easy access. But in its more recent growth the vehicle industry of the Northwest has sought port locations.

Under pressure from the Board of Trade the British car industry was obliged to decentralise from its Midland and metropolitan concentration in the early 1960s and to divert part of its expansion to the Development Areas. Merseyside proved overwhelmingly the most popular choice of the great car firms. Two, Vauxhall and Ford, now have major new factories at work on Merseyside, the former near Ellesmere Port, south of the estuary, and the latter at Halewood on the north shore. Both plants, though very large, are likely to be merely the nuclei for even greater future expansion, and a third company (Standard-Triumph, now part of the Leyland group) has plans to build a factory on Merseyside. Within a few years the Merseyside conurbation has become the most important concentration of motor-car manufacture outside Midland and metropolitan England. Though the establishment of the industry here was directly the consequence of government intervention, Merseyside has many positive advantages to offer to the industry: its port facilities, a pool of labour continually replenished by the high birth rate, access to steel from Irlam and Shotton and to the established components supplies of the east Lancashire engineering area.

Aircraft manufacture, the most modern branch of the vehicle industry, has a long history in the Northwest. The firm of Avro has been producing aircraft in or near Manchester since the First World War; it now has factories both at Chadderton and at its airfield at Woodford. But the Second World War brought an enormous increase of this industry in the relatively safe Northwest, and much of this wartime growth has proved to be permanent. The English Electric Company at Preston, once a manufacturer of the tramcars which swayed so majestically between Lancashire towns, began aircraft manufacture during the war and has continued since. De Havilland grew quickly during the war and post-war years in a complex of factories, including converted mills, in the Bolton area, and its airfield plant close to the Dee estuary has been one of the factors in Chester's recent industrial growth. But the aircraft industry is now passing through a process of rationalisation, though the northwestern factories have escaped serious closures.

Since the metal-using industries are so well developed in Lancastria it is perhaps surprising that the primary-metal manufacture is so small and so strictly localised there. Half a century ago the iron and steel industry of the Northwest was largely concentrated in Furness, where its quick growth in the late nineteenth century had been based chiefly on the rich hematite deposits in the nearby limestones and on coke brought by trans-Pennine railways from Durham. But the Furness hematites have been failing for many decades. Today they are virtually exhausted, though some production continues in the Millom peninsula, in the extreme south of Cumberland. Here, too, is the last of the many ironworks which for a long time made high-grade pig iron from the local ore resources, for the Barrow ironworks closed in 1963. The only significant (now precarious) survival of the

Furness metal industry is the Barrow steelworks which serves the still prosperous shipbuilding industry on which the town depends so heavily.

Today the chief centres of the iron and steel industry of Lancastria are in the extreme south, far from the orefields and away from the Lancashire coalfield. The two largest plants are both in 'coastal' locations, at Shotton on the Dee estuary and at Irlam on the Manchester Ship Canal. Curiously, the latter is more truly in a dockside location, though far inland, than the former. The greater part of the ore supply to the Irlam plants comes directly to its stockpiles along the canal; but the Dee is unsuitable for large ore vessels, and Shotton is supplied by rail from the Birkenhead docks. Both plants represent a movement from coalfield to coastal sites. The Irlam plant was originally located on the Lancashire coalfield near Wigan, but in 1930 the company moved to the new canal-side site, where a smaller ironworks already existed. The parent of the Shotton (Dee) plant is the Shelton iron and steelworks in north Staffordshire. Originally purely a steelworks and dependent on pig iron from the Potteries, the Shotton plant was converted into an integrated unit by the addition of smelting facilities in the 1950s. Two other steelworks exist in the Manchester area, at Trafford Park and Openshaw. Neither has smelters, and the output of steel shapes is for local industrial consumption. Though still one of the minor regions of British iron and steel production, the Northwest is a quickly growing one. During the period 1950 to 1959 iron output in the region grew from 311,000 to 1,044,000 tons, while steel production expanded from 1,292,000 to 2,025,000 tons. In both cases the regional growth rate has been far above the national average.

For more than a century Lancastria's chemical manufactures have been located chiefly in the mid-Mersey basin, aligned along the axis of cheap water transport, the Weaver–Sankey system, which joined the Cheshire saltfield with the southwestern angle of the Lancashire coalfield. By the closing years of the nineteenth century the greater part of the country's alkali manufacture was in several clusters along the Northwich–St Helens axis. At St Helens, the oldest centre of the industry, the obsolete Le Blanc process was still in use, and the technical backwardness of the plants here led to the extinction of the industry by 1921. Widnes, too, was a producer of Le Blanc alkalis, but it had long had somewhat greater variety in its chemical trades, with a stronger interest in the acid and metallurgical branches of the industry. Here the industry continues, though the obsolete Le Blanc process survives only for the production of by-products. Widnes now produces a wide variety of chemicals and is, appropriately, the headquarters of the I.C.I. miscellaneous chemicals division. But today the main mass of the Lancastrian chemical industry lies south of the Mersey, in the Northwich area. The great complex of plants at Winnington and Wallerscotes, producing alkali by the ammonia-soda process, has developed here rather than on the coalfield because this new process, introduced in 1873, requires little fuel but great quantities of salt, now piped to the plants from the Holford brinefield east of Northwich. A second technical revolution in alkali manufacture, the electrolytic process, had less profound effects on the location of the industry in the mid-Mersey region, though plants using the new process exist on the Mersey estuary near Runcorn and at Northwich (Plates 21, 23).

Most of these changes antedate the period with which this chapter is concerned. During the last thirty years the industry has been more stable in location, though small plants—for example at Middlewich—have closed. The Northwich complex of factories has continued to grow both in size and in the diversity of its products. But there has been only a slight growth in employment; indeed during the 1950s there was a very slight decline in the labour force of the Northwich industry, due to the further automation of production. In general, chemical employment has grown more strongly outside rather than within the traditional chemical zone of the mid-Mersey. There has been marked growth at Warrington, where the manufacture of soap and detergents has expanded and a new chemical factory has been built. Here employment in the industry grew by 53% in the three years 1955–8. On Merseyside, especially in the industrial zones on the southern shore of the estuary, this industry has grown with almost equal speed, partly through the expansion of the old-established soap manufacture but chiefly because of the further development of the Ellesmere Port oil-refining and chemical complex. In east Lancashire the chemical manufacture is relatively much less important, and its growth has been slower. The chief branch of the industry here is the manufacture of dyestuffs, especially in the large factories at Clayton and Crumpsall, in east and north Manchester respectively. The link with the textile industries is obvious, but the recent growth of chemical manufacture in the Manchester area has taken rather different forms. A large new plant at Carrington on the Manchester Ship Canal manufactures chemicals from oil, and a company making light chemicals has established itself in several factories in the Manchester area. There is a clear pattern in the recent growth of the chemical manufactures of the Northwest. In the nineteenth century they developed along the north–south axis of the Weaver–Sankey waterways, but since the Second World War their expansion has been much faster along the east–west axis from Merseyside to Manchester and particularly in sites close to the Manchester Ship Canal. But the west rather than the east of this belt has attracted the bulk of new investment and employment, and the mid-Mersey basin remains the chief focus of the industry, though changes are taking place in its detailed location.

Engineering and the chemical industry are male-employing, and they make little contribution to the provision of alternative work for the redundant women mill workers who make up two-thirds of the cotton industry's labour force. For women the clothing industry offers the largest alternative source of employment. Long established in Manchester, this manufacture has become more widespread in the coalfield and the textile towns, though it is no longer a vigorously growing industry in the region as a whole. In Manchester the clothing trade takes several forms; the manufacture of shirts, dresses, and similar garments from cotton and synthetic fabrics has an obvious link with the textile industries. A second important branch, dominant in Salford and north Manchester, is the production of rainwear from proofed fabrics, probably because Mackintosh experimented with the waterproofing of fabrics here. More recently a third branch of the clothing trade has developed in southeast Lancashire, though chiefly outside Manchester, the manufacture of ready-made suits. A large firm of Yorkshire origin has established several large factories in Lancashire, where the abundant female labour supply was a considerable attraction. Employment in the clothing trade declined sharply in Manchester during the 1950s, from 56,000 to 46,000, a more rapid rate of contraction even than that of the cotton industry. But the little clothing factories tucked away in the back streets of Manchester and Salford, many in converted houses or mills, remain the largest single source of female employment in the two cities.

Elsewhere in the Northwest the clothing industry is largely limited to areas with a textile tradition. It is insignificant on Merseyside, though it has grown in parts of the chemical and salt area, where it forms almost the only manufacturing work available to women. In the textile belt the clothing trades are now widespread, though they are of quite recent growth over most of the area. One of the chief reasons for the spread of this industry to many of the mill towns is that the decline of the cotton industry freed both premises and labour which were readily adaptable to the clothing firms. In the Bolton area two large mills have been converted by a tailoring firm, which also has a large new factory at the eastern end of the East Lancashire Road, while in Stockport and Manchester sports clothing is made in converted mills. Rossendale has had a flourishing footwear industry since the closing decades of the nineteenth century: the conversion of textile mills to clothing and footwear factories is still taking place here, but there has been little increase in employment in the clothing trades since 1945. Almost alone of the 'replacement' industries, the clothing trades have shown a marked preference for the textile towns. Perhaps, in the long term, this is unfortunate, for clothing is an industry with a contracting labour force.

The food, drink, and tobacco trades, like clothing, depend largely on women workers, but they are located chiefly in the west rather than in the east of the region. These are chiefly 'port' industries which depend on overseas sources for their raw materials and which therefore seek dockside locations. By far the greatest concentration is on Merseyside, where flour milling, sugar refining, and other types of food preparation are among the oldest of the industries of the port. In Manchester a considerable development of the food industries followed the opening of the Ship Canal; now tea packing, flour milling, and the manufacture of maize products are prominent in Manchester's 'dockland' and in Trafford Park. At Irlam, too, food processing has grown in canal-side plants.

Except at Manchester and on Merseyside, the food and drink trades are comparatively feebly developed, though both Board of Trade guidance and the conversion of old cotton mills have resulted in some localised growth in the textile towns. The great new canning plant at Wigan, in the South Lancashire Development Area, has greatly broadened the range of employment here, for it has attracted cognate industries (p. 215). Both at Middleton and Hyde old cotton mills have been converted for tobacco manufacture; but in general old mills do not lend themselves easily to the needs of the food-processing industries.

Paper making is one of the oldest industries of the northwest of England, and it remains an important source of employment, especially for men, over much of the textile region. Paper mills existed along some of the streams, especially of east Lancashire, by the early years of the eighteenth century, and during the period of the industrial revolution the industry became concentrated into a distinctive zone which extended from the Darwen valley between Preston and Blackburn through the middle Irwell basin near Bolton and Bury to the Pennine flank east of Manchester, where Glossop and New Mills (in Derbyshire) are two important centres. Pure water and power from the hill streams were the two main factors locating early paper making in this area, but at one time it also used large quantities of local raw material in the form of rags and textile waste. Today the traditional sites of the paper industry are less attractive. Pollution has so affected the river water upon which it depends that some firms can no longer produce fine white papers and have taken up the production of coarser qualities, and today the basic raw material is imported wood pulp, which comes chiefly through the port of Preston. Though paper making continues to flourish in east Lancashire—where new branches like wallpaper and packing board are developing strongly—much of the more recent growth has been farther west and south. New paper and board factories at Warrington, Eastham, and Wigan reflect this locational shift, which is common to so many Lancashire industries. Though Bury and Darwen remain the most important foci of the industry, recent growth has been quickest in the Warrington district.

The conversion of cotton mills

Most of Lancastria's newest and most quickly growing industries have made much faster progress beyond the coalfield and outside the textile zone than within the areas which have depended for so long on these two staple industries. Almost without exception the textile towns have attracted much less employment in expanding trades than they need to balance their losses in the traditional industries. Except in the two Development Areas which were centred on Burnley and Wigan, few new factories have been built in the cotton towns for almost forty years, and their industrial progress has depended chiefly on the conversion of empty cotton mills to new uses. This has been the spearhead of industrial diversification in the textile zone; without it the recent decline of the cotton industry would undoubtedly have brought unemployment and distress on a scale to rival the lean decade of the 1930s.

The adaptation of empty cotton mills for other industrial uses is no new feature of Lancashire's economic life. Hundreds of mills were closed during the inter-war period; and though many of these were so small, old, and isolated that they have simply crumbled away, the better buildings were put to a variety of new uses. But the pace of mill conversion quickened during the Second World War, for the cotton industry concentration scheme was specifically intended to free both space and labour for armament industries. Some of the companies which took over Lancashire cotton mills during the war left with the peace; but very many have stayed and have given a lasting diversity of employment to the cotton towns. Since 1945 two factors have stimulated the conversion of old mills: their very low prices during a period of quickly increasing building costs, and the operation of the government's industrial guidance policies. Space in sound cotton mills may be bought or rented at remarkably little cost, and the accelerating decline of the cotton industry has kept the price of old mills low. Young and struggling firms are particularly attracted to converted mills, and many have grown to considerable stature. In effect the old mills are an industrial nursery. But the operation of the Board of Trade's industrial guidance policies has been perhaps a greater stimulus than low cost to mill conversion. Except in the three Lancashire Development Areas, new industrial building has been strictly controlled and severely limited in the Northwest since 1945. A company which wished to expand or to build a new factory might well have its request for an Industrial Development Certificate refused. But it could buy and convert empty mills to accommodate its growth almost without formality, and so firms which otherwise must surely have been 'steered' to the Development Areas of Merseyside, Wigan–St Helens, or northeast Lancashire have had a freer choice of sites in the textile districts of the east (Fig. 35).

It is difficult to measure the volume of employment created by mill conversion. A tentative estimate for the decade 1951–61 put the number of jobs in adapted mills at about 120,000, which represented some two-thirds of the loss of textile employment over the same period. Though this may be an overestimate, it shows that the re-use of textile factories is the most important reason for the surprisingly slight distress in the cotton towns over the period of crisis in their staple trade. But this new employment is very unequally spread, for not all mills are worth converting. Single-storey weaving sheds are more readily adaptable to a wider variety of trades than

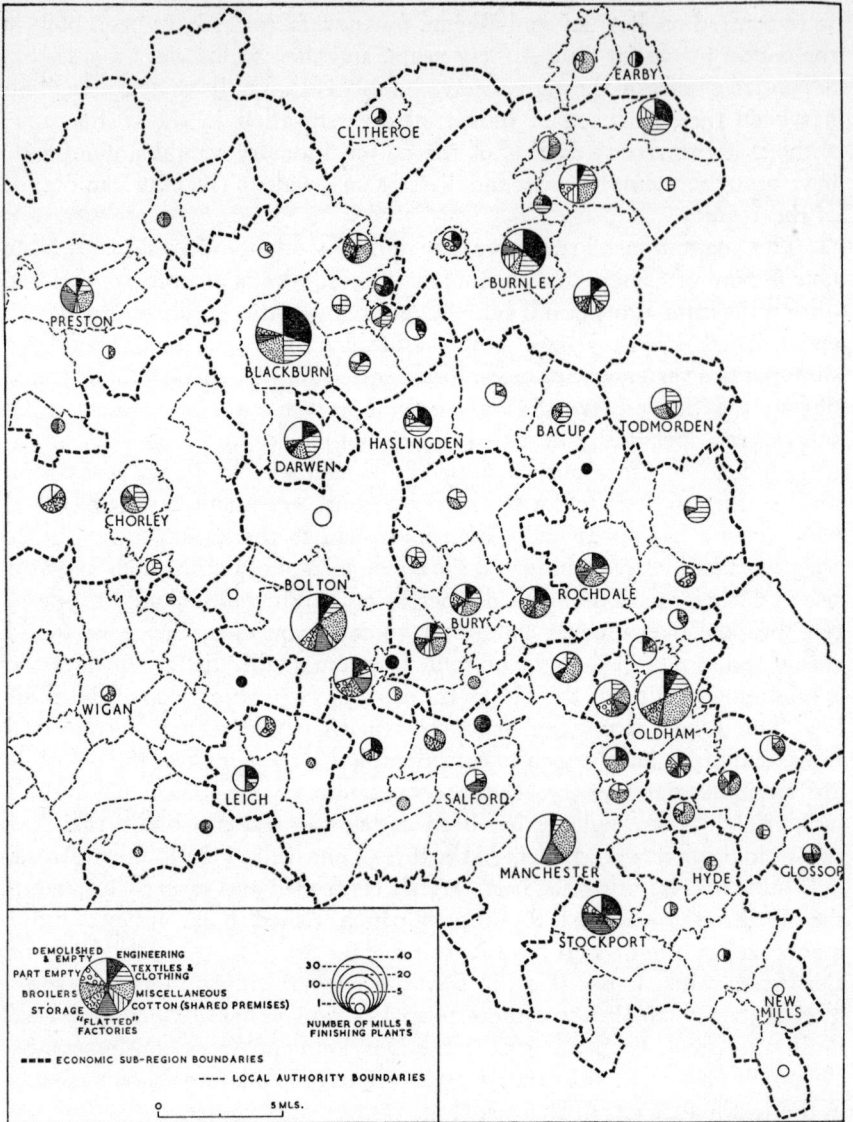

Fig. 35 NEW INDUSTRIES IN CONVERTED COTTON MILLS, 1951–62.

multi-storey spinning mills. With their unobstructed floorspace and roof lighting, old weaving rooms meet many of the requirements of light engineering firms, by which many have been acquired. But many of the tall spinning mills, old, ill-lit, and poorly provided with handling facilities, are much less adaptable, except for trades which require large areas of cheap floorspace, like the mail order firms. Most of the towns of the weaving belt have acquired a valuable range of new industries during the last decade;

146

but mill conversion has been less successful over some parts of the spinning zone, though there are marked local differences. At Royton several vast, elderly spinning mills are empty or in process of demolition, while nearby, at Middleton, most of the abandoned spinning mills are already converted. In and near Manchester the clearance of small industries in the course of redevelopment schemes has given a stimulus to mill conversion, and some of the largest spinning units have become 'flatted factories' with a dozen or more small firms in them. Few mills, even large spinning units, stand empty in central Lancashire, for most of the examples here are modern buildings of very sound construction which are soon sold to new trades. But the oldest mills of the first phase of the cotton industry's growth, in remote valleys or in inaccessible sites on stagnant canals, rarely interest other manufactures.

The variety of new manufactures in old cotton mills is so great that a list of them reads almost like the standard industrial classification. Engineering in all its forms is one of the oldest and today the most important 're-occupier' of empty mills: a large electrical engineering firm grew first near Oldham in converted premises and has now spread widely in the Manchester area both to old mills and new factories. More recently, chiefly during the Second World War, aircraft manufacture has grown in and near Bolton, again partly in empty mills; in northeast Lancashire a variety of electrical engineering is carried on in old weaving sheds. These are some of the more significant examples of the development of engineering in old mills; but many scores of smaller companies making a very wide range of specialised products have taken similar premises. Clothing firms, too, are common users of converted premises, for even multi-storey spinning mills are easily adapted for this purpose. At Bolton and Stockport, for example, the growth of this industry has added to the volume of female employment. Old mills are used to house manufacture of plastic products such as domestic utensils and foam sheeting, and a number have been converted for the purposes of food preparation and cigarette manufacture. Even broiler chickens are reared on an industrial scale in adapted spinning mills, which with their immense floorspace and heating facilities are well suited to this curious re-use. This variety of re-use is shown in Figure 35.

Though a mill may be re-used after the cotton firm has closed, the new company may provide far less employment than the original occupant. Few mills used for storage purposes employ more than a mere handful of workers, though the mail order companies are an exception. But some of the new occupiers may provide even greater employment than the textile firms: clothing, cigarette manufacture, and the production of plastic articles generate a high density of employment to the site acre, and in many cases conversion to these uses has increased the employment provided by the mill. Unfortunately many of the new industries use unskilled female labour,

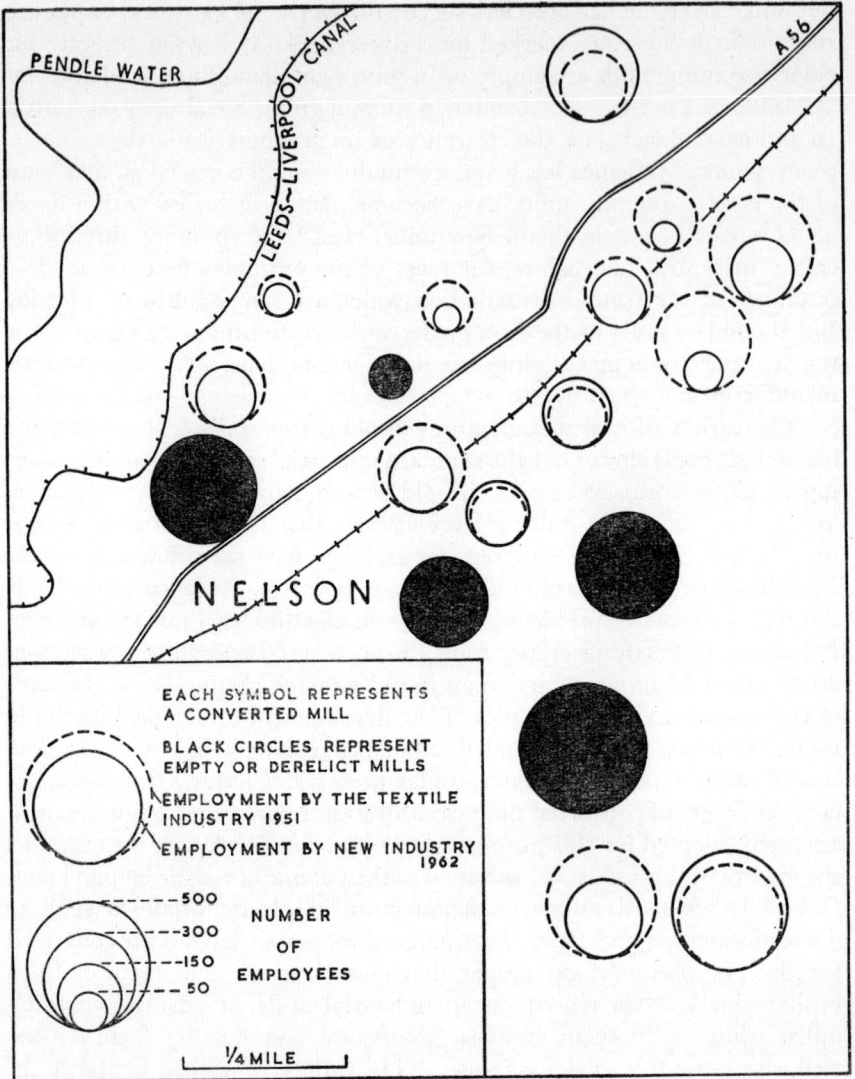

Fig. 36 EMPLOYMENT IN MILLS BEFORE AND AFTER THEIR CONVERSION FROM TEXTILE TO OTHER USES. Nelson. The authors are indebted to Mr R. L. Holt, M.A., for this map.

and the skilled male mule spinner may find little opportunity in the new industries, except as a labourer. It is quite impossible to generalise about the relationship between employment in mills before and after conversion. Sample studies have shown very great local contrasts; in the more fortunate towns the new trades provide virtually as much employment as the old mills. But it is not so everywhere: Nelson has lost heavily, as shown in Figure 36 and discussed on page 210.

148

Changes in the general distribution of industrial employment

During the period since the end of the First World War radical and apparently irreversible changes have been taking place in the general distribution of industry, and therefore of employment, in Lancastria; and these industrial trends are the root causes of the great changes in population distribution reviewed in the regional chapters which follow. In essence, the industrial transformation of the present century has reversed many of the consequences of the economic revolution of the late eighteenth century and the nineteenth. Now the great nodes of industrial growth are not in the Carboniferous uplands of the east or along their flanks, or even in the coalfield, but rather in the Triassic plain of south and west Lancashire and north and west Cheshire. There has been a marked shift of both industry and population towards the west and south, from the Carboniferous outcrop to the Triassic, from the highlands to the lowlands of the region.

Two maps summarise these changes. The first (Fig. 37) shows the distribution of new industrial building licensed by the Board of Trade since 1950. The unit-squares show the total floorspace constructed, while the bars reveal contrasts in the amount of new building *per capita* of the insured population of each of the subregions. Industrial development has clearly been most vigorous in an east–west belt between the two major conurbations along the twin axis of communications of the Manchester Ship Canal and the East Lancashire Road. But it is significant that growth has been much faster on the shores of the Mersey estuary than in the Manchester lowland. Manchester's high actual total of new building is in fact small when expressed in *per capita* terms, and the cotton towns in the north and east of the conurbation have attracted new development only on a trivial scale. Only the Cheshire fringes of the conurbation have seen industrial progress at an adequate rate. The movement of industry away from the Victorian congestion and disorder of an old coalfield environment to new lowland sites so characteristic of the Manchester conurbation reflects the national and the regional trend in miniature. The same southward tendency may be observed on Merseyside, where the Wirral has attracted much more development, *per capita*, than the Lancashire shore. Warrington, too, has secured more new floorspace than the coalfield towns to the north. The quick and direct road and rail links across Cheshire to the threshold of the industrial Midlands are also reflected in Figure 37, for the towns of the salt district—mid-Cheshire and the southeast border of the county—have attracted a considerable amount of industrial building in relation to their small size.

Direction of industrial growth through Development Area policy is reflected in the pattern of Figure 37, but perhaps not as strongly as might have been expected. Certainly the Northeast Lancashire Development Area, instituted in 1953 after the first of the post-war textile recessions, stands

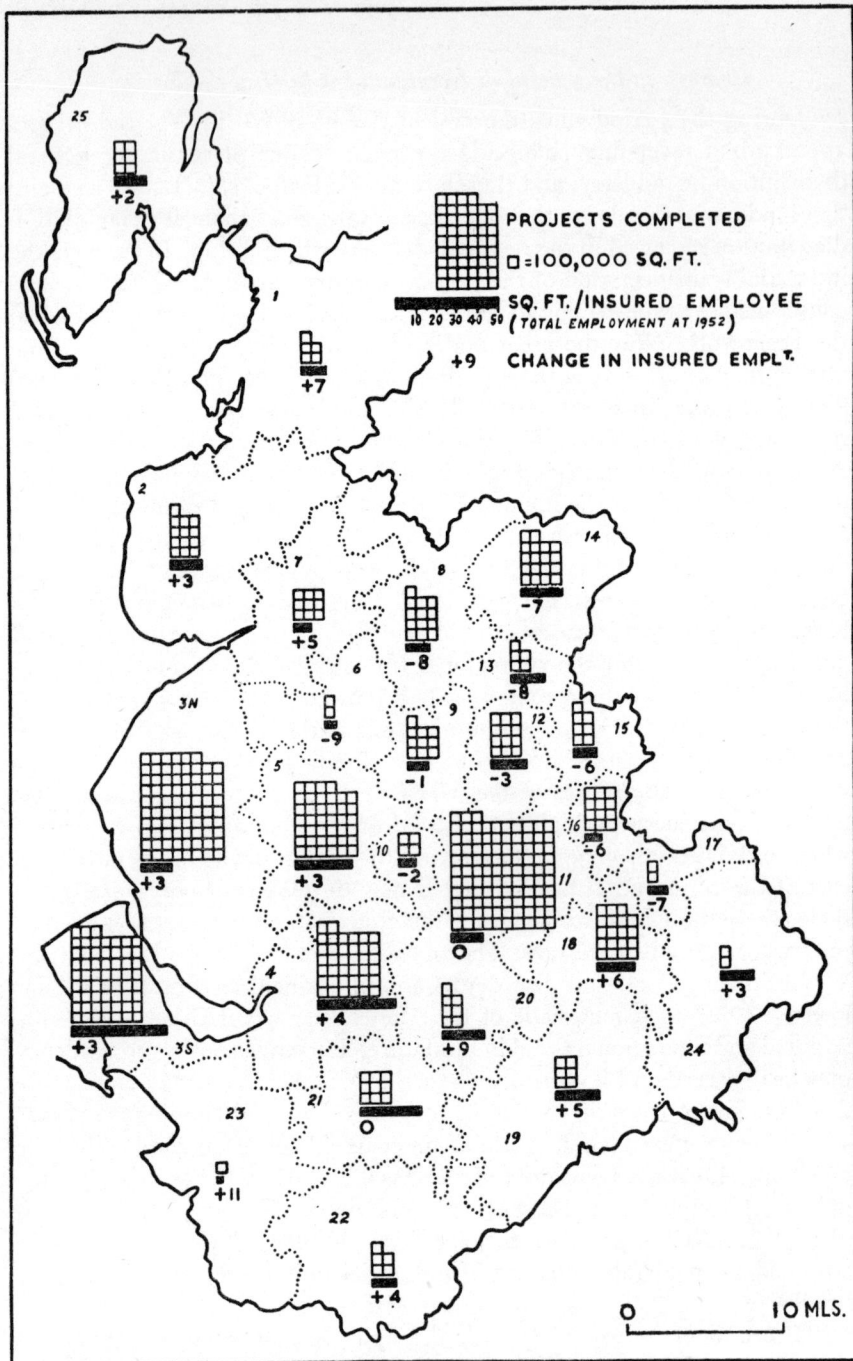

Fig. 37   NEW INDUSTRIAL PROJECTS AND MAJOR EXTENSIONS IN THE NORTHWEST, TO
1959. First published in *Problems of Applied Geography II, Geographia Polonica,*
Warsaw (1964), 223.

out among the textile districts of the east as the strongest node of new industrial growth, chiefly because of the miserably poor records of the other cotton towns. The older Merseyside and South Lancashire Development Areas, established in 1950 and 1946 respectively, are among the districts with the highest totals of new building, chiefly in the trading estates of Kirkby and Speke in the former and Parr and Lamberhead in the latter. But in general the scheduled Development Areas have attracted a surprisingly small share of the region's industrial growth: clearly Board of Trade guidance falls far short of complete control of industrial development.

In Figure 38 all the diverse trends and changes in the distribution of industry in Lancastria are summarised; for this map shows, by subregions, the over-all change in total employment between 1952 and 1958. A clear and sharp contrast can be seen between the textile province of the east and the newer industrial areas of the west and south in which so much of the modern growth of manufacturing has been concentrated. Almost all the cotton towns suffered heavy losses of employment during the period, which rose as high as 15% per decade in the worst-affected areas. This is clear evidence that, until 1958 at least, the conversion of old mills had failed to balance the quick loss of work in the old staple trades. But over most of the region the total volume of work available is rising strongly: along the Merseyside–Manchester axis, in north and east Cheshire, along the coastlands of west Lancashire there have been consistent increases in employment. This map demonstrates that a high level of new factory building does not guarantee a strong increase in the work available. In mid-Cheshire there has been a quick increase in industrial floorspace but no growth in employment—the result of increasing mechanisation and automation in the chemical industry; on south Merseyside the enormous investment in new industrial building has resulted in only a modest increase in employment.

The re-distribution of population

In no region of the country is the distribution of population changing more quickly or more radically than in the Northwest. In outline these changes are simple and easily described, for they faithfully reflect the industrial trends reviewed above. The three maps (Figs. 39–41) show that the numbers both of population and households have risen at rates that far exceed the national average over much of the west and south of the region, in southwest Lancashire and the Wirral, along the whole of the coast as far north as Morecambe Bay, and across north Cheshire from Merseyside to the suburban areas south of Manchester. Where losses have occurred in these areas, as at Liverpool, they are easily explained by short-range suburban movement, for example to Kirkby. In total contrast, the textile region of the east has lost population at an alarming rate, and the few instances of substantial growth—chiefly at Worsley and Middleton

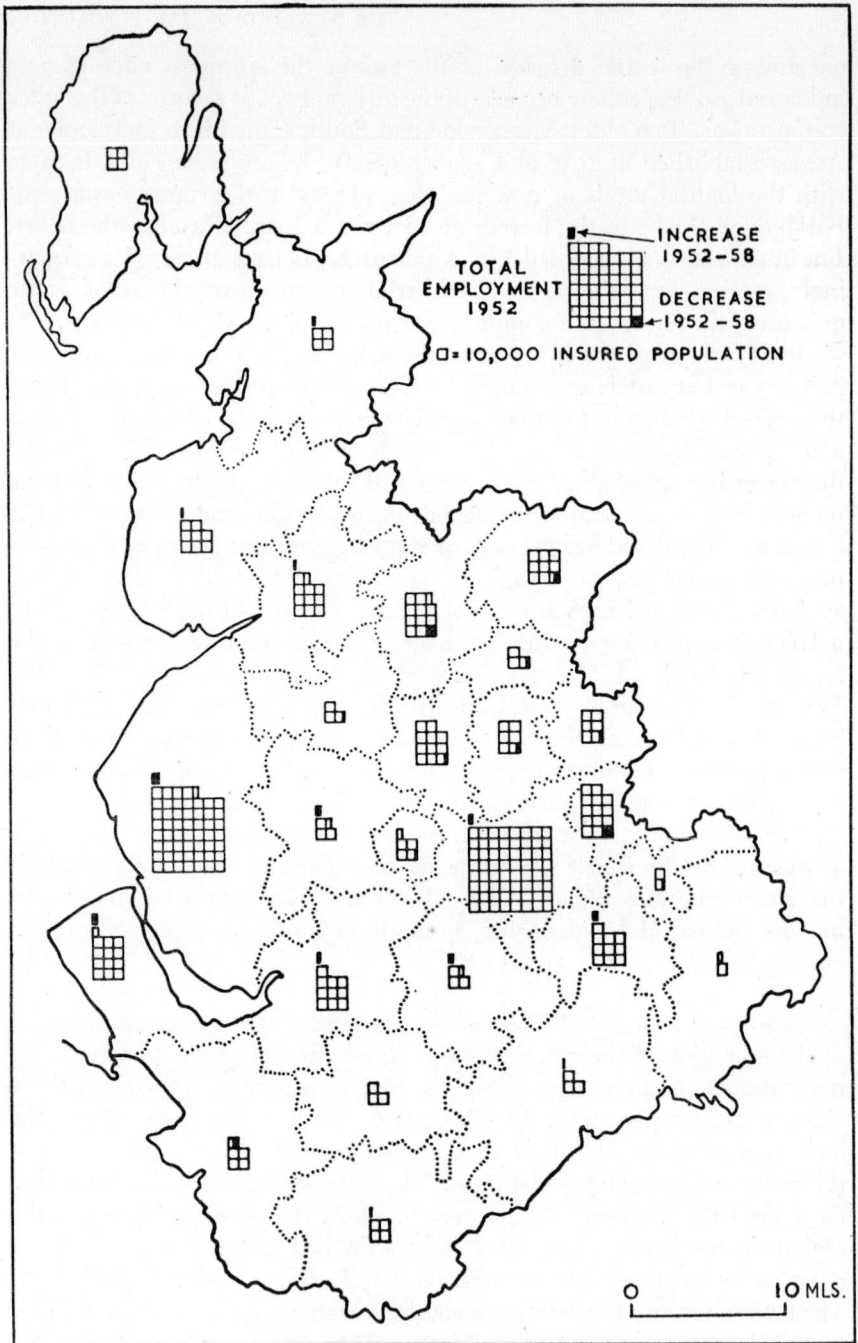

Fig. 38   CHANGE IN THE DISTRIBUTION OF EMPLOYMENT IN THE NORTHWEST, 1952–
1958. First published in *Problems of Applied Geography II, Geographia Polonica,*
Warsaw (1964). The sub-divisions on this map and Fig. 37 are the official planning
sub-regions.

—are the direct results of suburban overspill from nearby cities of rapid population loss. These contrasts between east and west are seen most clearly in a comparison of the Manchester and Liverpool conurbations. Given their 1951 definitions, neither grew significantly between 1951 and 1961, but if recent overspill development contiguous with the main urban mass is included, for example at Kirkby on the landward side of Liverpool, then the Merseyside conurbation grew by some 3.5% over the decade, while the Manchester conurbation increased only by 0.3%. Nor is this a mere trick of definition: if both conurbations are given their semi-official 'extended' forms—so that Liverpool includes the Southport area and the whole of Wirral and Manchester is given a deeper bite into north Cheshire —then the growth of the former was virtually tenfold that of the latter.

It is not proposed to discuss the geography of population change in detail at this point, for it is examined closely in the regional chapters which follow, but rather to enquire into its causes. The districts of strong growth may be divided between those in which there is a high rate of natural increase and those which are growing chiefly by inward migration, though there are a few favoured areas in which both forces are at work. An extensive area of unusually quick natural increase exists: centred on Merseyside it extends northwards to Preston, eastwards to Warrington and the coalfield about Wigan and southwards into mid-Cheshire. All these areas have rates of natural increase above the national average: most of them have strong Catholic communities in their populations, chiefly but not wholly of immigrant Irish origin. Where dispersal from the Merseyside conurbation has created young communities of strongly Catholic nature, particularly at Kirkby, the birth rate has reached almost Oriental proportions. Were these areas of strong natural increase able to absorb the whole of their population increment into local employment their growth would be remarkably vigorous, but in most of them the loss by migration during the last decade has been at least half the natural increase.

Parts of the zone of quick growth of population have rates of natural increase below both the regional and national averages—or indeed an actual excess of deaths over births—and here population increase depends entirely on inward migration, not only from other parts of the Northwest but also from beyond the region. The Fylde and north Lancashire have attracted a steady stream of migrants, many of them elderly and retired, without which their substantial growth would be converted into a loss. Preston and its surroundings is one of the few areas in which inward migration adds to a strong natural increase, but the growth throughout north Cheshire is largely migrational and chiefly the result of suburban dispersal from the Manchester conurbation.

An alarmingly large area of eastern Lancastria is suffering population loss which is partly attributable to a natural decrease. The indirect result

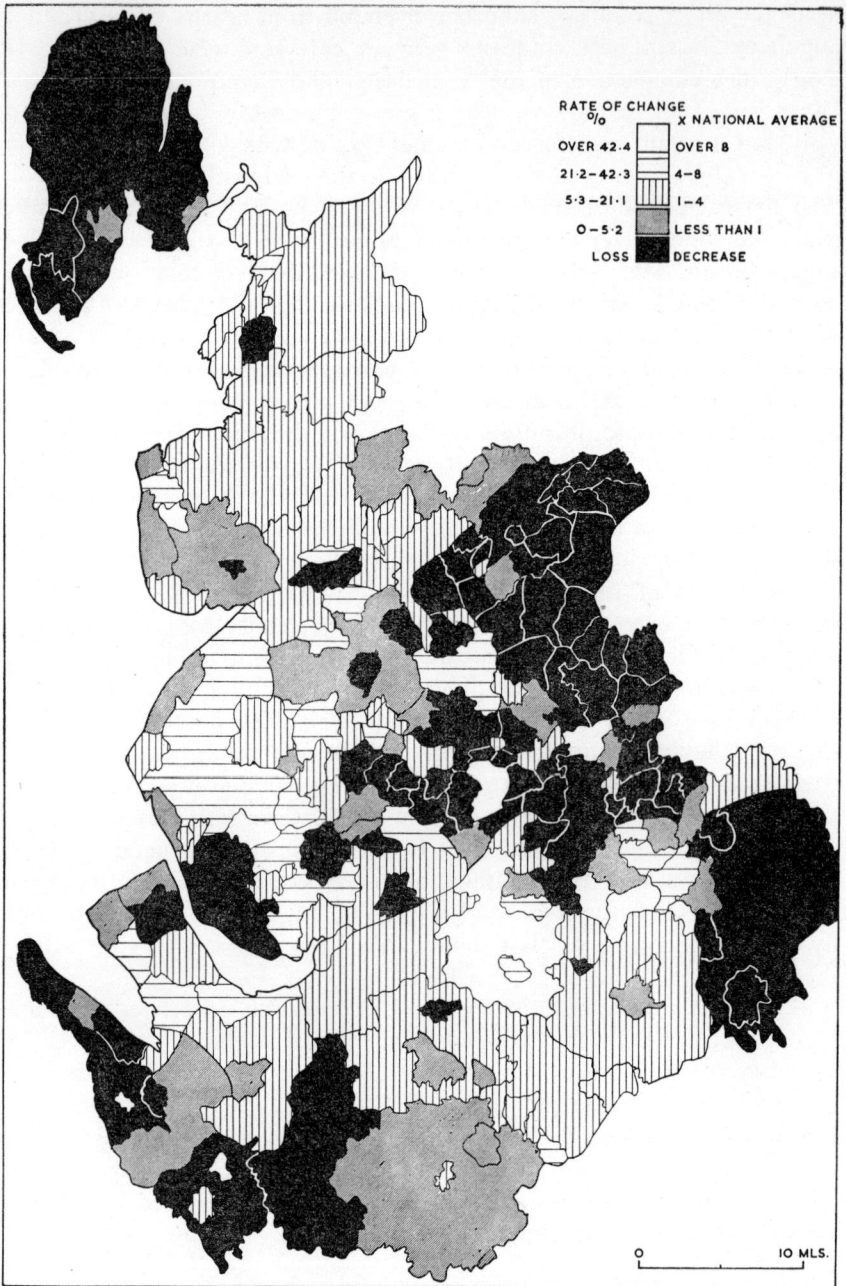

Fig. 39 POPULATION CHANGE IN LANCASHIRE AND CHESHIRE, 1951–61.

154

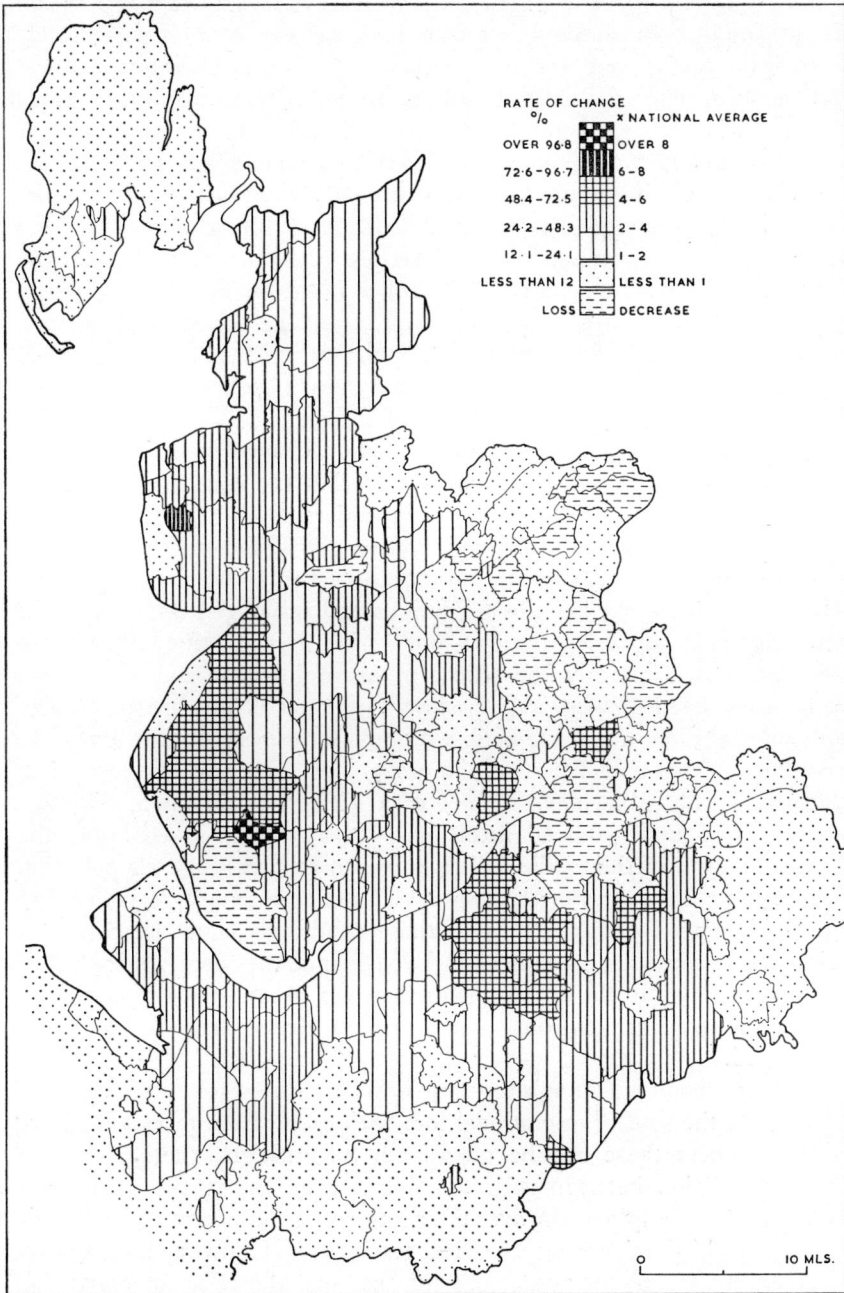

RATE OF CHANGE
%
OVER 96·8
72·6 – 96·7
48·4 – 72·5
24·2 – 48·3
12·1 – 24·1
LESS THAN 12
LOSS

x NATIONAL AVERAGE
OVER 8
6 – 8
4 – 6
2 – 4
1 – 2
LESS THAN 1
DECREASE

0   10 MLS.

Fig. 40   CHANGE IN THE NUMBERS OF PRIVATE HOUSEHOLDS, 1951–61.

of prolonged age-selective migration is to remove a significant proportion of the young, reproductive population. This has now spread widely through the textile zone, for in the weaving belt and in Rossendale almost every town registered a natural decrease in population during the decade 1951–61, which rose as high as 3% in some cases. But this condition is not yet serious in the textile areas of southeast Lancashire or the worked coalfield. Since these natural excesses of deaths over births reflect a distortion in the local age structure and a deficit of young adults, they are likely to persist. But much the most serious cause of population decline in the textile region is migration to other more fortunate areas, partly within but chiefly outside the Northwest. Even the sub-regional figures, which suppress the effects of local population shifts, show migrational losses which rise as high as 5% over the decade 1951–61, and data for individual towns show much higher rates of loss.

Migration is clearly the key to population change in the region, for apart from its direct consequences it underlies the contrasts in natural trend. Its causes are by no means fully understood, largely for want of accurate data. Both economic and non-economic factors are involved. Unemployment is the classic, but not necessarily the present, cause: indeed there has been little or no serious and prolonged unemployment in the textile areas during the post-war period, but migration from them has continued. Certainly the threat of unemployment and short time working has been present, and the low wage rates of much textile work, especially for men, may have been a serious factor in migration. But non-economic factors may have been more potent than any of these. The drabness of the urban environment of a Victorian mill town, the high proportion of unfit—indeed intolerable—housing that it contains, the weeping climate of the textile valleys prone to fog, frost and air pollution may be the chief causes of the region's loss of so many of its young and early-middle aged people. None of these conditions could be corrected quickly, and some are ineradicable. Even if industry were guided much more effectively into the textile towns than has so far been the case there is no certainty that migration would be halted, though it would doubtless be reduced.

It is easy enough (though too simple to be entirely sound statistically) to correlate the rate of migrational loss with each of the factors likely to cause it, where these can be quantified. Surprisingly, there is only a feeble association between migrational loss from the textile towns and their rates of unemployment over the post-war period. Certainly there has been a surge of migration from the textile area following each of the recessions in the cotton trade, but this has had the effect of correcting unemployment. Even in the years of almost 'overfull' employment between recessions some migrational loss has continued. A much better correlation exists between rate of loss by migration and the proportion of local

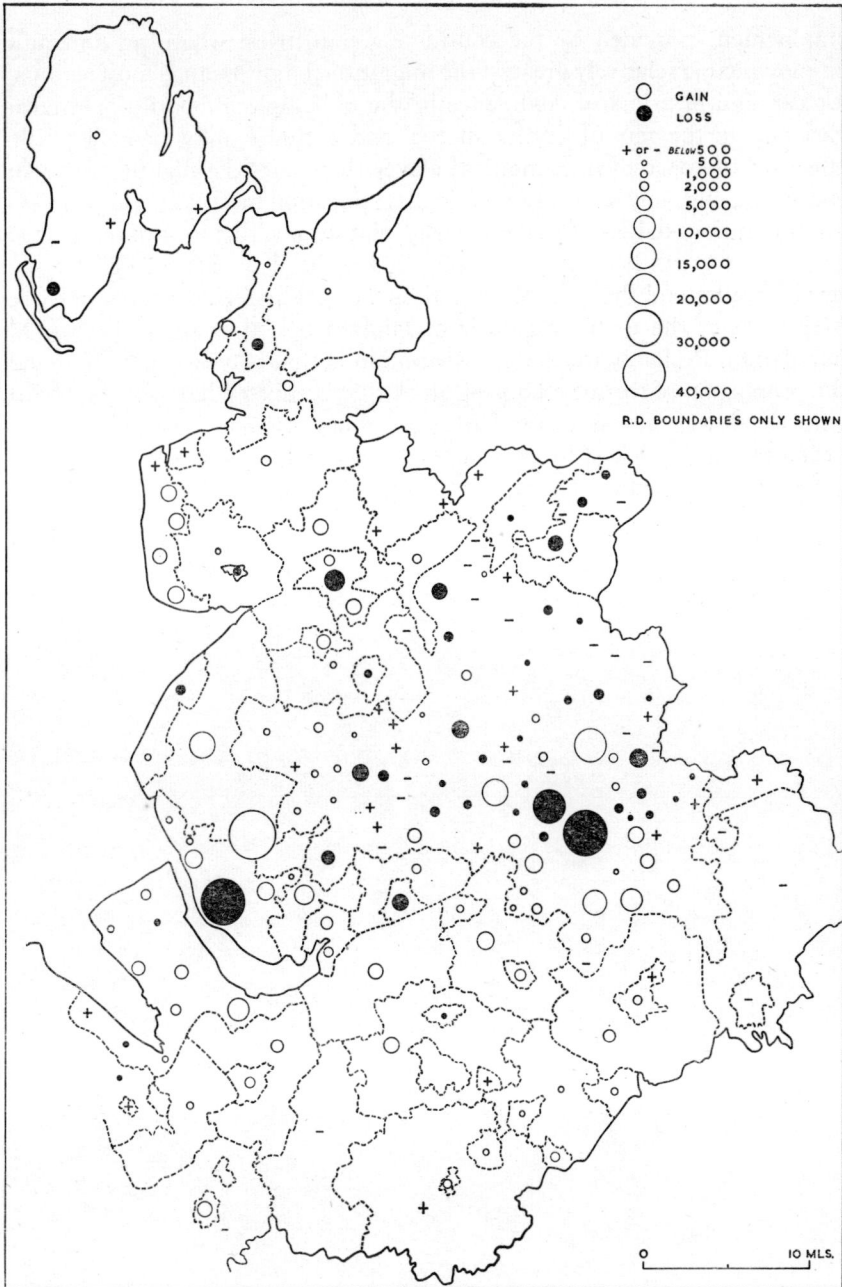

GAIN
LOSS

+ or − BELOW 500
     500
   1,000
   2,000
   5,000
  10,000
  15,000
  20,000
  30,000
  40,000

R.D. BOUNDARIES ONLY SHOWN

0   10 MLS.

Fig. 41   THE LOCATION OF POPULATION LOSSES AND INCREASES, 1951–61. The only boundaries shown are those of the Rural District Councils. This and the two preceding maps were first published in *Problems of Applied Geography II, Geographia Polonica*, Warsaw (1964).

157

employment provided by the contracting industries: where pit and mill employment is relatively greatest the migrational movement is most serious, a clear sign of a loss of confidence in the old staple industries. Yet local variation in the rate of decline of coal and cotton employment has little effect on the pace of migration: whatever their fate, the flight from them continues, and only where economic diversification has made real progress has migration halted. It is especially significant that a strong inverse correlation exists between the proportion of local work provided by the service trades and the level of migrational loss. The feeble growth of these over most of the textile region is certainly a potent factor in its loss of population. Probably the closest association is that between migration and the proportion of the local housing stock that is substandard, for the towns with the lowest housing standards are, almost without exception, those losing families quickest by movement to areas which not only offer better paid and more secure work but also superior housing and urban amenities.

CHAPTER 7

The Essential Cheshire

CHESHIRE covers slightly more than 1,000 square miles with a population in 1961 of 1,369,000. But of these, almost two-thirds are in the areas of Cheshire that belong to the Merseyside conurbation, with 408,000, or the Manchester conurbation, with 467,000; these two conurbations together include 183 square miles of Cheshire, less than one-fifth of its area. Statistically Cheshire is overwhelmingly urban, as only 209,000 people, or 15%, live in areas that are officially rural districts; and at least one-quarter of these are people working in adjacent towns. Although hardly more than one-tenth of Cheshire's population are on the land, or closely associated with the farming community, the county is still dominantly rural in appearance. In this chapter, the areas of Cheshire that now belong to the two great conurbations of the Northwest are excluded; they are treated in Chapter 8 as part of the Mersey industrial belt, focused in modern times on the Manchester Ship Canal. Even though one separates the Mersey industrial belt from the rest of Cheshire, there is still a strong industrial tradition in its towns. One of the oldest and most characteristic, Nantwich, already had a long industrial tradition by 1831, when Lewis noted the strength of the cotton and glove manufactures, chiefly the latter. Both these trades have gone now, though there is a strong ready-made clothing industry in the town. And this story is not untypical of Cheshire towns, though the type of industry has varied. To some extent the towns of Cheshire have shared in the general industrialisation of the Northwest, though only those against the Pennine flank share Lancashire's textile tradition, seen, for example, in the silk and cotton manufactures established in the eighteenth century at Congleton and Macclesfield. Outside the conurbations, Cheshire towns have some evidence of antiquity such as an old or rebuilt church and a number of Tudor or eighteenth century houses; exception is Crewe, a new town of the railway period with nineteenth century housing, churches, and public buildings.

The threat to rural Cheshire lies not only in the possible further outward spread of the conurbations but also in the spread of the existing towns. Nantwich and Crewe have been joined together by ribbons of suburban settlement and the ring of housing estates and privately built houses around

Northwich has noticeably invaded a rural area. Here the main recent economic growth is associated with the chemical industry, as also in towns of the mid-Mersey basin such as Widnes, Runcorn, and Warrington. Figure 42 shows those areas of Cheshire which had marked increases of population between 1931 and 1951: there is a clear spread of housing around Macclesfield, in a few outer residential areas to the south of the Manchester conurbation, around Chester, in a few areas around Alsager close to the Potteries, which acquired an ordnance factory during the Second World War, and in villages that have attracted a dormitory population and, in some cases, industries. Rural Cheshire and its towns are in

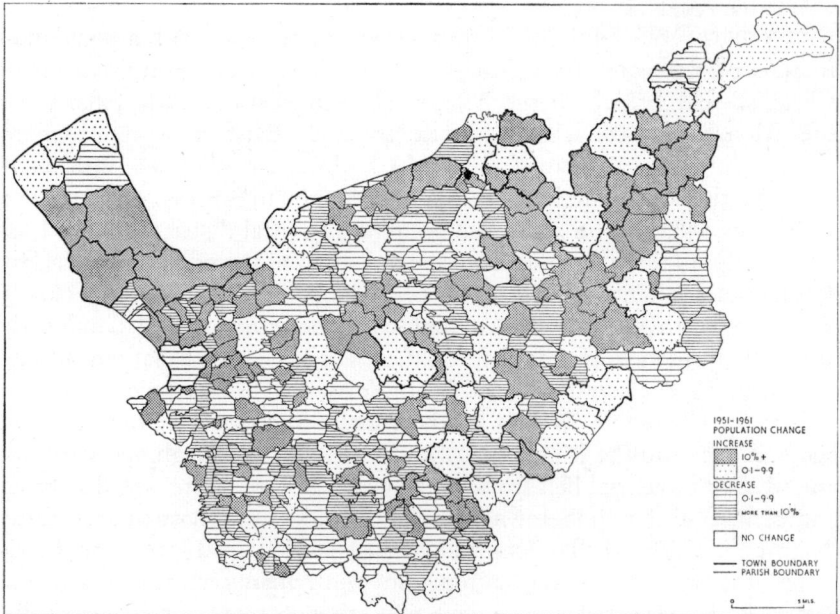

Fig. 42 POPULATION CHANGE IN CHESHIRE, 1951–61. This map shows changes at the parish level and so supplements Fig. 41.

many ways attractive to industry. There are excellent rail communications, good roads, and open sites in contrast with the congested areas of the conurbations; some industries, such as the making of lorries at Sandbach, owe their location to personal initiative rather than any marked geographical advantage. A negative reason for industrial location is seen at Mobberley, where a photographic factory was placed in the deep countryside because the air was clearer than in the city. Only to a limited extent is agricultural produce used industrially as the sale of liquid milk pays well, though there are factories for cheese, dried milk, and other milk products in the salt towns of Winsford and Middlewich and in a number of villages, notably Wrenbury. Another agricultural industry is the making of Benger's Food at Holmes Chapel, on the main railway line from Manchester to Crewe.

Although there are clear signs that Cheshire may be an attractive area for industry, the landscape is likely to remain primarily agricultural. If one excludes the Mersey industrial and residential belt discussed in Chapter 8, the areas shown as having more than 400 to the square mile in Figure 43, and the districts showing a recent heavy increase in population (Fig. 42); the remaining area is almost entirely farmland, as only one-twentieth of the county is agriculturally unproductive. Of the unfarmed land, the largest single area lies in the Cheshire Pennines, though there are smaller fragments of wasteland in the Bickerton and Peckforton hills, a

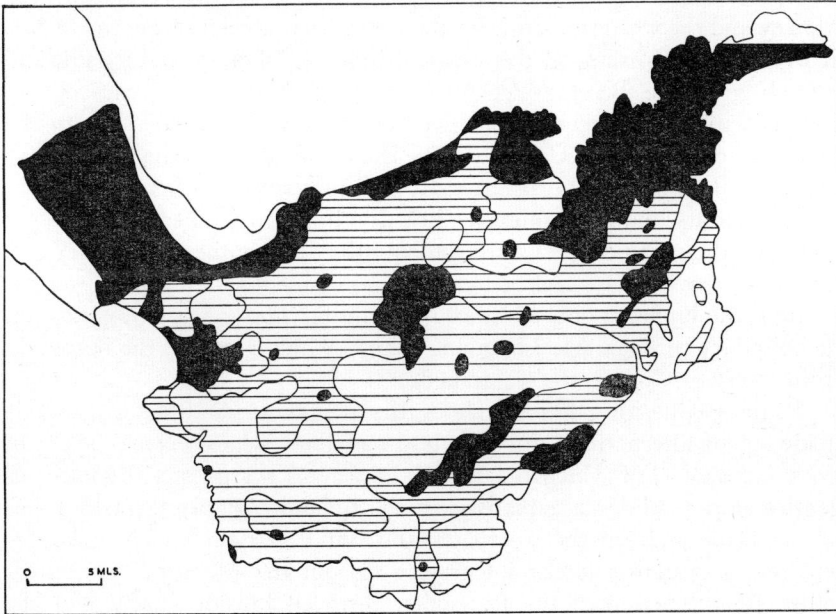

Fig. 43 POPULATION DENSITY IN CHESHIRE, 1961. This map was compiled with a dot map as a base. The areas shown in solid black have over 400 to the square mile, those with the close lines 101–200, with wide lines 1–101. The blank areas are uninhabited.

few woods (notably Delamere Forest), and some heaths and mosses that have escaped reclamation. Approximately half the rural area has a density of 101 to 200 per square mile, but lower densities, of 51 to 100 per square mile, occur over a considerable area, particularly between Northwich, Winsford, and Crewe, and also in the extreme south of the county, including the fringes of Shropshire. The deep rural areas, especially those of the great dairy farms, have a low density of workers in relation to area. To a great extent, agricultural activity in Cheshire has been adjusted to the needs of the consuming markets in the towns, with market gardening and arable cropping in the north and milk with cheese farther south. The rural scene possesses rich verdant pastures and fine croplands, but much of the fertility is due to long-continued manuring and especially to the use of marl to strengthen areas of light soil. Generally the farms are large, with big houses, flanked by a range of outbuildings on three sides of a yard.

Physical features and agriculture

Pennine Cheshire. In southeastern Cheshire the county boundary follows the long ridge, formed of grits, which is so clearly seen from the railway line through Congleton to Stoke. This ridge, in fact a cuesta, has three marked summit areas, all over 1,000 feet, in Mow Cop, Congleton Edge, and the Cloud: it forms the watershed between the Trent and the Mersey and the western margin of the Potteries coalfield. From this ridge, at Mow Cop for example, the westward view is of the Cheshire lowland extending to the Beeston–Peckforton hills with the radio telescope at Jodrell Bank as an incongruous element in so rural a scene. But to the east and south of Mow Cop there lies the coalfield and industrial area of the Potteries and its suburbs, a vastly different scene; so here if nowhere else the county boundary follows a line dividing two markedly contrasting areas. To the north of the Cloud the boundary enters the Dane valley and follows the river to its source in moorland country some 4 miles west of Buxton: the highest point of Cheshire, Shining Tor (1,834 ft.), is now on its boundary through an adjustment of 1936 which removed the boundary from the river Goyt to the watershed.

Pennine Cheshire, like much of the neighbouring upland areas, is made up of alternating anticlines and synclines which expose layers of grits and shales, of which the former appear as scarps and the latter as gentler slopes. Many streams dissect the upland, notably the tributaries of the Dane and, on the west side, the Bollin, a river which makes its leisurely way across lowland Cheshire to join the Mersey. These river valleys, combined with the frequently terraced hillsides formed of the grits and shales, give this part of the Pennines a scenic diversity that attracts a considerable number of day visitors: for this reason it is perhaps appropriate that it should be part of the Peak District National Park. The area virtually corresponds with the Macclesfield Forest, of some 70 square miles, established under Edward I. Until the seventeenth century this was probably heavily wooded to 500 feet, and more sparsely wooded in places to 1,000 feet, above which there were open deer moors. Steadily during the seventeenth and eighteenth centuries land was enclosed, and the farms are now mainly small family concerns, of some 40–50 acres of improved land, almost all in grass, used for dairy cattle and for sheep which find some pasture on the moors. The demand for liquid milk has given hill farmers some source of income (but with subsidies), though the general movement has been away from the upland farms. Boon described the area as 'a land of steep green fields enclosed by dark gritstone walls and of deep wooded valleys sheltering sombre gritstone farmhouses'.

Apart from the woods surviving on steep slopes—a characteristic Pennine valley trait—the only wood is a coniferous plantation in the Bollin valley around the Langley reservoirs.

The north Cheshire grass-arable belt. On the north this belt merges into the agriculturally rich areas close to the Manchester conurbation, which include the market gardening districts of Carrington Moss and Baguley; to the east there is a gradual transition to the grassland farms of the Pennine fringe, and on the west it reaches the poorer mid-Cheshire uplands. On the south this grass-arable belt may be distinguished from the far-famed grass-dairying belt of deep Cheshire by a line drawn from Helsby to Kelsall, then eastwards to Winsford and Middlewich, and south to Sandbach and Alsager. Many varieties of farming practice are found within the grass-arable belt. The soils include both clays and sands of glacial origin, but there has been long-continued and careful fertilisation, formerly by the addition of marls to light sandy soils and of sand and peat to heavy clays. Another source of fertility was the abundant manure brought from the towns, especially from Manchester by canal (Plate 4).

Climatic influence is seen in the varying proportion of permanent grass, which may cover much more than half the land on the flanks of the Pennines, or as little as one-tenth, and even less, on the drier districts near Chelford or High Legh (south of Lymm). At its best, for example in the area around Lymm, this area has good arable land with high crop yields, such as 8–10 tons of potatoes, and as much as 25 cwt. of hay to the acre. On the drained alluvium of the Mersey as many as seven consecutive corn crops have been grown. In the Lymm area potatoes are less likely to be damaged than on the rich but low-lying mosslands with their liability to frosts. The grass-arable farm in its most characteristic form has rotation grass, oats, potatoes, and wheat as the main crops: hay is made into silage on many farms. On some farms there is one cow to 1 or $1\frac{1}{4}$ acres, and milk is sold wholesale through the Marketing Board or retail in the outer suburbs of the Manchester conurbation. The farmers sell wheat and potatoes as cash crops, and oats are fed to stock. But there are many variations in farming practice, though the combination of arable cropping and grass husbandry is often regarded as sound, as a bad cereal year may be a good grass year.

On one farm near Bowdon, of 200 acres, with soils ranging from a medium loam to alluvial meadowland, there were over 100 stock, with a yield of 1,000 gallons a year as an average, 100 pigs, over 500 deep-litter poultry, but no sheep, owing to the menace of dogs close to a suburban neighbourhood. Many of the large and handsome fields are sown to potatoes in the first year, wheat or oats in the second, laid to grass for two years, then used for peas for a canning factory at Stockport. Most of the oats is used for stock and large quantities of silage are made, and considerable quantities of fodder crops, such as mangolds and kale, are grown.

The land is heavily fertilised with farmyard and chemical manures. On this farm, all the stock are reared, but on an efficient hill-foot farm near Macclesfield known to the author all the stock were bought, mainly from Galloway, and the 750 poultry were kept in batteries. This farm had some 70 cattle and 110 sheep, fed on grass and concentrates. On some farms, conspicuously those nearer the Pennines, 'flying herds' are kept: young stock are bought, used for one milking season, and then sold for beef, or in some cases as store cattle. Only to a limited extent can one ascribe the difference between these two efficient farms to differences in their situation, for opinions differ widely on methods of farming. Along the roads of north Cheshire it is now not unusual to see signs outside cottages advertising 'free range eggs' on the assumption that they must be better than those raised any other way.

Apart from differences due to the choice of individuals, in some areas natural soil characteristics have a clear influence on farming. There are, for example, some areas in which heavy boulder clay has virtually dictated dairying without cropping, as in an area of some 2 square miles of first-quality grassland to the northeast of Mobberley, where one farm of 140 acres has 110 cows, of which some are sent to summer grazings in Derbyshire. This area extends to Lindow Common, a peat area not yet entirely reclaimed, but partly divided into small-holdings, some of as little as 5 acres used mainly for flowers and vegetables, or for poultry. Many of these holdings provide only a part-time occupation, but the reclamation of mosses has added substantial areas of market gardening land in the Northwest, though some peat still remains, for example at Dane's Moss near Macclesfield. Not all the market gardens are on peat: immediately south of Manchester airport, around Styal, vegetables and flowers are grown on light, well drained loams, with some glasshouse production of tomatoes, cucumbers, and early vegetables. Scattered through north Cheshire there are patches of horticultural land, used for flowers and vegetables, with a number of nurseries, of which some are run by firms in Manchester and others seek wider markets. Some of these garden-type holdings are run by people displaced when Wythenshawe was built, but the Timperley–Baguley area still retains some of its significance for market gardening (see p. 184). The flowers and plants are sold in the shops and markets of Manchester and other towns, or even from stalls and sheds on the holdings to passing motorists.

Delamere Forest and the mid-Cheshire ridge. Approached from the Weaver valley between Northwich and the Mersey, the Delamere area appears as a diverse and hilly area, formed of Keuper sandstones terminating on the north in an abrupt scarp at Frodsham and Helsby and on the west in a similar scarp from Helsby to Kelsall. Rising to an altitude above 500 feet, both Delamere Forest and the ridge farther south are made a marked scenic feature by the lowlands around them, notably in the south, where Beeston Castle and the Peckforton hills stand up magnificently above the 2-mile wide Gowy gap, used by road, canal, and railway between Tarporley and Beeston. Delamere is the northern part of the mid-Cheshire hills, but belongs rather to the grass-arable belt of Cheshire than to the famous dairying area discussed below. Long-continued and careful fertilisation has made excellent farmland from former waste, but meres and peat bogs still remain, and the heathery ground vegetation in some of the woods suggest the heaths with which much of the area was at one time covered. In 1795, Aikin spoke of Delamere as 'a black and dreary waste, composed of deep sand and sterile heath and chiefly inhabited by rabbits'. Much of the reclamation dates from the nineteenth century, though in 1941, E. P. Boon wrote that 'the land still bears, to some extent, the mark of a "pioneer stage" which never quite reached completion'. And this is still true. If it were not for planning control, the forest might easily become invaded by new houses inhabited by people travelling to work by car (Fig. 44, Plate 3).

Forests survive mainly in a central triangular area traversed by a secondary road from Frodsham to Tarporley and by the old Cheshire Lines railway from Northwich to Chester. The largest patch of forest covers more than 2 square miles, but there are numerous woods elsewhere, of which some cover several hundred acres interspersed with patches of heath. Like all 'beauty spots' of Cheshire, the forest attracts a considerable number of day visitors from the towns. The Old Pale dates back to the thirteenth century as a clearing and the New Pale, on the west side, to the seventeenth century: apparently these two areas had natural medium-loam soils contrasting sharply with the sterile glacial sands found elsewhere. Some of the reclamation was done from 1760 to 1809, but under an Act of 1812 further encouragement was given to the creation of farms: this Act (of Enclosure and Soil Improvement) preserved half the central forest belt for the crown and permitted settlement only on its margins. Many of the trees planted were oaks but in recent times coniferous trees have become general. The farms made in the nineteenth century were not unusually of 50 acres, originally with 10-acre fields. This process of settlement continued vigorously until the 1850s, though some farms were made later under crown leases.

Fertilisation was at all times the major problem, and marling was the chief method used. There is some evidence that it was employed as early as the thirteenth century both to lighten clay soils and to strengthen sands. In Delamere sand prevails, though there are some patches of drift-clay at the surface. Good marl always contains lime—indeed, it is not strictly a marl without this lime content—but a variety of strengthening manures was used, including boulder clays (clay marls) and shales in the Keuper marls and waterstones (slate marl). Strahan described the marling of an area of 800 acres on the north side of Eddisbury Hill from a bed of dull

165

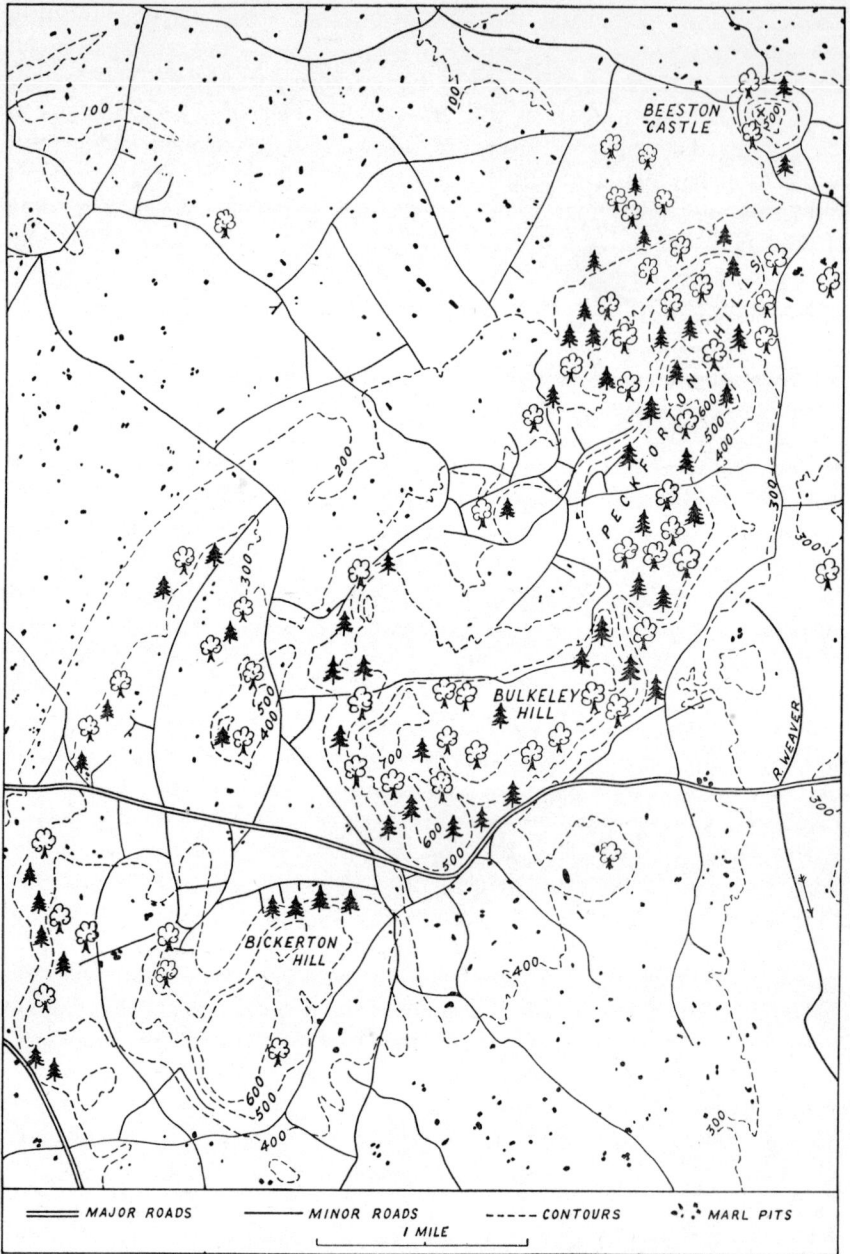

Fig. 44   THE MID-CHESHIRE RIDGE NEAR TARPORLEY. The enormous number of marl pits on the heavier drift soils of the lower ground is a striking feature. The ridge, a marked feature of the Cheshire landscape, is continued farther north in Delamere Forest to Frodsham and Helsby near the Mersey.

red clay under the northeast slope of the same hill in 1861–3. A bed of marl 12 to 15 feet thick, resting on a bed of sand and round pebbles, was worked, carried an average distance of 2 miles and spread on the land at a total cost of nearly £8,000, and the value of the land was increased from 5s. to 32s. 6d. an acre. In recent times the fertility of the land has been guarded by the use of farmyard manure, crushed bones, and chemical fertilisers. Some farmers in the nineteenth century specialised in cheese making, but now milk and poultry are sold in the towns, and surplus crops such as oats and potatoes also command a ready sale. In its general complexion the farming is similar to that of the grass-arable belt of Cheshire, with dairy cattle as the main economic resource, crops grown primarily for the stock but with a surplus for cash sale in many cases, and a large expenditure on fertilisers and feedstuffs.

The grass-dairying area. This, the most wide-famed of the agricultural areas of Cheshire, extends southwards into Shropshire and Staffordshire and westwards into Denbigh and Flint. The soils, largely derived from glacial and fluvioglacial deposits, include a variety of clays, some of which are of particularly heavy quality in the west and southwest. East of the Peckforton hills, however, there are sands and gravels, some of which provide, with fertilisation, excellent soils for crops. In general dairying remains the main resource, and the crops are used mainly as feedstuffs, though in a few places, notably on the islands of Bunter pebble-beds near Churton (seven miles south of Chester) and also around Farndon and Holt (the latter in Denbighshire), light, easily worked, warm, and early soils are used for market gardening. Though the Peckforton hills rise only to 746 feet, they form a clear ridge between the Dee and Weaver valleys. Much of this ridge consists of Triassic sandstones devoid of glacial drift, acting as a natural reservoir which is tapped on the east side to supply water for Stoke-on-Trent. Here, as in the Delamere Forest area, it is not difficult to see that the limit of farming has been pushed forward into an area of heath mixed with forest, notably on the western side facing the wide part of the Dee valley to the south and southeast of Chester. There are some large farms with cattle rearing and dairying, and also some well-tilled fields for crops. But much of the Peckforton hills remains a heath, and is greatly appreciated as an open space. There are woodlands on the steeper hillsides and also in the grounds of Peckforton Castle. To the south the Bickerton hills, 694 feet at the highest point, rise sharply from the lowland and consist mainly of heathland; to the north, Beeston Castle rises above the Gowy gap as a kind of sentinel on its sharp hill (Fig. 45, Plate 2).

Although the grass-dairying belt still remains predominantly green, with fine meadows and pastures, excellent crops are also grown, and the farmers now wish to be as self-sufficient as possible in feedingstuffs. In 1938 it was said that many Cheshire farmers lived on 100 acres of grassland

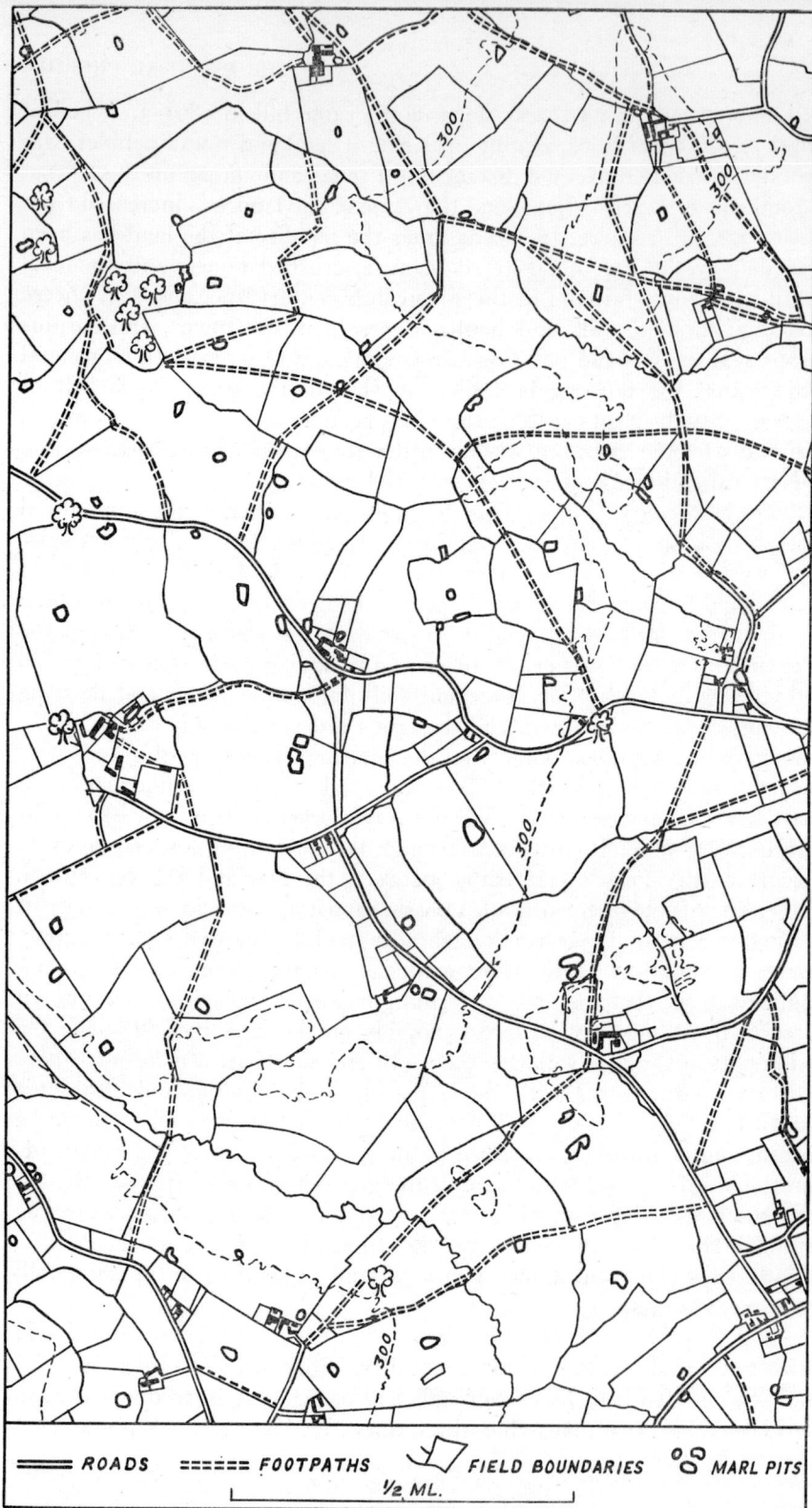

Fig. 45   PART OF THE CHESHIRE DRIFT COUNTRYSIDE. Much of Cheshire has dispersed settlement, a chaotic system of lanes, and innumerable marl pits. It is still possible for the horse-rider, or even the leisurely motorist, to wander through a rich rural landscape little changed during the past fifty years.

in Cheshire and 200 acres of New World grain, as there was no silage and no grass drying; but as a result of the intensification of farming during and since the Second World War the farmers now grow a substantial part of the feedstuffs. The farms, strongly mechanised, have for many decades been worked with enterprise. Normally two-thirds of the land is grazed and one-third sown, and the use of silage pits and towers has steadily increased; many farmers have their grass dried, though so far few have their own drying plants. E. S. Simpson, in his excellent article on this area, has said: 'Today the fields of the central dairying area are a patchwork of permanent grass, ley grass and arable fodder crops which contrast greatly with the unrelieved expanses of permanent grass in the nineteen-thirties.'[1] The cereal crops include mixed corn and oats, and the green crops kale, mangolds, and turnips.

Even now, in some districts, as much as four-fifths of the land is in grass, especially on the heavy 'gley' soils which never burn up in summer, and in spite of all the changes the cow still reigns supreme, for Cheshire has the highest density of cows of any county in England or Wales, and the yield per animal is one-fifth higher than the national average. Pigs are now kept in numbers equal to those of prewar years, but since the decline —fortunately not total—of farm cheese making, little whey has been used and there has been a heavy dependence on imported feedstuffs. Sheep were never very important, as they were either 'flying flocks' for one crop of lambs or merely a flock of fattening lambs fed on the aftermath of the hayfields and sold before Christmas. Essentially the appearance of this belt has changed little since 1938, when there was 'a patchwork of small, green, thorn-hedged fields carrying in summer a multi-coloured population of dairy cows, especially red and roan Shorthorns. At the bottom of each well-kept hedge ran a ditch into which drained the outfall of the pipes beneath the heavy-soiled fields. The fields themselves often had an undulating surface of regularly shaped ridges and furrows (the "butt and reins" of the Cheshire farmer), evidence of earlier attempts to drain the surface of the heavy land.' Since 1938, however, there has been a considerable change of stock from Shorthorns to Friesians and Ayrshires, which are favoured owing to their higher milk yields (Fig. 45).

There are large farmhouses, some dating back to the eighteenth century or earlier, with dairies and cheese-storage rooms, and farm buildings where beasts could be sheltered for five months each year. Excellent piggeries exist on most farms, many of them of a Danish type. Almost all the liquid milk is sold: for example, in 1949–50 it was found that less than 1% was retained for cheese making, which was produced on 34 farms within the county and another 29 in neighbouring counties. By 1964, the cheese-making farms numbered only 46, of which 28 are in Cheshire (Fig. 46).

[1] E. S. Simpson, *The Cheshire grass-dairying region*; Institute of British Geographers, Transactions and Papers 1957, Publication No. 23.

The cheese-making farms occur in the countryside between Crewe and Nantwich to the east and Chester to the west and south of Nantwich towards Market Drayton and Whitchurch, the latter a Shropshire town which formerly had cheese fairs. Milk from farms in the north and west supplies the Merseyside market and from those in the north and east the

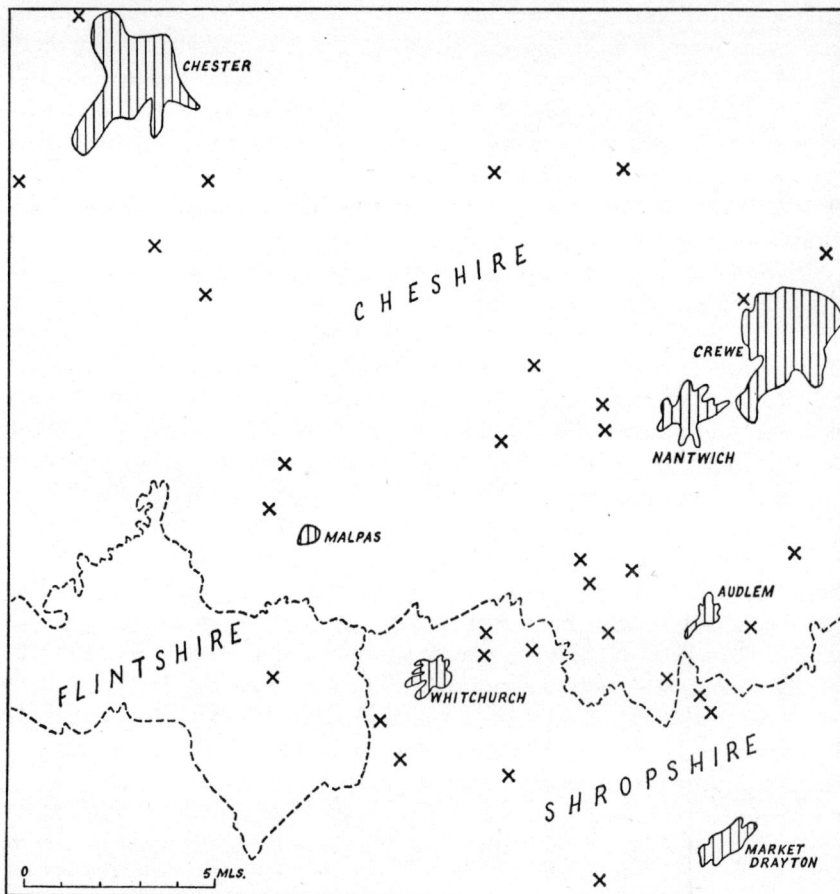

Fig. 46 CHESHIRE CHEESE FARMS. The few farms where cheese is made on the premises are chiefly in the far southwest of Cheshire and in neighbouring areas of north Shropshire. Compiled from information provided by Mr F. W. Foulkes, 25 High Street, Whitchurch.

Manchester conurbation. Manufacturing depots are found mainly in the southern part of the county, for example at Wrenbury on the railway line from Nantwich to Whitchurch, at Audlem, and at Haslington near Crewe.

Population

Country and town population in Cheshire. Figures 41 and 43 show that there has been some invasion of Cheshire's countryside by settlement from neighbouring towns, but only within limited areas; it is based on the census figures, together with fieldwork. Somewhat similar work done by the compilers of the county's Development Plan reached comparable results. Having excluded the few parishes that showed marked increases of population from 1921–48, they estimated that over much of rural Cheshire there had been a net loss of 20% by emigration in twenty-seven years, though the actual decreases were far smaller, owing to the excess of births over deaths. About half the parishes had an increase, as the rate of growth through excess of births is relatively high (for example, 1931–51, rural districts of Nantwich over 8·9%, Bucklow over 7·6%, but Tarvin only 4·6%) yet the essentially rural population has declined: one may note, for example, that the number of workers on the land was reduced from 29,950 in 1931 to 27,250 in 1951, less than 5% of the employed population. From 1951–61 the highest population increase was in the Bucklow rural district (over 44%), owing to new housing near the Mersey at Partington, and at Mere near Knutsford. The former is associated with the expansion of the chemical industry near the Ship Canal and is in effect an outlying growth of the Manchester conurbation (p. 197). At Mere the development is mainly of expensive modern houses close to a lake ('mere') and a country club. If it were not for some form of legislative restriction the type of development seen at Mere would probably be widespread in Cheshire for people working in the conurbations, in Stoke-on-Trent, in the industrial towns such as Northwich, and for many more. Essentially designed for the two-car-to-a-family household, such houses might easily make a 'rururban' belt within ten or twenty years. As this is not at present possible (and definitely not desirable), some business people buy up old farmhouses, recondition them inside, and farm the land with the help of a bailiff. Old cottages and outhouses are eagerly sought for conversion into country homes, and sophisticated suburban hospitality is provided with cows peering in at the drawing-room window. Even so, from 1951–61, the increase of population in the Nantwich rural district was only by 163 persons, a mere 0·6%, and in Tarvin rural district there was a decline of 0·5%; these represent the deep rural fortresses of Cheshire, even though some of the suburban growth between Nantwich and Crewe is within the Nantwich rural district. To summarise, over most of rural Cheshire the population has declined, or very slightly increased, and the addition of about one-quarter to the totals for the rural districts from 1931–51 and of over 11·6% from 1951–61 is due to an overflow into a few areas, especially those near to the towns of Chester, Crewe, and Nantwich, Northwich, Congleton, and Macclesfield, and on the fringe of the Manchester conurbation. In the Macclesfield rural district, for example, there was an increase in population of 18% from 1931–51, but 14 of the 27 parishes had decreases, and the increase was due primarily to outer suburban spreads in such places as Adlington, Gawsworth, Poynton, and Prestbury. In

1951–61 there was an increase of 8%, similarly localised, with decreases in 11 parishes. In the neighbouring rural district of Congleton, with a population increase of 22% to 1951 (and over 6% from 1951–61), all except 4 of the 20 parishes added to their numbers from 1931–51; but this is not an increase of the agricultural community as in most cases the visible sign of this expansion is the addition of a dozen or twenty houses in a village, of which some are privately built and others represent schemes of the rural district council. In 1951–61, 12 of the 20 parishes recorded increases. Some farmers complain that such schemes do nothing to solve their labour problems, as the new houses are in many cases occupied by town workers, or by retired people.

As a statistical unit, the Tarvin rural district is perhaps most representative of the true, deep countryside of Cheshire. From 1931–51 its population increased only from 14,400 to 14,600, and in 39 of its 69 parishes a decline was registered; between 1951 and 1961, there was a decline to 14,500, with a decrease in 44 parishes. Having no places defined as towns in its area of almost 100 square miles, this rural district had its main additions of population in its larger villages, such as Farndon on the Welsh border (580/690),[1] Malpas, an old but small market centre (1,100/1,220), Tarvin on the main road from Nantwich to Chester (1,250/1,500), and Kelsall on the edge of Delamere Forest (870/1,030). A comparable increase is seen at Tarporley (1,380/1,540), an old town with a charter for markets dating back to the thirteenth century, described by Lewis in 1831 as having 'one long street, which is well paved and terminated at the end by the ancient manor-house'. The failure of these places to grow significantly during the past hundred-odd years is partly due to their lack of railway stations (Tarporley's station, for example, is 2 miles distant, at Beeston Castle); but motor travel has helped to revive them. To what extent industry should be dispersed through rural Cheshire is clearly a contentious matter, though there are signs of growth in several villages; for example, Holmes Chapel, on the main railway line from Crewe to Manchester, with a population of over 1,000, has work available in food and wallpaper factories. It is perhaps a safe assumption that planning control will prevent any wholesale invasion of the countryside for residential and industrial purposes, but some planners have expressed the opinion that a limited enlargement of various Cheshire market villages might be advantageous, since with a larger population such places could provide more varied social and recreational facilities. One post-war plan of Cheshire suggested that places such as Audlem, Malpas, Tarvin, Tarporley, and several more could be expanded with advantage. Over much of Cheshire villages are sparsely distributed, and the main pattern of settlement is dispersion, both of farmhouses and of labourers' cottages.

[1] The figures are for 1931 and 1951; estimates for 1961 are Farndon 820, Tarvin 1,400, Kelsall 1,200, Tarporley 1,550.

Town population. Of all the county's towns, perhaps none is more characteristic in appearance of a slowly growing, ancient market centre than Nantwich, even though until 1856 it had salt working as a traditional, if declining industry. But there is so much surviving from the past, including some half-timbered houses, of which one in the central square, marred by a modern shop front, is dated 1584. There are some seventeenth-century almshouses now restored and used as a restaurant, and a large country house of 1577 originally built outside the town, also used as a restaurant. There are domestic buildings of later centuries in rich variety. But the life of the place centres around the square, made in 1872 by the removal of a block of shops. Beside the square stands the large parish church, of the fourteenth century, surrounded by lawns with venerable trees (oddly enough, and fortunately, not yews but birches) on the site of the graveyard. Most of the town's offices and shops are within a couple of hundred yards of the centre, and so also are the main hotels. Not far from the church there is a fine Georgian terrace of houses with large gardens at the rear, for in Nantwich, as in many old towns, a considerable number of houses have plenty of ground behind them. In appearance a typical market town Nantwich, with a population in 1961 of 10,450, has a long industrial tradition which is still vigorously maintained; but boot making ceased in 1925 and glove making and cotton ceased earlier, though the tannery has remained prosperous and the largest industry at present is clothing. Rural industries are represented by milling, largely of oats, and by an egg-packing station serving a large area from Warrington to Whitchurch and employing more than fifty people. One enterprise of special interest is the Cheshire, Shropshire, and North Wales Farmers' Supply Association, which is run on a co-operative basis and employs fifty people; founded in 1871 and now operating within a radius of approximately 30 miles, it deals in feedingstuffs, seeds, fertilisers, and agricultural machinery, markets all kinds of crops and dairy produce and undertakes grass drying, crop spraying, agricultural contracting, and even the construction of farm buildings. The amenities of Nantwich include a brine swimming bath and a praiseworthy attempt to brighten the centre under the Civic Trust (Plate 5).

Crewe, 4 miles away, is in sharp contrast, for in effect it is a new town of the railway era, which acquired its lines from 1837 to 1858 (p. 88) and its famous railway works from 1843. Having only 200 people in 1841, Church Coppenhall parish, which assumed the name of Crewe, grew to 4,570 by 1851, to 17,800 by 1871, and to 42,100 by 1901, since when growth has been slow and intermittent, though the population was 53,200 in 1961. Having become a borough in 1877, Crewe was extended in 1892 and again in 1938, when for the first time the railway station was brought within the boundaries of the borough. Never an attractive town, Crewe has a large number of 'neat cottages of four apartments' built by the

173

railway company, now regarded as ripe for clearance, a great variety of Nonconformist chapels of indescribable architecture, and until recently few shops of much attraction. As early as the 1871 Census it was noted that Crewe workpeople were settling in neighbouring villages, such as Haslington and Shavington, from which they travelled to work by horse bus or brake, and from the 1890s by bicycle also. Willaston had a railway station now closed, and became a suburban village by the early twentieth century. Wistaston also has become suburban, so that there is virtually no gap in building between Crewe and Nantwich along the main road. Including the suburbanised villages, this area had a population of 75,000 in 1961 compared with 71,000 in 1951 and 64,000 in 1931. The industrial basis of Crewe has been steadily broadened to include motor cars and engines, rolling machinery, and clothing, but the number employed in the railway works has declined. At times Crewe is mentioned as a town that might be expanded in population and industry, partly by movement from industrial Lancashire: a small overspill estate for Manchester people is planned.

Six miles east of Crewe, Alsager has grown rapidly in recent years and with some 5,600 people in 1951 had almost doubled its population from 1931. There was a further increase, by about 40%, to 7,800 in 1961. Traditionally residential, partly for the Potteries, Alsager was used as a site for a large government factory during the Second World War. East Cheshire's strongest towns are Congleton (16,800 in 1961) and Macclesfield (37,600), both of which have ancient markets dating back to the thirteenth century. Macclesfield has a fine church on a commanding site above a deep valley tightly built up with the railway, mills, and houses. Congleton is spread on hilly ground mainly on the south side of the Dane valley and here too mills and houses are jumbled intricately. Both towns are strong market centres; both have a long industrial tradition, and have grown only slightly in population during the past century. There are considerable similarities in their industrial history. In Congleton the older industries included the making of gloves and leather laces (known as Congleton points) but from the middle of the eighteenth century these enterprises were superseded by silk and ribbon manufacture. In Macclesfield the early trades were thread twisting and button making, but the first silk mill was established in 1756, with a cotton factory two years later. In spite of changes which include the transformation of some of Macclesfield's many mills for new trades such as engineering, it is still a major centre for silk weaving: here, as at Congleton, the traditional industry survives. Both towns now have clothing factories, and both share the problem of rehousing a considerable part of their population owing to the inheritance of nineteenth century cottages now urgently in need of replacement. Congleton was at one time suggested as a new town for Manchester overspill, but at present it appears more probable that Macclesfield will be extended; in fact, the reception of Manchester families has begun. Three miles away, Bollington (5,600) is a small, mainly stone-built, hill-foot cotton town, but its mills are now used for a variety of industries including paper, printing, and plastics. Bollington has the appearance of many Pennine towns that seem to have grown out of the hills around them.

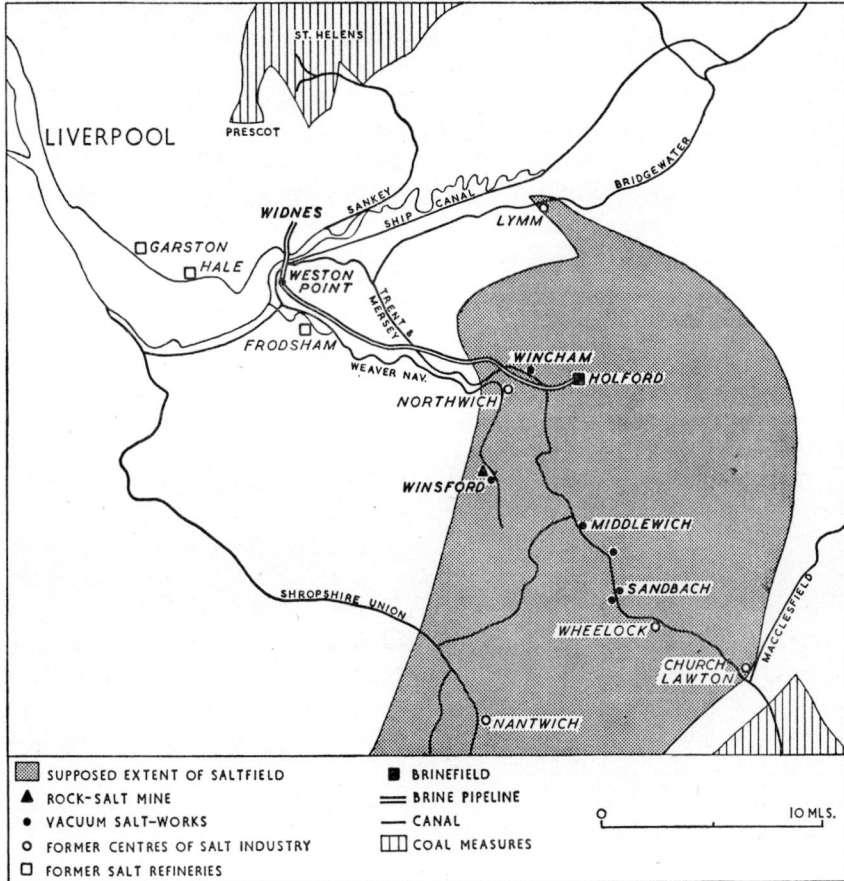

Fig. 47 THE CHESHIRE SALTFIELD AND ITS TRANSPORT LINKS WITH THE MERSEY ESTUARY.

Central Cheshire has its traditional salt manufactures, now extinct in Nantwich but still surviving in varied forms at Sandbach, Middlewich, Winsford, and Northwich. Sandbach (9,900) is an urban district including the old town of this name and two industrial villages, Wheelock and Elworth, all of which are fusing into one another. At Elworth there are famous diesel lorry works; other industries include silk textiles and a brine-pumping station for the manufacture of table salt. A small flash, due to subsidence, is visible here from the main-line railway; but the greater effects of past salt working are seen in the flashes of Northwich and Winsford and in the shoring-up of houses in and around these towns and Middlewich. During the nineteenth century, apparently due especially to the pumping of natural brine (cf. p. 62), subsidence became a serious problem, and in some places dramatic effects were seen quite suddenly, as for example when Winsford flash was formed through a sudden collapse in the 1870s. But the most serious subsidence resulted from the flooding of old workings to give 'bastard brine' from 1873 to 1935; in the first year a lake of 5 acres was formed which spread until it was many times that size, and serious subsidences occurred in 1880, 1893, and 1912. In 1911 controlled pumping was begun and the brine taken by pipes to Weston Point, near Runcorn, outside the area likely to experience subsidence. The only surviving salt mine is at Winsford, and the main area of extraction is now on the Holford saltfield, to the east of Northwich, where the scene is like a Texas oilfield with the derricks of the brine pumps scattered through farmland, and agricultural activity is little impeded by the use of the underground resources. Very different, however, is the nightmare landscape of devastation due to subsidence to the north of Northwich, though the flashes are now sealed off and used for dumping chemical refuse (Figs. 47, 48).

Northwich (19,500) is one of the strangest towns in Britain. Its main street has been raised and its buildings are on frames so that they can be jacked up when the need arises. A considerable amount of land has been sterilised for building, and in the past a number of buildings have been destroyed. The town has a ring of suburbs at some distance from its centre, including Lostock Gralam, Rudheath, Davenham, Hartford, Weaverham, and Barnton, which give Northwich in effect a population of over 40,000. Here, as at Middlewich (6,900 in 1961), salt and chemicals are the major industries, though there is also some engineering and clothing manufacture at Northwich. Some of the chemical industry's raw materials and finished products are still carried by the Weaver navigation, and vast supplies of lime are drawn from the Buxton area by rail (Fig. 49). Winsford (12,800) is an old salt town now being transformed. After years of decline, it is taking overspill from Manchester and Liverpool, and will expand to 30,000, possibly 60,000, inhabitants. A new industrial estate already has a wide variety of factories, some attracted by the proximity of the M6 motorway.

In many ways these salt-chemical towns are a scenic blot on Cheshire, and one could wish that the suburbs had been developed with more taste. But fortunately there is a wide rural area between Northwich and the fringes of the Manchester conurbation, occupied by rich farmland and having in Knutsford a town almost untouched by industry. Profiting from a strong rural trade, Knutsford is also a residential centre for Manchester, some 16 miles away: out of its 1,123 residents who worked

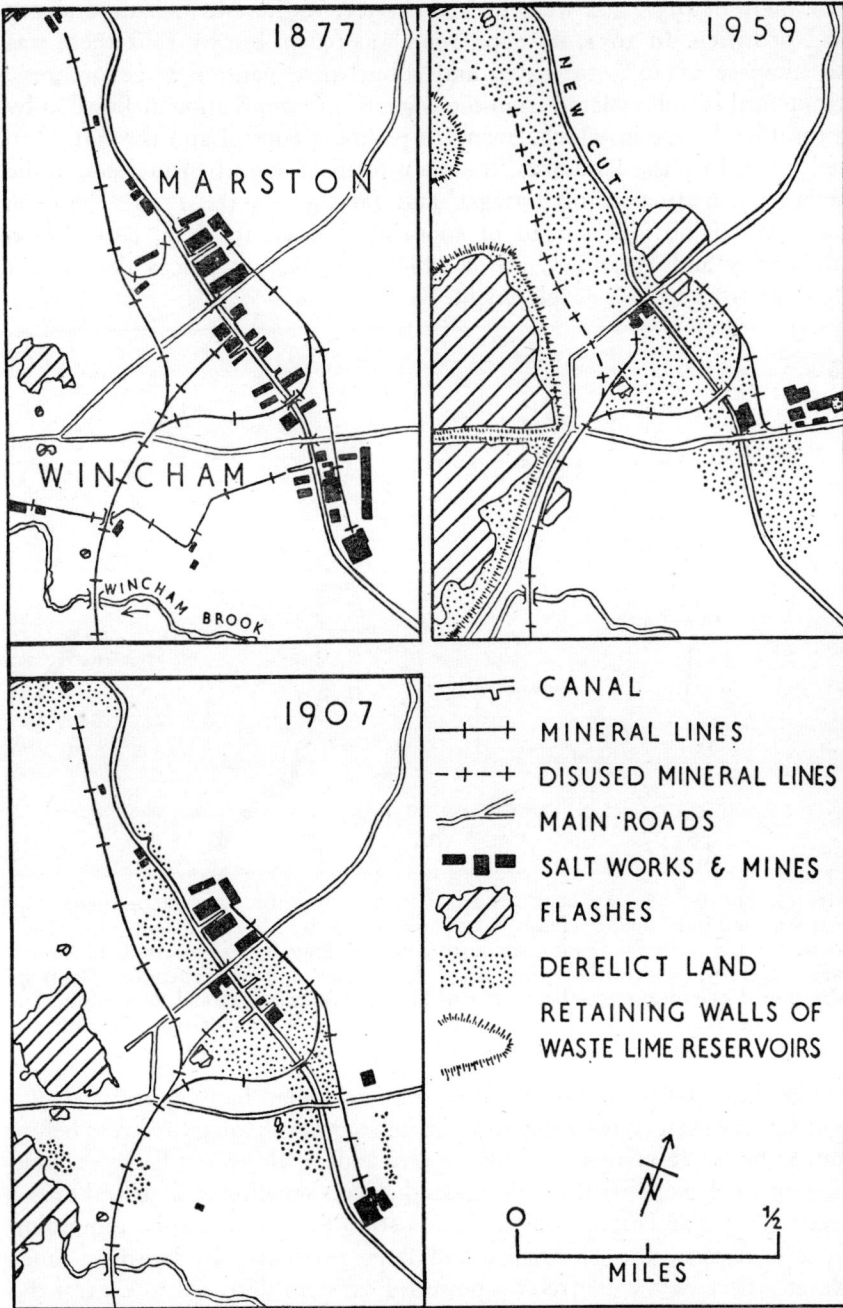

Fig. 48 DERELICT LAND NEAR NORTHWICH, 1877–1959. First published in *Geography* 45 (1960), 274, by Mr K. L. Wallwork, M.A., to whom the authors are indebted.

CANAL
MINERAL LINES
DISUSED MINERAL LINES
MAIN ROADS
SALT WORKS & MINES
FLASHES
DERELICT LAND
RETAINING WALLS OF WASTE LIME RESERVOIRS

MILES

elsewhere in 1951, 262 went to Manchester, 169 to Altrincham, and 113 to Northwich. In 1951, its population was 6,600, but by 1961 there was an increase of 42% to 9,400, and suburban expansion is in progress. Knutsford is well isolated from the edge of the conurbation at Bowdon by a rural landscape in which, owing to planning control and the refusal to sell ground by the landlords, the main form of suburban invasion is the lavish reconstruction of cottages and farmhouses (p. 171). There is, however, an obvious spread of suburban houses at Mere, and also at Mobberley and Prestbury, all of which are pleasant places though not immune from ribbon development.

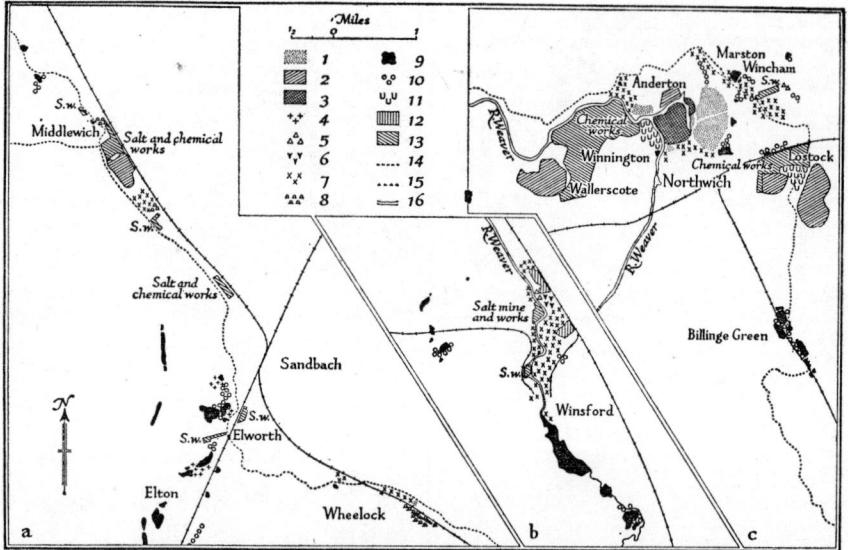

Fig. 49 SUBSIDENCE AND DERELICT LAND IN THE CHESHIRE SALTFIELD, 1959. This map was first published in *Geogr. J.* **126** (1960), 194, by Mr K. L. Wallwork, M.A., to whom the authors' thanks are due. The key may be summarised: Chemical waste 1, 2, 3; Salt works' waste 4, 5, 6; Derelict salt and chemical plants 7; abandoned chemical waste heaps 8; subsidence flashes 9; seasonal flooding due to subsidence 10; restored chemical waste 11; restored industrial dereliction 12; major salt and chemical plants 13; canals 14, 15; river Weaver 16.

Of all the Cheshire towns none is more eloquent in its appearance of a long history than Chester itself. Made into a great legionary fortress before A.D. 80 by the Romans to defend the civil zone of Britain, it had an oblong playing-card shape with four gates and streets meeting at a central cross-roads. This plan (Fig. 50), modified, is still discernible despite rebuilding by the Saxons, the Normans, and later residents. In Norman times Chester became the centre of a powerful earldom designed to control the Welsh, for here was the first crossing place of the Dee, the natural line of entry to North Wales, and a port beneath the walls which had been used from Norman times. The threat to Chester as a port was stated in a request by the mayor and burgesses for a reduction of their dues in 1445, on the ground that they were losing trade to Beaumaris and Liverpool, and the harbour was silting up so that merchant ships could not approach within 12 miles of the city. Early in the seventeenth century Camden said that Cheshire had 'lost the advantage of a harbour, which it enjoyed heretofore'. By 1674, small ships of 20 tons could come no nearer than

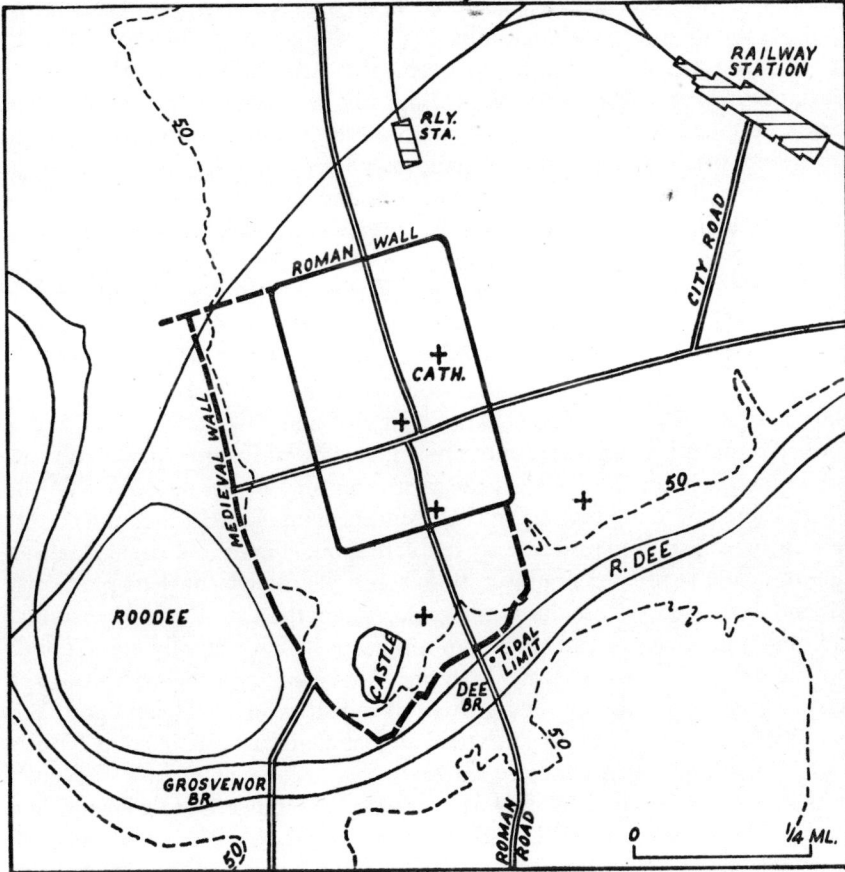

Fig. 50   ROMAN AND MEDIEVAL CHESTER. The sites of some early parish and other c urches are shown with a cross.

Neston (the New Quay of the sixteenth century), and Defoe (p. 55) noted that it was no longer significant as a port. In 1735–7, the New Cut was made through the sands of the Dee to revive Chester's trade, but by this time Liverpool was supreme. Even so, Chester had some fame as a port in medieval times, especially for Ireland (Plates 6–8).

Although Chester acquired canals to the Mersey and to Nantwich in the late eighteenth century (p. 65), the abiding strategic advantage of the town lay in its roads and, from the 1840s, its railways. In modern times

Chester has become a city to avoid for its traffic, but its by-pass system is still incomplete, and thousands approach North Wales along its roads as well as through its railway station. It has become the headquarters of the Crosville motor bus organisation which serves a large part of Cheshire and of North and Central Wales. The 1961 Census of Retail Distribution showed that its shops employed some 4,800 full-time workers and that its trade was valued at nearly £20,000,000, an average of £333 a head for its population of 59,000 (incidentally, Crewe with 53,000 had only 2,600 full-time workers and a trade of £10,500,000). Around Chester there are a number of unabsorbed suburbs, technically in rural districts, which have a total population of some 21,000; with these the population increased (for the same area) by 26% from 61,500 to 78,000, between 1931 and 1951. Chester itself had 57,000 residents in 1951 and 59,300 in 1961; the outlying suburbs had some 25,000 people by 1961.[1] Undoubtedly trade is drawn into the retail shops from these areas, and also from a much wider area, including towns and industrial villages of the Flintshire coast and parts of Merseyside conurbation in the Wirral peninsula, which is well served by trains and buses from Chester to Birkenhead. The 'Rows' disliked by Defoe (p. 55) provided a natural pedestrian way for shoppers centuries before such features became characteristic of new town centres. The two-mile circuit of the walls still remains a favourite walk, and sporting events still take place on the Roodee, the vast river-side open space. Within the town there are many fine eighteenth century houses, including one stately group in Abbey Square close to the cathedral. There is a dreary artisan quarter close to the main railway station, and the suburbs have no particular distinction. Apart from its commercial strength, Chester is the county administrative centre and the see of a diocese which virtually corresponds to the county. It has chemical, engineering, and food factories; but the city is affected by the marked growth of industry on the cheap open land south of the Dee, where works extend almost continuously for some 8 miles into Flintshire. Near Chester, aircraft and steel making are the chief industries. Although these factories are some distance from Chester, and across the border in Wales, they have stimulated its recent growth, particularly on the west side, and there is a heavy movement daily to Broughton and Shotton.

The individuality of Cheshire

It has none, it could be said. If one travels south into the neighbouring parts of Shropshire and Staffordshire, or even west towards the Welsh hills that form so attractive a backcloth to rural Cheshire, one sees much the same farming, and not dissimilar towns. All this has some element of

[1] In 1965 the Local Government Commission proposed to change Chester's boundaries so that its population would be 75,000. This did not include Saltney, with some 4,000 people, continuous with Chester but in Flintshire.

truth and Cheshire may reasonably be thought of as part of the marcher country or the western fringe of the English lowland, traditionally pastoral in much of its farming, yet possessing excellent arable land also. Generations of skilled farmers have made Cheshire fertile, have cleared all save a few small fragments of its peatbogs and forests, have drained its thick clay soils or enriched its sandy soils. Many of its farming families have tended stock and tilled fields on the same land for hundreds of years. To a great extent the intensification of agriculture is due to the nearness of a vast consuming market in Lancashire, never more exploited than now; even so, Cheshire cheese has been widely renowned for centuries.

Cheshire towns are fundamentally market centres, having excellent shops, particularly ironmongers and grocers. In Nantwich, for example, the retail sales average £204 a head, in Knutsford £193, in Macclesfield £179, but in the rural districts only £54; the average figure for the county is £141 (1961 Census of Distribution). But the imprint of industry is clear in most Cheshire towns, in three forms: first, the historic salt working has been transformed into a branch of the chemical industry, and left its problems of subsidence, especially around Northwich and Winsford; secondly, there are clear influences of the spread of textile industries in such east Cheshire towns as Congleton and Macclesfield; thirdly, modern engineering has grown in several towns, notably Sandbach, Crewe, and Chester. In fact, Chester has a variety of trades and owes much of its modern growth to its fine strategic position, but Crewe in contrast is as much a creation of the railway as Swindon or Wolverton. Deep in the heart of rural Cheshire, it is the least indigenous of its towns, even though it now has graduated, as it were, in the ways of Cheshire by adding a vast cattle market. As well as its major towns, Cheshire has a number of market villages, now showing signs of growth, partly due to their residential attractions. In spite of the obvious influence of industry in Cheshire, its canals, railways, and fine motor roads have not so far removed its essentially rural character: it still has its deep countryside of fields and stately farmsteads, best seen by the traveller who leaves the main roads to wander along its minor roads and lanes and hardly seen at all by travellers along the M6 motorway.

CHAPTER 8

The Mersey–Irwell Belt

As one enters this belt from the south, a new landscape appears. What has been described as 'the essential Cheshire' in Chapter 7 gives place to the industrial Northwest focused in the west on Liverpool and in the east on Manchester, with Warrington, a historic river-crossing place, approximately half-way between them. The Cheshire scene is agricultural, punctuated here and there by industrial areas such as Northwich and its suburbs, Crewe and Nantwich with the sprawling suburbia between them, Macclesfield and Bollington, and even the age-old Chester with its industrial outgrowths on the reclaimed Dee marshes in the Welsh borderland. If one approaches the Manchester conurbation along the Chester road, the last farms are seen in the Bollin valley with their splendid large fields of crops and their rich green pastures, and a suburban landscape appears on the southern edge of a low ridge, 200 feet high at Bowdon. From this point northwards there is continuous town for 20 miles, interrupted only by the flood plain of the Mersey and by the limited areas north of Manchester that have not so far been used for building.

Rivers, canals, and roads

Industrial growth in this Mersey–Irwell belt has long been associated with rivers and later with canals, and its modern development owes much to the construction of the Manchester Ship Canal. A main artery of commerce which carries an ocean highway to Manchester over 30 miles inland, this canal has become the county boundary between Lancashire and Cheshire over most of its course. It is crossed by few bridges, though more are being built and others reconstructed to carry the heavy traffic of modern times. Before the canal existed, the main lines of water communication were the Mersey and the Irwell, made into a river navigation in the early eighteenth century, and the Bridgewater Canal (Fig. 51). The Mersey is formed by the junction at Stockport of two streams, the Goyt and the Tame, both of which rise in the Pennines; at Stockport the Mersey flows through a rock gorge, filled up with a line of ancient mills and crossed by a massive railway viaduct that dominates the lower part of this hilly town, unfortunately so ugly though possessing so fine a site. West of Stockport

Fig. 51 THE MERSEY–IRWELL NAVIGATION AND THE BRIDGEWATER CANAL. This map, from the 1:10,560 Survey of 1848, shows one of the 'cuts' made to ease navigation on the Irwell and, in the top right-hand corner, the course of the Bridgewater Canal with the position of its famous aqueduct at Barton.

the Mersey valley broadens out into a wide belt of alluvium with gravel terraces used for sports grounds, pastures, and arable farming. The Irwell rises in the Rossendale upland, and receives numerous tributaries on its way to join the Mersey, notably the Roch, the Irk, and the Medlock. The initial advantages of the site of Manchester included the existence of an easy crossing-place of the Irwell to Salford on its west side, the opportunity of industrial use of these rivers for water power and the processing of textiles, and—perhaps most important of all—a central location in an extensive lowland that through its possession of water and coal became a pioneer manufacturing area of the Industrial Revolution. The many roads that meet at Manchester do not, as often said, follow the river valleys, but rather the interfluves between them.

Though of considerable significance in the whole growth of Manchester, the Irwell's inky waters, having flowed through the city in a somewhat furtive manner, are now merged into the Ship Canal for more than a dozen miles. Careful observation on the ground shows relics of its former course where these are not in the line of the canal itself, but even the former Mersey junction is hard to discern now, for this river joins the canal on the east bank, opposite Irlam, and its channel is controlled by a weir. The propensity to flooding of the Mersey has necessitated careful control, and even yet there are floods in some years in the section of its course through the Manchester suburbs. Like the Irwell, the Mersey loses its identity in the Ship Canal for several miles, though it reappears in the lowland north of Lymm, and flows through Warrington, having in this section some interesting 'cuts' that are relics of earlier improvements in the river. These channels and the main river combine to give Warrington a network of waterways. It is ironic that here the Ship Canal forms not only the modern boundary between Lancashire and Cheshire but also divides Warrington from its main southern suburbs, Stockton Heath and Grappenhall; as noted on page 159, there has been a considerable suburban overflow from Lancashire into Cheshire, particularly in the last sixty years and most of all since 1919. Between Salford docks and Warrington the canal runs mainly through a lowland with wide views, though there are some cuttings in Triassic red sandstones that are impressive when seen either from bridges or from a boat, particularly at Warrington. Some of these sandstone cuttings, however, weathered badly and had to be filled up with bricks in the soft places, as for example at Trafford Park. Between Cadishead and Warrington (Fig. 24), the scene is agricultural on both sides, though Lymm, on a site elevated above the flood plain, is suburban both to Warrington and to Manchester. A plan to build a new town here was defeated after a public inquiry, partly because much fine agricultural land would be lost, and partly through the fear of making a continuous urban belt from Warrington to Manchester.

To the west of Warrington the canal runs through the widening Mersey floodplain to Runcorn. In this section the Mersey becomes tidal, increasingly broad and winding, and uncrossed for over 6 miles from the bridge at Warrington to the new road bridge between Runcorn and Widnes. This fine erection replaces the Transporter bridge, whose passing few will regret, though it was an interesting experience to cross the Mersey and the canal on a piece of roadway (packed with vehicles and people) suspended by cables from the superstructure, and propelled by some motive force of a jerky and creaking character; stories of breakdowns half-way across are numerous. Pedestrians could walk by the footway beside the railway viaduct (opened in 1869) which carries the London to Liverpool line. In 1964, an area of 11 square miles based on Runcorn was designated as the site of a New Town, to house 70,000 people drawn from Liverpool and district; the population is expected to rise to 90,000 by natural increase (Plate 28). From Runcorn, the Ship Canal runs immediately beside or very close to the Cheshire shore of the Mersey. The west side of Runcorn, known as Weston Point, has the Weaver Canal close to the Ship Canal, and a lock connection upwards to the Bridgewater Canal, which is joined at Preston Brook to the Trent and Mersey Canal. This has proved to be a favoured industrial site, and among the various works is the Salt Union's plant, located here in 1911 because it is an area free of subsidence! Salt is pumped as brine from the Northwich area (p. 176) for processing. The lower Weaver, once tidal to Frodsham Bridge, is now brought into the Ship Canal, which has sluices into the Mersey to regulate its level. For 5 miles onwards to Stanlow, the canal crosses the desolate Frodsham, Helsby, and Ince marshes and the main scenic attraction is the view of the northern edge of Cheshire's central sandstone ridge which extends far south into the county through Delamere Forest to Beeston, Peckforton, and beyond.

At Stanlow, on the Gowy marshes, a large oil port with refineries has been built since the site was drained by the work of prisoners in the First World War. In 1922 large docks were made at Stanlow, in a small hill of sandstone, so that ships of 16,000 tons could be brought to the refinery, and a new dock has now been made at the entrance to the canal, from which oil can be pumped direct to the refinery, but the great increase in the size of tankers has necessitated the construction of a deep-water terminal at Tranmere. Combined with other industries of Ellesmere Port (Plate 31), the Stanlow refinery has helped to make an industrial area of great significance on the outer edge of the Merseyside conurbation, separated by a few miles of residential suburb, interpenetrated by a Green Belt, from the no less interesting area of Port Sunlight. The latter, however, owes its origin to a choice of site by Mr Lever in 1888 rather than to the existence of the canal, which joins the Mersey estuary at Eastham locks. Eastham itself is a pleasant old village with a red sandstone church and a few suburban roads running off here and there in characteristic if regrettable Wirral fashion; in such a place the nearness of a vast industrial concentration may easily be forgotten.

Without the great entry of the Mersey, no ship canal would have been built. Its inception at a meeting in a private house in a Manchester suburb was due to the wish to bring cotton more cheaply into Manchester and so remove the stranglehold of the Liverpool merchants. Optimists also envisaged the creation of a vast industrial belt on the southern margins of Lancashire, and particularly the continued and increasing prosperity of Manchester. Cartoons of the time pictured a day when Liverpool would have fallen into complete decay as all its trade passed eastward to the new ocean port. In fact, cotton has never been a main import to Manchester by canal, and so far there is not a continuous industrial belt, though there have been some striking industrial advances, notably in Trafford Park, Manchester, which fronts the last 3 miles of the canal on the south side. From the 1890s to the beginning of the cotton slump in the 1920s Mersey-side and the Manchester conurbation—and indeed the whole of industrial Lancashire—remained pulsatingly prosperous, so that when Patrick Geddes wrote *Cities in Evolution* shortly before the First World War he foresaw, perhaps by intuition rather than exact analysis, the growth of a 'city region' extending from Merseyside to the Pennines east of Manchester. From the 1890s there was a relatively greater increase of population on Merseyside than in the Manchester conurbation (p. 153), for the areas most dependent on textiles began to show signs of stability, and even of slight decline, before the First World War.

In the propaganda advocating the Ship Canal, stress was laid on the centrality of Manchester as a distributing centre to a natural hinterland of vast population and resources, virtually equal to that of London. This exaggerated claim has been constantly reiterated in textbooks, though at present there is a far greater population within a radius of 50 miles from London than the 11,000,000 people resident within 50 miles from Manchester Town Hall. The original canal circular said:

> A radius of forty miles from Manchester includes a greater population than any similar area in the United Kingdom, the population of north-east and south-east Lancashire, mid- and east Cheshire, North Staffordshire and the West Riding of Yorkshire being in round numbers 5½ million—Manchester, therefore, as a convenient food-distributing centre has no equal in the country.

At that time several comparable canals, such as that from Amsterdam to the North Sea, existed. In Britain the Clyde had been transformed by engineering works into what was virtually a ship canal from the 1840s, and the Tyne had been greatly improved by its Commissioners during the 1860s, partly to offset the competition of Hull and other east-coast ports. In 1861–81, it was noted, the trade of Liverpool had been increased by only 59%, compared with 85% on the Tyne and 103% on the Clyde. According to Bosdin Leech, the minor advance of Liverpool was due partly to the curious administration of its port; but after the canal was built the charges were lowered and a phase of expansion began. The initial Ship Canal circular inspired emulation of what others had done in its statement that 'by connecting the Mersey–Irwell into a Lancashire Clyde, Manchester has it in her power to secure advantages as great, nay, even greater than Glasgow'.

Liverpool now depends on the maintenance of a dredged approach for access at all states of the tide, though the narrowness of the estuary for 4 miles upstream from New Brighton is a natural asset. Everywhere less than a mile wide, the outer estuary narrows to a channel only 1,000 yards wide at the landing stage, and then broadens out to 3 miles at Ellesmere Port before narrowing at Runcorn; this inner part of the estuary accumulates a large quantity of water during the flow of the tides, which on the ebb scours the narrow channel opposite Liverpool. Before any docks were built, ships had to moor in creeks such as those at Wallasey, Tranmere, and Bromborough or in the Pool beside the medieval nucleus of Liverpool. The town became a borough in 1207, and its port was used especially for the transport of men and supplies to Ireland, although Chester was a strong rival until the fifteenth century, when the silting of the Dee initiated its decline as a port. But the real rise of Liverpool came in the eighteenth century when the first dock was opened in 1715; through this, wrote R. Hodges, the Mersey was 'transformed overnight from a dangerous harbour where vessels lay at the mercy of fast-running tides into a port where they could berth in comparative safety when loading and unloading their cargo'. Apart from the main docks of Liverpool and those of the Wallasey Pool on the other side of the estuary, there are other docks at Bromborough, associated with the Port Sunlight works and at Garston on the north side. Originally pioneered by the St Helens and Runcorn railway company, this port became the nucleus of an industrial town now merged into Liverpool by boundary extension.

In all, more than 4,000,000 people live in this Mersey–Irwell belt, if it is taken to include the Merseyside conurbation, the twin towns of Widnes and Runcorn on either side of the river, Warrington and its suburbs, and the Manchester conurbation. Though perhaps marginally placed, St Helens has been termed a 'Merseyside' town by its most recent historian. Obviously it is not on the Mersey, yet its industrial growth was due to the building of the Sankey Canal from the Mersey (p. 64), which stimulated the growth of glass manufacture and carried raw materials for the new chemical industry based on salt from Cheshire with local supplies of coal. Of this industry all that now remains is a landscape of dereliction, hideously ugly, with masses of chemical waste, still very little quarried for any purpose. A possible northern boundary of the Mersey–Irwell belt is the edge of the coalfield, approximately on the line of the East Lancashire road. On the Cheshire side no unequivocal line can be drawn, though the whole of the two conurbations are included, together with Runcorn and the

Cheshire suburbs of Warrington, including Lymm which is only in part suburban to Warrington. As will be shown (pp. 189–91), the spread into Cheshire is recent and, one may add, still continuing though subject to planning control; fear is expressed of the unending suburbanisation of such places as Helsby and Frodsham, and of various villages in the vicinity of Chester. Equally, there are fears that a growing Chester may eventually meet a growing Ellesmere Port. If, however, one regards this belt of north Cheshire and south Lancashire not only in terms of its vast industrial potential, but in terms of its land use on the ground, an entirely different picture emerges, for the rich arable farming of north Cheshire merges into an agricultural landscape at least as rich, and in places even more intensively cultivated, in south Lancashire. The intensive character of the agriculture is due largely to the certainty of the demand for the farmer's produce in the large town markets, as well as to fertility of soil, both inherent and induced. Nowhere is this better seen than from the Ship Canal, which runs largely through farmlands. In places there are sharp contrasts, notably at Irlam, where there is a vast steelworks with its own quay for ore on the north side of the canal, and farms (now threatened) on the south side. A recent growth here has been the vast expansion of the Petrochemicals plant, with new gas and electricity works, west of Trafford Park (Plate 18).

Rivers and canals gave an initial stimulus to the growth of trade in the Mersey–Irwell belt from the eighteenth century (p. 80), and the railway promoters of the nineteenth century connected Liverpool and Manchester by 1830 (p. 85). These two cities became the nuclei of large conurbations through the building of railways and the use of the roads for horse buses and—far more significant—motor buses after the First World War. In the Merseyside conurbation the spread to the Cheshire side of the river began when ferry services were established from 1816, and though the ferries now carry fewer passengers than in former years they still make a substantial contribution to the transport of workers to Liverpool. The Mersey railway, electrified in 1903, and the road tunnel opened in 1934 carry a heavy traffic beneath the river. To a great extent the economic strength of the Mersey–Irwell belt has been developed and maintained by communications though these were provided not as a social service but in the expectation of profit. Until the 1930s there were complaints that most of the roads were little more than a network of country lanes, widened and straightened in places, but not everywhere, through the years. In the 1930s some new roads were built which presaged the motorways of the 1960s; these included the East Lancashire road which runs from the northern and newer dock area of Liverpool to a junction with the A6, the main London and Carlisle road, on the northeast side of central Manchester. Since 1963 connections have been made with the M6, the Birmingham–Preston motorway. The East Lancashire road, now being transformed into a four-lane highway, was designed for speed, with cuttings, embankments, and bridges across by-roads: like modern motorways, it avoids towns, for it runs south of Tyldesley and Leigh, and well north of both Warrington and St Helens. It has, however, proved to be a magnet for new industries on the northeast side of Liverpool, where the recent spectacular development of Kirkby is based partly on industries served by road transport: some of the coalmines close to this road use it for lorry transport. A road development of more local interest was seen in the building of the Queen's Drive (1934) at Liverpool as a ring road around the suburbs of the inter-war period, and the construction of the parkway in Manchester to give quick access to the Wythenshawe area. The Queen's Drive gives a useful arterial route through the suburbs of Liverpool, which have spread far beyond it on the plain of southwest Lancashire. Manchester's parkway has American affinities and provides a way through the outer parts of the city with green lawns, trees, shrubberies, and flower beds which are both attractive in themselves and separate the road from the nearest houses and their gardens.

Unfortunately such roads are all too rare in Lancastria. One of the most historic roads of Britain, the A6 from London to Carlisle, crosses the Manchester conurbation diagonally from southeast to northwest, passing through industrial quarters of Stockport, through Piccadilly and Market Street in the city centre of Manchester, and across the Irwell to Salford, which it traverses from its grimy beginning to its suburban end. The A6 has, since 1963, been superseded by the M6 as the main trunk route. But the A6 is of Roman lineage even though probably not now on the exact line of its original ancestor, and from it ran a 'Watling Street' that, beginning at Mamucium, went on to Deva, or in modern terms, Chester. The present Chester road, with much the same course, has become a fine highway, but in stretches beside it there are little-known relics of the Roman road. As a whole the road system had no grand strategy such as the Romans devised, but grew rather as a piecemeal development from pack-horse trails, country lanes, and turnpikes designed to link one town or village with another. Most of the modern road plans for the Mersey–Irwell belt hark back to the same idea that the Romans possessed—a provision for speedy and unimpeded transport between major centres; and the same idea is apparent in the by-passes such as the fine one around Northwich which departs from the line of the Roman road between Manchester and Chester, but even more in the motorways of which the first here was the 8-mile stretch from Sale to Worsley with a fine bridge across the Ship Canal, west of Trafford Park (M62). The Birmingham–Preston motorway crosses the Mersey to the east of Warrington and is likely to stimulate industrial growth in its vicinity (Plates 29, 30).

The distribution of population

For the places having definite urban boundaries in the Mersey–Irwell belt, the population in 1961 was almost 4,150,000, approximately 50,000 more than in 1951. In the two major conurbations, Merseyside and Manchester, the change of population has been slight, but in the former the new artisan district of Kirkby is not included: constituted an urban district only in 1958, it had 3,100 people in 1951 but 52,200 in 1961. Both in 1951 and 1961 the Merseyside conurbation had about 1,386,000 people; but within these ten years the population on the Lancashire side declined by about 26,000, from 1,004,000 to 978,000 while on the Cheshire side numbers increased from 382,000 to 408,000. Between 1951 and 1961 the main movement on both sides of the estuary has been a suburban spread revealed partly by the increase in the number of dwellings by 14% to house much the same population. Only a short distance separates the outer edge of the Merseyside conurbation from Widnes (52,000) and its twin town Runcorn (26,000) on the Cheshire side of the river and the Ship Canal. Similarly, the urban district of Huyton-with-Roby, which within thirty years has increased in population from 5,200 to its present 63,000, virtually joins the old industrial centre of Prescot (13,100), which in turn joins St Helens (108,000), widely famed for its glass industry. Warrington (75,500) is so narrowly defined as a town that it appears to be comparatively small in population and to show a decline from 1951 to 1961, but in fact some 50,000 people live beyond its boundaries in contiguous suburban areas on either side of the Ship Canal.[1] Though excellent agricultural lands lie between Warrington and the Merseyside conurbation, there are increasingly clear signs of both industrial and suburban growth on the Lancashire side, and in Cheshire at old villages such as Frodsham and Helsby. When one reaches the Manchester conurbation, however, entry is made into one of the great urban areas of Britain, and indeed of the world. Within the 379 square miles shared by its 52 separate local government units, live 2,427,000 people; not all this area is built up at present, and some of it—but only a small proportion—consists of Pennine and Rossendale moorlands which are technically 'urban', as they lie within old parishes that were the bases of modern administrative units. Here, as in the Merseyside conurbation, the movement to suburbs has been strong for more than a century, and during the period from 1951 to 1961 the population in the Cheshire part of the conurbation increased from 421,000 to 467,000 while that in the Lancashire part declined from 2,002,000 to 1,960,000. And in this conurbation, as in Merseyside, population densities are decreasing in the central areas of towns as they are rebuilt with blocks of flats in place of congested slums. A serious, indeed challenging, problem of both Manchester and Liverpool is posed by the heritage of poor, and in thousands of cases definitely bad, houses that are relics of the early advance of these two cities to industrial greatness in the nineteenth century.

Though the increase of population in the Mersey–Irwell belt was small

---

[1] In 1965, the Local Government Commission suggested a boundary revision that would give Warrington a population of 125,000. The Cheshire suburbs would be included.

from 1951 to 1961, the number of separate dwellings has increased by 14% in the Merseyside conurbation and by 11% in the Manchester conurbation. In the larger towns between them, Warrington had 11% and St Helens 15% more dwellings, though in both cases there was a decline in population. This increase is partly due to the progress made in housing during the 1950s and to the economic prosperity which enabled people to acquire a house or flat rather than to share accommodation. The average number of persons now occupying 10 dwellings is 31, though there are differences from one area to another: in the 1961 Census both Manchester and Liverpool were recorded as having exactly 210,690 dwellings, yet they were occupied by 661,041 persons in Manchester (average 3·1) and by 747,490 (average 3·6) in Liverpool. Hardly any urban district shows a decline in the number of dwellings, though in Salford there was a decrease from 50,745 in 1951 to 50,039 in 1961 (−1·4%) with a decline in population from 178,000 to 155,000 (−13%). This case is particularly interesting because part of the city policy in Salford has been to limit its formidable loss of population by building flats of several storeys to replace its outworn houses: inevitably through lack of building land within the bounds of the city some of its inhabitants have been moved to a new estate at Worsley, where the urban district council has built houses for them. As the density of population falls in central town areas, through the replacement of congested slums and the decline in the size of the household, so the need for more land must arise, and already Manchester is building houses in the land of other authorities, notably Middleton, and more recently Heywood, both on the north side (p. 285). There are also various other overspill sites in Cheshire, including those at Hazel Grove and Bramhall, Hyde and Wilmslow within the conurbation, and outside it at Knutsford, Macclesfield, and Winsford. But the largest scheme is to settle 14,000 families at Westhoughton, on the northwest margins of the conurbation.[1] Though between 1951 and 1961 the conurbation's population was virtually stable, the present problem is one of redistribution to provide better living accommodation and more space for industries, roads, and various social essentials such as schools, other public buildings, and open spaces.

Merseyside with the Wirral peninsula

An officially recognised conurbation, Merseyside is dominated by Liverpool, though much of the recent industrial and residential growth has taken place at Kirkby on the north outside the conurbation, and at Ellesmere Port in the Wirral, which became a borough in 1955, and by 1961, with nearly 45,000 people (an increase of 37% since 1951), was within sight of its expected eventual population of 60,000. In many ways Liverpool

---

[1] This contentious project has been discussed for several years: at one time a virtual new town of 50,000 people was proposed, but it now seems likely that a more modest scheme will be implemented.

presents a fruitful subject for a study of the cycle of town growth—if there is such a cycle—for at one and the same time it shows both change and stability. Always associated with the sea, it has its great warehouses and numerous factories beside its 7 miles of dock frontage, gradually built and extended from 1753 to 1927. The original town centre near the river with its old parish church has long since been obliterated by the spread of the commercial offices, many of them associated with shipping, which are as characteristic a feature of Liverpool as the great textile warehouses are of Manchester. There is still a clear trace of the residential city of the eighteenth century, particularly on the sandstone ridge now dominated by the Anglican cathedral where several streets and squares survive, though the houses are no longer occupied by the social classes for whom they were originally built but in many cases are transformed into offices or institutions, including departments of the university. Unfortunately some of the former homes of the merchant and professional classes have become squalid tenements beyond any reasonable hope of repair. As the dock system developed, Liverpool acquired its characteristic elongated shape with no great breadth from the waterfront, for its workers were employed mainly in the docks and the associated warehouse and industrial belt. On both sides of this commercial core many square miles of nineteenth century artisan houses spread north along the Scotland Road to Bootle and south through Edge Hill and Everton towards Toxteth. It is here that the main problem of rehousing lies. Although various housing estates such as Speke have been built it is recognised that many thousands of people wish to be near the dockside belt and therefore flats of several storeys are being built. To quote a Liverpool M.P., Mrs Bessie Braddock: 'I say to my constituents—if you won't go up, you must go out' (Fig. 26, Plates 35, 36).

Inevitable and compelling as the association with the dockside must remain, industry has spread along the line of the Leeds–Liverpool Canal, completed in 1816, and to other areas such as Edge Hill and Old Swan, and Fazakerley and Aintree, all of which have excellent railway communications. In the docks area many of the factories deal with imported commodities such as sugar, oil and oil-seeds, and newsprint; the suburban industries, more varied, include foods such as biscuits, sweets and jam, metals, rubber, rayon, soaps, and polishes. The grain-milling industry has now been transferred to the Cheshire side of the river, where the first docks were opened in 1847 and the others were added by 1870 except for Bidston, on the extreme inner side of the Pool, which was finished in 1933. Garston docks, originally developed as a railway enterprise, include one constructed by the St Helens and Runcorn Gap railway in 1830, with others added in 1869 and 1909. Here a number of industries have developed, including saw-milling, engineering, tanning, timber goods, and bottle making; in addition Garston is the main coal port of the Northwest, and has many other imports, including pit props, ores, and tropical fruit.

On the Cheshire side, the earliest industrial developments were at Birkenhead, where the initial growth came through shipbuilding and general port industries similar to those on the other side of the river. The Laird shipbuilding yard was founded in 1824 and gradually extended to its present size on the river between Tranmere and Woodside. By 1841 Birkenhead had over 8,000 inhabitants, including both labourers for the growing industries and people of ampler means who were developing the suburbs on higher ground, at first in Oxton and later on the various other sandstone ridges of the Wirral peninsula. Suburbs also grew close to the sea in Hoylake and West Kirby and along the Dee estuary, for example at Neston and Heswall, which have views of the mountains in North Wales. Much the same suburban tendencies were seen in Liverpool, whose suburbs were established on ridges such as Mossley Hill, Sefton Park, and Woolton, all of which had a number of large houses built by Liverpool merchants; similarly there was a movement towards the dune-backed coast at Waterloo, Crosby, and Formby, as well as to Southport. The main population growth in the Wirral peninsula dates from the second half of the nineteenth century, from 57,000 in 1851 to 209,000 by 1901, and then to 408,000 by 1961. It was at first associated with the ferries, combined with the railway from Birkenhead to Chester from 1840, but the main growth came from the 1880s, when a line was built from a station near Seacombe ferry in 1884 and connected to Birkenhead in 1886; a line to New Brighton was added in 1884. But the most significant advances were the opening of the Mersey tunnel in 1885 and the electrification of the system in 1903. Nevertheless, until the end of the First World War much of the Wirral remained virtually immune from suburban growth, as under the transport conditions of the time it was inaccessible. Here as elsewhere it was the motor bus and the private car that threatened the whole of the peninsula and induced Rideout to comment in 1927: 'It cannot be long before the extensions from Liverpool and its satellites in the north, Ellesmere Port in the east, and Chester on the south, spread over what remain the most delightful rural townships in all Wirral.' From 1951 to 1961 the most marked population increases were in the areas of Wirral farthest from Liverpool. The urban district of Neston increased from 9,700 to 11,900 (over 20%) and the Wirral urban district, which includes the old centre of Heswall and three villages that have grown recently, Barnston, Pensby, and Irby, from 17,400 to 21,900 (over 30%): the number of dwellings increased in Neston urban district by 39% and in Wirral urban district by 45%. But there are now defined Green Belts, and the recent addition of houses and population hardly raises a serious problem of amenity destruction.

A development of great interest has been the growth of industry at Ellesmere Port, on the fringe of the conurbation—in fact so much on the fringe that many of the residents regard their town as definitely separate from it; the argument is supported by the existence of a narrow Green Belt between the town and Bebington. The first signs of settlement here date back to the canal period in 1795. By the 1840s iron ore was brought from Whitehaven and Ulverston to Ellesmere Port for transhipment to the Midlands, and Welsh slates, grain, and Cornish china-clay for the Potteries were also handled. The construction of the Ship Canal added further industrial strength to the neighbourhood, and the drainage of the Gowy marshes by prisoners during the later stages of the First World War gave a site for the vast Stanlow oil refinery, which now employs several thousand workers; a new dock has been constructed at the Ship Canal entrance from which oil is sent direct from the tankers to the refinery. There is also a wide range of prosperous industries, including flour milling, steel products, electrical trades, and newsprint: the 1951 Census of work places showed that Ellesmere Port received 8,079 workers from other areas, and that 2,759 travelled daily to other areas; its occupied population was 14,955. Some of the recent growth of population is due to planned immigration from Liverpool, and eventually some 5,500 families are to be settled.

Port Sunlight, within the borough of Bebington, is a fine example of an earlier industrial settlement of the same vintage as the Cadbury estates in Bourneville and that of the Rowntrees at York. It originated in 1887 when Mr Lever came from Warrington in search of cheap land, and gradually expanded into the present vast plant with many thousands of workers; from soap, its products have extended over a wide range of commodities. The village of Port Sunlight was begun in 1888 and was widely studied as an example of a planned industrial estate. Two attractions of the site were the nearness of the Bromborough Pool, which from 1852 had a candle factory, and the existence of a tidal creek to the works. Some of the raw materials are still brought to the private docks at Bromborough and the works are provided with railway sidings connected both with the docks and the main line through the peninsula.

For many years both before and after the Second World War, an unemployment rate above the national average caused concern in the Merseyside area. Constituted a development area, it achieved considerable success: the Speke and Kirkby industrial estates attracted many firms in the engineering, metal and rubber industries, and the building of the two great motor plants at Halewood and Hooton brought a further expansion of employment (Plate 22). Though reconstituted a Development District in 1960, Merseyside now seems capable of growth without artificial assistance; by 1970 it will have the largest concentration of the British vehicle industry outside the Midlands and the London area. This is due to the Board of Trade's policy of guiding industry to an area of relatively high unemployment, though Merseyside has locational advantages for the industry in its port and the nearness of the great strip-steel plant at Shotton on the Dee estuary. But as the new industries are located on the fringes of the conurbation, at Speke and Huyton in Lancashire and at Hooton in Cheshire, some land must be taken from agricultural use for the plants and for houses.

Merseyside's abiding problem, made the more acute by a high rate of natural increase, is the housing of the population, for it is estimated that almost two-fifths of Liverpool's houses are far below modern standards. To a great extent this is due, as in the Manchester conurbation (pp. 197–205), to the rapid growth in the first three-quarters of the nineteenth century, but it is due also to the decay of the large houses once occupied by the middle classes but turned into tenements. As noted on page 192, in Liverpool many thousands of workers wish to be near the docks and the allied industrial belts, and so blocks of flats are being built in central areas. There are also large housing-estate areas in the suburbs, and the outer towns of Huyton-with-Roby (63,000) and Kirkby (52,200). These towns have a total area of 12 square miles, of which the greater part is already allocated for housing, institutions, industries, or open spaces. Liverpool has by far the most severe housing problem within the conurbation, yet Bootle has also several thousand houses in need of replacement, and on the Cheshire side the older-settled areas—Birkenhead and the more industrial and artisan parts of Wallasey—face comparable problems. If it be agreed that a Green Belt should be preserved in the Wirral to prevent its indefinite submergence under houses, and also that some of the richly farmed agricultural hinterland of Liverpool and its neighbours should be retained, then the only possible solution—of necessity not a complete solution—is a New Town; and in 1961 legislation was passed to establish one at Skelmersdale, west of Wigan, on the outskirts of the central Lancashire coalfield. The issue is really quite simple: a Green Belt can be defined and one of Britain's richest agricultural areas retained, only if at least one New Town is provided. So far no such town has been built in the Northwest, for places like Kirkby and Huyton, though administratively independent of Liverpool, are in effect extensions of it—in short, they could be regarded as satellite towns rather than New Towns.

The middle belt

If one travels from Manchester to Liverpool by Wigan it is easy to see the continuous spread of housing and industry that is characteristic of central Lancashire, but if one travels through Warrington, the rural enclaves are more apparent. And in spite of the attraction of industries to sites near the East Lancashire road, and recently of the new mines of the coalfield's southern extremity, the journey reveals the existence of the rich agricultural area of south Lancashire. Its greater richness, however, is seen to the south of the East Lancashire road in areas nearer the Mersey and Irwell, particularly in the mosslands to the east of Liverpool. The Ship Canal runs mainly through the drained marshlands of the floodplain, which is still largely pasture; on the Cheshire side the edge of the floodplain is marked by rising ground and in places by a red sandstone bluff. The arable belt of north Cheshire has large fields with fine crops, farms, and villages of brick and sandstone with churches of red sandstone, built of the local Triassic rock.

Fortunately urban growth is not yet continuous between Liverpool and Manchester, so that the prognostications of Patrick Geddes nearly fifty years ago that in Lancashire there was growing 'another greater London as it were' have not come true. Yet signs of such development are not lacking. Should one travel from Liverpool and Huyton to Prescot and St Helens, little of the rural scene appears on the road, and nearer the river there is now hardly more than two miles of open country between the most easterly extension of Liverpool's Speke estate and the outer suburbs of Widnes. Similarly the modern industrial expansion of Stanlow, on the outskirts of Ellesmere Port, is separated by only a couple of miles of farmed countryside from Helsby, which, though within a rural district, is in fact largely suburban in character; and Frodsham, on the west side of the Weaver, a compact suburbanised village, is rural only in name. These places are attractively situated at the northern end of the sandstone ridge of Cheshire (p. 16); many of the old villages now have a new suburban element in their population. At Widnes the river narrows, and gives the first reasonably easy crossing, used by both road and railway. Long known as the Runcorn Gap, this crossing became a centre of the chemical industry, which still survives here though it has disappeared from St Helens (p. 141); here too the timber trade has been successful. Together these towns had a population of 78,200 in 1961 compared with 72,700 in 1951. Beyond Runcorn, the Cheshire side of the river is almost entirely agricultural for half a dozen miles to Stockton Heath, Warrington's main Cheshire suburb (Fig. 52).

Warrington, formerly a site of strategic importance, apparently declined in population by 6% (to 75,000) from 1951 to 1961, but in fact the loss was due mainly to the removal of people to outer suburbs beyond the town boundaries. The continued prosperity of Warrington is due to its wide range of successful industries. Long associated with the chemical industry, it has now a smaller proportion of its population employed in them compared with some 40% in Runcorn and Widnes, for its industries include metal trades, leather, brewing, saw-milling, paper, and clothing. The suburban extensions from Warrington on the north side of the Ship Canal include Great Sankey and Penketh on the west side, Winwick on the north, Poulton and Croft on the east; and in Cheshire, Stockton Heath, which is linked to the east with Grappenhall, Thelwall, Statham, and Lymm in an amorphous urban growth extended for over 5 miles. Lymm in 1961 was an urban district of 6½ square miles with a population of 7,300 (over 14% increase since 1951). East of Lymm an agricultural area extends to the fringe of the Manchester conurbation at Bowdon, fusing naturally into the richly farmed lands of north Cheshire described on page 163.

The Manchester conurbation

That Manchester is the heart of this conurbation is undoubted, for it stands out as one of the major regional capitals of Britain now as for more than two centuries, even though its population (661,000 in 1961) has steadily

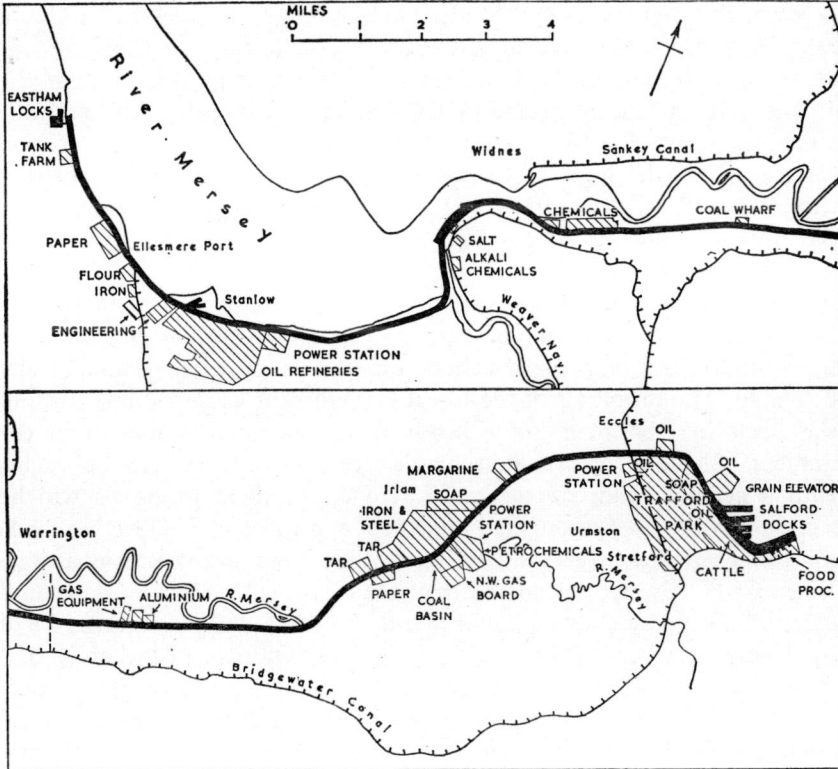

Fig. 52   THE MANCHESTER SHIP CANAL. Reproduced from North, G., 'Lancastria', in Mitchell, J. B. (ed.), *Great Britain: Geographical Essays* (Cambridge 1962), 404.

fallen from the peak figure of 736,000 in 1921. This decline has been due to the fall in the average size of household within the past forty years (the 210,690 dwellings of 1961, a 5% increase over 1951, housed 6% fewer people), and also to the outward movement of population to new suburban areas beyond its bounds. Nevertheless, the conurbation as a whole has for thirty years shown virtual stability of population (p. 153); but its appearance has been greatly changed by redistribution. At each succeeding census some of its 52 administrative districts have shown a marked increase of population: from 1951 to 1961, for example, Middleton in Lancashire increased its numbers by 74%, from 32,600 to 56,700, largely owing to the addition of the Langley estate by the city of Manchester. In this case, the building of more than 7,000 new dwellings is obviously a significant land-scape change. In Cheshire the main extensions were in the urban districts of Hazel Grove and Bramhall, Cheadle, and Gatley. The former increased in population by 55%, from 17,700 to 30,000, and the latter by 45%, from 31,500 to 45,600; the number of dwellings increased by 61% in Hazel Grove and Bramhall, by 53% in Cheadle and Gatley. Yet the conurbation is reasonably well defined; it has no modern outgrowth such as Kirkby in relation to Merseyside (p. 195), and its Green Belt on the Cheshire side seems likely to be preserved, at least for a time, though it is not, like the London Green Belt, protected by legislation, only by control through the Cheshire County Planning Office. Even so, the recent acceleration of train services along the lines to Crewe, now electrified, may induce further suburban settlement in rural Cheshire—indeed, some of the comments by the railway authorities suggest that they expect and hope for such growth near their stations.

Basically the conurbation is nothing more than an area of continuous building on the ground, for it has no common voice, no over-riding adminis-trative unity, nor indeed any cohesion except as an entity geographically definable. The proposals of the Local Government Commission, given to the Press in December 1965, involved a substantial reduction in the number of administrative units by the creation of large new boroughs, with a general conurbation council. No doubt these proposals will be strenuously opposed, though all the recent expansion of housing has made the conurbation a firmer unit on the ground than at any previous time. When C. B. Fawcett considered this area in 1932, he spoke of its central core, in effect Manchester, Salford, and Stretford, and its outer girdle of significant towns, Bolton, Bury, Rochdale, Oldham, Stockport, and Altrincham, all of which are some 7 to 10 miles from Manchester Town Hall. The conurbation has grown both by the development of its central nucleus and through the expansion of its numerous other town and industrial villages; but it became a clear unit of interlocking towns only during the 1930s through the building of housing estates served by motor buses. Nevertheless the signs of such an interlocking were clear several decades earlier, for as long ago as the late 1840s there was virtually con-tinuous building along the main road from Manchester to Oldham, and in time an uninterrupted spread of industries along the canal parallel to the road. Similarly, the 6 inch to 1 mile map of 1848 shows that there were ribbons of settlement along the roads between Ashton, Hyde, and Dukinfield. 'Ribbon development' provided the first expression of the conurbation, not only in the areas mentioned, but along many other roads such as those of suburban Manchester, where houses were placed beside the main roads to villages which, like Didsbury, eventually became the shopping and social centres of suburbs. But beyond the ribbons of settlement along the main roads there was generally open country, and it was to this land that the house builders of a later time turned for space.

Historically this conurbation grew round a number of towns possessing a marked individuality and in most cases a long industrial tradition, such as Bolton, Bury, Rochdale, Stockport, and Altrincham, though other towns within the conurbation such as Oldham, Stalybridge, and Hyde were creations of the Industrial Revolution (see also pp. 116–17). Some of the conurbation's present problems have their roots in the early growth of industry and the survival of 'dark satanic mills' and associated poor houses long after they had become obsolete. This is not always obvious from the main roads, as on them many sites have been used for new premises: the survival of old mills and houses is far more apparent in the backwater areas of the towns, particularly in the vicinity of the rivers and canals. By 1801 the area now forming this conurbation already had 322,000 inhabitants, of whom 84,000 were in Manchester and Salford, and within the next fifty years the numbers trebled to 1,063,000, then doubled again to 2,149,000 in 1901. But in the 1901–11 census decade the increase was only 9%, to 2,350,000, and since the First World War the population, 2,427,000 at the 1961 Census, has remained virtually stable. Until the 1920s it was assumed that economic growth would be continuous in the future as—with a few setbacks such as the cotton famine during the American Civil War—it had been for a century and a half; but the catastrophic and continuing decline of the cotton industry has removed any such illusions. In 1959 legislation aimed at a rationalisation of this once staple industry by scrapping almost half the spindles and two-fifths of the looms, many of which were idle when the Act was passed. Of 80 spinning mills closed, half were in Oldham and Bolton, which, like many other places in Lancashire, still possess the appearance of cotton towns, but have a wide variety of industries within the old mills. In general, the cotton texile industry has now less than one-third of the workers which it had in 1921. Manchester still remains an internationally known centre of the cotton trade; but it has virtually ceased to be a cotton-manufacturing town, though it has a strong clothing industry, particularly in women's garments made of cotton and other materials.

The effects of the decline in the cotton-textile industries would have been far more serious but for two main factors: first the expansion of both mechanical and electrical engineering, and secondly the developments associated with the building of the Ship Canal, which gave the district a major port (actually in Salford though its docks bear the name Manchester) and encouraged the growth of Britain's first and largest trading estate, Trafford Park (situated in Stretford and Urmston), with some 55,000 workers. Mechanical engineering grew initially with the demand for textile machinery but has long since spread into a far wider range of enterprise, and electrical engineering came here partly by the chance purchase of an old mill at Oldham by a member of the Ferranti family and the settlement of a vast concern on the Trafford Park estate. One less fortunate event was the departure of the Ford motor company from Trafford Park to Dagenham in 1929; and it seems ironic that the return of Ford to the Northwest is to Merseyside rather than southeast Lancashire. The present industrial future is a matter of some concern, though many cotton mills have been taken by industrialists providing a wide range of goods, including many consumer products. And there are other signs of expansion on some of the industrial sites such as those provided at Wythenshawe, Manchester's satellite housing area developed from 1929 (p. 201). Another hopeful feature is the success of the modern chemical industry, particularly at Carrington, on the western edge of the conurbation, south of the Ship Canal, where the vast new plant and new residential property is an obvious extension of the conurbation. The chemical industry has a long history in southeast Lancashire, partly in association with dyestuffs, and this industry is now located largely in the northeast of Manchester. Aviation is represented by large factories at Woodford and Chadderton. In general, the industrial complexion of the area becomes steadily more varied, even though its two basic industries, coal and cotton, are in decline. Within Manchester, the only surviving mine is at Bradford and all mining has now ceased in areas east of the city such as Oldham and Ashton with their surrounding districts, though it still survives in the northwest of the conurbation where the new Agecroft colliery has recently been constructed; the coal from both these large collieries is used for power stations. No longer is Lancashire self-supporting in coal and the railway line from Sheffield was electrified in 1954 to carry coal from Yorkshire.

A recent survey has shown that Manchester and Liverpool each have a larger wholesale trade than any other provincial city and together handle four-fifths of the wholesale trade of the Northwest[1]; each city also handles approximately one-fifth of the provincial bank clearances. In the wholesale trades the two cities are complementary to one another rather than rivals, for Liverpool handles most of the raw cotton and Manchester the clothing and textiles, with four times the quantity of groceries handled by Liverpool. In central Manchester the offices and warehouses of the textile trades are more obvious than the depots of the grocery and allied trades, which are handled through wholesale markets and auction rooms as well as by dealers whose supplies are sent from various warehouses of which many are hidden away in back streets and even include discarded chapels. For many years central Manchester has been under reconstruction; recent additions include many office blocks of modern design and some much-needed hotel accom-

---

[1] In the official sense of Lancashire, Cheshire, and northwest Derbyshire. See page 1.

modation. Especially notable perhaps is the large area given to warehouses, which fuses into the office quarters with the headquarters of several large banks and insurance companies between Market Street and Albert Square. Administration is represented by the town hall and its associated office blocks, culture by libraries and art galleries, not to mention the music available in the Free Trade Hall, religion by a variety of churches, entertainment by four live theatres and several cinemas as well as by numerous restaurants. The long-term extension of the university, with other colleges, will eventually provide a 'precinct' over a mile long, extending from the fringe of the shopping area southwards.

But the heart of the city has become almost entirely non-residential, and as long ago as the 1840s it was noted in the census that the central areas were losing population. Some of the social aspects and indeed the problems of this outward movement have been vividly described in Lady Chorley's book, *Manchester Made Them*. This perspicacious work shows that once the railways came people able to afford the journey were willing to travel as much as 10 miles to suburban homes in the Cheshire countryside as well as to nearer suburbs such as Didsbury, Withington, Fallowfield, and Chorlton on the south, or Broughton, Cheetham Hill, and Prestwich on the north, and Eccles on the west. As in other cities, not all the Victorian residential areas have remained prosperous. By the late 1850s most of these suburbs were firmly pegged out by the pioneers of the successful professional men and merchants of Manchester, whose working days were spent in Manchester but whose leisure in their suburban neighbourhoods, except for an occasional visit to the theatre and—particularly—the Hallé concerts. As Lady Chorley shows, it was never contemplated by these suburban settlers, deeply philanthropic as many of them were, that eventually even the artisan classes might move to similarly remote locations, but Manchester eventually provided in Wythenshawe an excellent example of an inter-war estate that was to combine some of the features of a New Town with those of a satellite, for in addition to a population of some 90,000 (now in fact over 100,000) it was also to offer, in its new industries on trading estates, some 30,000 jobs.[1] For Wythenshawe to be self-contained, however, was not regarded as possible, and transport was planned by a service of express buses including some to the centre of the city and others to Trafford Park. In fact the movement to work within the conurbation is vastly complicated, as apart from a heavy inwards movement to the central area, there are also movements to a number of industrial districts, such as those which ring round the central area in what has been termed an 'industrial collar', and also to the industrial areas of Stockport, Broadheath (Altrincham), and many more. In the northern areas of the conurbation the movement is apparently more local in scope, for towns such as Bolton,

---

[1] By 1965, some 14,000 jobs were available in Wythenshawe.

Bury, Rochdale, Oldham, Ashton, Hyde, Dukinfield, Stalybridge, all have their central commercial and their industrial areas, and their suburban areas from which workers come, as well as their inner areas of housing close—often all too close—to the factories and mills. Yet the position may arise that different members of a family may travel in different directions, and so far the problem of providing work when possible at no great distance, though understood and constantly discussed, is not easily solved. To some extent the choice is individual. Now as for more than a century, a journey of 10 miles or more by train or car will mean little to many professional workers; but an investigation on the new Langley estate in Middleton showed that some of the families found the cost of daily journeys high and were also bothered by the cost of week-end journeys to relations left in inner areas of Manchester.

Two maps illustrate the complex web of interlacing journeys to work in the Manchester conurbation. The first (Fig. 53) shows the intricate detail of which the main outlines have been described above; the outflow of workers from Manchester has been omitted from this map for the sake of clarity. In fact there is a considerable movement from the city each morning to industrial areas beyond its bounds, especially to Salford, Stockport and to the Trafford Park industrial estate, shared administratively between Stretford and Urmston. The second map (Fig. 54) classifies the towns of the conurbation from the point of view of their daily export and import of labour. The relative sizes of the two semi-circles show whether a town is a net 'importer' or 'exporter' of labour, and the stippled sectors indicate the sizes of the inward and outward movements to work. Suburbs like Sale and Audenshaw with a large outflow of workers and limited local employment are distinguished from the strongly industrial towns with large daily inflows. Nevertheless, few districts can be described merely as suburban or industrial. Residential areas like Cheadle and Hazel Grove, and especially Stretford and Urmston, have very high totals of industrial employment and large daily inflows of labour. Indeed all these areas and others too experience a twice daily change in population as their suburban 'white collar' commuters leave for the city and a blue-overalled labour force moves in to staff their factories. Scarcely any town in the conurbation is even remotely self-sufficient and self-contained for purposes of employment and labour supply. The resultant movement is one of the unifying forces which bind the conurbation together as a socio-economic entity, though it is notable that the Manchester dormitory area is much less extensive than the conurbation as a whole and fails to penetrate into its northern and eastern margins.

On the ground it is not hard to see the social and economic history of the Manchester conurbation reflected in its buildings. In central Manchester, many of the offices still show traces of the former town houses whose occupants left for the suburbs. And some of the small factories are converted houses, particularly in streets once fashionable and now decrepit near the central area. But from the 1840s, hundreds of workers' houses were pulled down as the land was needed for new roads, shops, warehouses, factories, railway yards, though in some areas one can see where the demolition

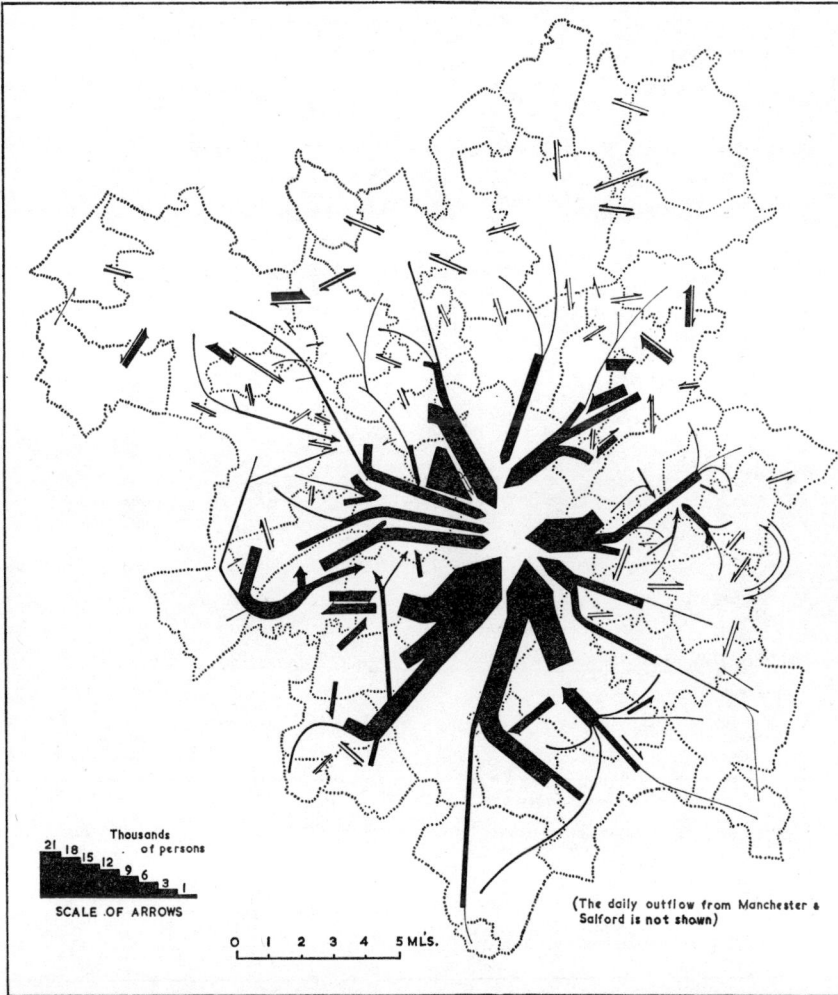

Fig. 53 THE DAILY JOURNEY TO WORK INTO THE CHIEF CENTRES OF EMPLOYMENT IN THE MANCHESTER CONURBATION, 1951.

of houses ceased and the early-nineteenth century houses have survived. Houses of a later age are now being pulled down for extensions of the university or for other purposes, including the building of new flats. And, on a smaller scale, much the same development is seen in the other towns of the conurbation, for only by some clearance of old houses can land be

203

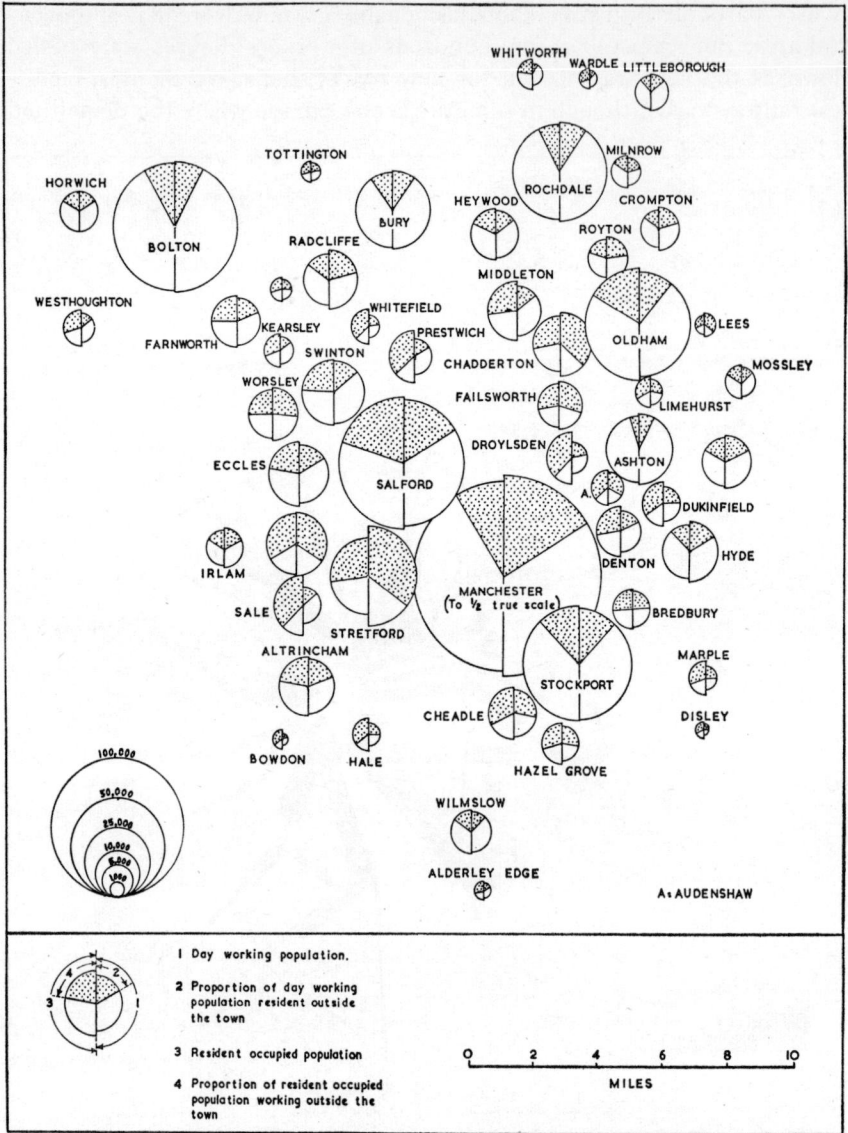

Fig. 54 THE RESIDENT OCCUPIED AND THE DAY-WORKING POPULATIONS OF THE MANCHESTER CONURBATION, 1951. Each constituent unit is represented by two semi-circles. The right-hand semi-circle shows the daytime, working population, the stippled sector indicating the proportion drawn from outside the town. The left-hand semi-circle shows the occupied resident population, of which the proportion shown by the stippled sector leaves each morning for work elsewhere. The contrast between suburbs and industrial towns is clear.

204

provided for civic and industrial purposes and for the needs of modern transport. To some, the process of change will seem all too slow, yet it is apparent all the same, and not least in the creation of a new Manchester skyline with such high buildings that it bears at least some resemblance to that of Rotterdam or Stockholm (Plates 24–27, 32–34, 37, 38).

CHAPTER 9

The Lancastrian Coalfield: its Industrial Regions and their Social Problems

AT no time has the coalfield of Lancastria contained the whole of the region's industry. But of the four divisions into which Lancastria has been broken for the purposes of regional description the coalfield was the most heavily and generally industrialised by the economic revolution of the eighteenth and nineteenth centuries. Almost the whole of the cotton industry was concentrated within it by the need for cheap fuel; so, too, was the engineering industry, which grew initially to serve the textile trades. And wherever the coal was workable—even high on the bleak moors of Rossendale—mining communities grew to supply the rapidly growing industrial concentrations. By the late nineteenth century the classic economy of the coalfield of Lancastria had been shaped. Two basic industries, textile work and coalmining, yielded the great bulk of employment. The mill and the pit were the twin symbols of the area's genuine prosperity; indeed they dominated it physically, for the terraced rows of these compact, congested towns lay in the shadow of the mill chimney and the pithead gear.

The nineteenth century was the golden age of the Lancashire coalfield, and the Edwardian period marked the zenith of its economic fortunes. In the harsher world of the inter-war period the simple, over-specialised economy of the region was brought to the brink of ruin. Both the basic industries contracted catastrophically, for both were relatively high-cost producers exposed to external competition from rivals able to produce more cheaply. The growth of cotton manufactures in Lancashire's traditional markets, for example in India and Brazil, and the appearance of cheap exports on a large scale from Japan brought the Lancashire textile industry to the point of collapse. Mills closed in their hundreds, and the loss of this local market for coal had immediate consequences on the mines, which also faced increasing competition from cheaper Yorkshire coal. Unemployment, industrial decline, emigration, and general economic stagnation were the inevitable results of these irreversible changes. But perhaps the most serious problem of the coalfield during the inter-war years, and indeed up to the present time in many districts, was its inability

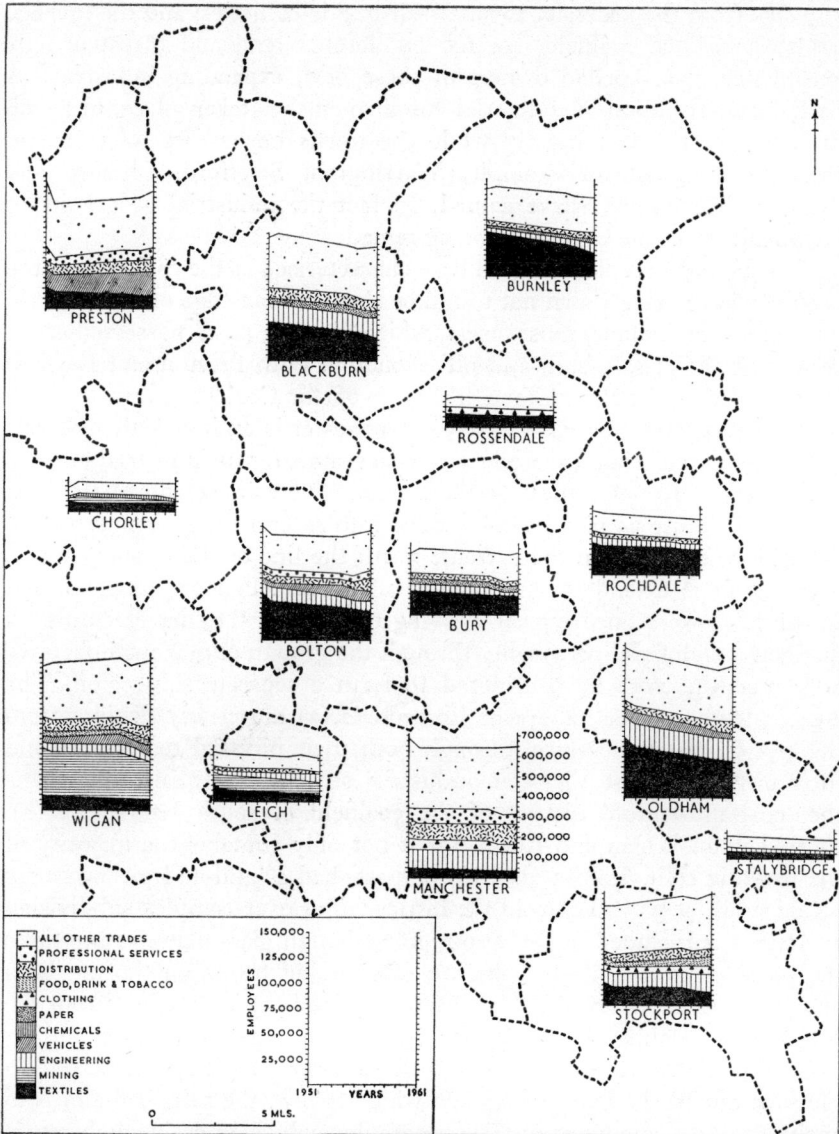

Fig. 55 THE CHANGING INDUSTRIAL STRUCTURE OF THE TEXTILE REGION. The authors are indebted to Mr R. L. Holt, M.A., for this map.

to attract new, 'replacement' industries to balance the loss of its traditional trades. In the nineteenth century the great mass of Lancastria's industrial development, apart from a few specialised manufactures like the chemicals of the mid-Mersey area, was concentrated on the coalfield; but, in conspicuous contrast, the newer and 'safer' trades have sought locations off the Coal Measures. The use of electricity and of road transport has freed industry from the necessity to site itself beside collieries; and the ravaged landscape of the coalfield, scarred by derelict land and threatened by subsidence, has repelled owners of these new, expanding industries. A partial redistribution of industrial employment has taken place, in which the coalfield has lost heavily while the towns beyond its western and southern margins—for example, Warrington, Stretford, Chester, and those on Merseyside—have gained. In fact the industrial geography of Lancashire is in the process of being remade.

The boundaries of the region here characterised as the coal-and-cotton province have been drawn not to follow slavishly the edge of the coalfield but rather to include those areas which, in the past, possessed some variant of the classic 'mill-and-pit' economy. Both Preston and Leyland are placed with the region, though they lie off the Coal Measures, for both have a textile tradition. Conversely, Manchester is excluded, though part of the city is underlain by productive coal seams, for its industrial breadth and balance are not typical of the region. The mining and textile area shown on Figure 55 may be subdivided into several parts for purposes of detailed description. In the extreme north the line of the weaving towns (sub-region 1) extends from Colne to Blackburn. Preston, Leyland, and Chorley (2) were once typical weaving towns, but they have acquired a distinctive industrial personality through the growth of new manufactures and must therefore be considered to form a separate sub-region. The austere towns of the valleys of Rossendale (3) are clearly distinct from the rest of east Lancashire, through both their physical remoteness and their narrow, almost Victorian industrial structures. Equally distinct is the 'coal-and-cotton' district of the coalfield of south Lancashire (4), centred upon Wigan and Leigh, for it not only contains the majority of the working collieries but also, in the past, had a 'mill-and-pit' economy of the simplest type. To avoid the intricacies of over-complex subdivision St Helens is included in this sub-region, though glass manufacture takes the place of cotton. Lastly, the arc of spinning towns on the northern and eastern margins of the Manchester lowland (5) is detached from the rest of the conurbation and considered as a separate sub-region, for industrially these towns now have little in common with Manchester. In the accounts of the five sub-regions which follow, the principal aim is to analyse their changing industrial geography, which leads inevitably to a discussion of their urgent economic and social problems.

The weaving towns

The line of towns which occupies the continuous trough of the Calder–Darwen valley, on the northern flank of Rossendale, has been closely associated with the cotton-weaving industry for more than a century. This Coal Measure lowland, enclosed between the sheer gritstone scarps of High Rossendale on the south and a smooth, hog-backed grit ridge on the north, made only slow industrial progress until the period 1830–50. It was remote from the focus of the growing cotton industry in the Manchester lowland, with which it was linked only by road and, circuitously, by the indirect course of the Leeds and Liverpool Canal. Improved rail connections after 1847 made this almost virgin coalfield ripe for faster and more intense industrialisation; it was at this time that the full mechanisation of cotton weaving was making quick though belated progress, and thus the association of the weaving branch with the Calder–Darwen valley was mere historical accident.

By 1914 the weaving area was distinguished by the narrowest industrial economy in the Lancashire coalfield: it depended upon a single branch of a single industry. In the Burnley district 72% and in the Blackburn area 63% of all insured employment was provided directly by the mills.[1] Alternative employment was scarce throughout the area and for both sexes, especially so in the smaller towns and for working women. Nine of every ten Burnley women in employment were mill hands, while 83% of the total labour force of Great Harwood was in textile work. Even the mines were unable to provide an effective alternative, for the shallow seams near Blackburn were already exhausted, while even in the deeper Burnley basin the pits employed less than one-tenth of the male labour force.

Clearly the weaving belt of Lancashire could be classed with Jarrow, west Durham, and South Wales in the extreme specialisation of its industrial economy; and when the depression struck the area it did so with great force, though with local variations in its impact. There had long been contrasts within the belt between Nelson and Colne, which specialised in fine weaving, the Burnley–Accrington district with a tradition of medium-quality work and, lastly, the coarse-weaving area centred on Blackburn. This system of local specialisation has been almost destroyed by the decline of the industry, but it had a powerful influence on the fate of the area in the 1930s. The coarse-weaving towns of the west suffered much more than the fine-weaving district of the east. Blackburn lost two-thirds of its mill employment between 1931 and 1951, but the average rate of decline in the Nelson–Colne area was only half this, owing to the slighter sensitivity of the fine-weaving trade to Asian competition. Since no part of the weaving belt was able to attract any significant volume of work in new industries before the late 1930s, the employment available shrank catastrophically, and prolonged unemployment led to continued emigration. Blackburn's population fell by 9% and Burnley's by 13·5% between 1931 and 1951, and the decline continued at closely similar rates (−4·5% and −5·3% respectively) during the decade 1951–61.

[1] These data are from the Ministry of Labour returns for 1929, which provide probably the best general guide to the structure of employment in Lancashire on the eve of the economic disaster of the 1930s.

The east and the west of the weaving belt have had unequal success in their efforts to attract new industries to balance the loss of the older trade. The Blackburn area, which so desperately needed new employment in the inter-war years to take the place of its coarse-cloth manufacture, has made much greater progress in remodelling its economy than the Burnley–Colne district, where the delayed decline of the fine-weaving trade postponed the crisis until the 1950s. In the west of the weaving belt electronic engineering is the largest of the new trades. A single firm has established several factories here, in part to take advantage of the known adaptability of local labour and its traditional manual skill. Blackburn, too, is near enough to Leyland and Preston to 'export' labour daily to the prosperous engineering industries there.

In contrast, the Burnley–Colne group of towns has made much slower progress towards the modernisation of its economy. Even after 1945 these towns continued to depend on their fine weaving, which had successfully weathered the stresses of both the depression and the war without radical contraction. Here, indeed, an essentially Victorian economy survives, for this is one of the very few parts of Lancashire in which male employment is still largely in the textile mills. In several of these towns half the men are mill hands, while in the Blackburn group the proportions are between 10% and 20%. In short, the continued decline of the cotton industry is a far more serious threat to the fine weaving than to the coarse-weaving towns, for it can no longer be assumed that the demand for fine cotton fabrics will remain heavy. Figure 36, page 148, shows that in Nelson several large mills are no longer occupied and that of the thirteen mills used by replacement industries only four had more workers in 1962 than in 1951. Many had only a small fraction of their former number of employed workers.

The industrial weakness of the Burnley district was clearly demonstrated by the 1952 recession, when unemployment rose almost to the level of the depression years. In direct consequence the fine-weaving towns were scheduled as a Development Area in 1953, in the hope that the guidance of new industry into it would restore its stability. Much progress towards economic diversification has been made: but the growth of the replacement industries has been slower than the decline of the cotton manufacture, for northeast Lancashire has been far less successful in attracting new enterprises than the other Development Areas of the county. The reasons for this are complex; some are local, others national. So mercurial were the recent fortunes of the cotton industry that the recession of 1952 was followed by years of such brisk demand that a labour shortage resulted. Both this and the prospect of a progressive decrease in labour supply through emigration and a low birth rate have tended to repel new industries. There is no doubt, too, that the physical remoteness and indifferent communications of this Development Area have hindered its economic progress. But quite apart from these local problems, northeast Lancashire has been unfortunate: it was the last Development Area to be listed, and in the radical revision of the government's policies of industrial guidance following the Act of 1960 it lost its special status.

For all these reasons the flow of new employment into northeast Lancashire has been inadequate, and it is largely confined to Burnley itself. The most significant progress has been the growth of domestic equipment manufactures, for example washing machines and kitchen cutlery. Electrical equipment for motor cars is another substantial new trade. And, more recently, the conversion of old weaving sheds for a variety of small new enterprises has made faster progress. But even the forced contraction of the cotton industry by the 1960 Act has not destroyed the dominant position of the mill in the area's economy, for much of the labour made redundant by closures quickly found work in other mills now operating on a shift system. In short, the fine-weaving district is, industrially, almost a nineteenth century survival, while the coarse-weaving towns have almost completed a second industrial revolution. This contrast, it will become apparent, is repeated on a larger scale throughout the Lancashire coalfield.

Rossendale

Many of the problems of northeast Lancashire are repeated, with little modification, in the ribbon towns of the deep valleys of the Rossendale upland. For almost two centuries Rossendale has lived by its cotton manufacture and by very little else. There was not even mining to offer alternative employment on a significant scale, for the upland seams are mostly poor and thin. Yet there is some variety in the textile manufacture of the upland. It never quite abandoned its old woollen industry, which still survives on a small scale and has recently proved more stable than the younger cotton manufacture. The wool-felt trade developed into a new industry which has made steady progress since its foundation in the 1870s—the making of felt slippers and, later, women's and children's footwear. Even within the cotton industry there is unusual breadth: spinning and weaving are almost equally balanced and the finishing trades, attracted to the upland valleys by their ample supply of clean soft water, are well established. This is particularly fortunate, for they have been much more resilient since 1945 than the manufacturing branches. Though Rossendale was as distressed as any part of Lancashire in the inter-war period, its cotton industry has proved remarkably stable in recent years. It escaped almost unscathed from the reorganisation scheme. Specialisation in heavy cloths for industrial purposes and in the cotton-waste trade are among the reasons for this, for heavy textiles have so far suffered little Asian competition.

It is fortunate that the traditional trades of Rossendale have survived so strongly, for remoteness and poor communications, perhaps also the 'weeping' climate and the gloomy, cramped appearance of the valley towns, have combined to repel new enterprises. In the three towns of central Rossendale (Rawtenstall, Haslingden, and Bacup) 41% of the employment is still in the mills and 22% in the footwear factories. Engineering occupies only 3% of the insured population, and—as in so many parts of Lancashire—the service trades are very feebly developed. In England and Wales 54% of the total employment was provided by service industries in 1959, but in Rossendale the proportion was only 24%. In fact an economy of almost Victorian simplicity survives here. Whether it can endure much longer is uncertain, but the fate of these isolated towns should their textile industry collapse would be serious.

No part of Lancashire reached its population peak as early as Rossendale: the total has declined throughout the present century, from 72,000 in 1901 to 56,000 in 1961. Between 1931 and 1961 the three chief towns lost from 10% to 12% of their populations, chiefly through emigration. Because of this long-continued flight, chiefly of young people, natural increase has almost ceased; indeed, Rawtenstall lost 3% of its population by natural decrease between 1951 and 1961. Despite its industrial insecurity Rossendale was not included in the nearby Development Area in 1953, and so there has been no artificial stimulation of new enterprises here. Paradoxically, any new industries which might have come into these towns could not have been sure of a labour supply, for the mills have been short-handed during most recent years. This is the dilemma of economic planning in regions such as this. The absence of short-term unemployment means that there is no urgent and compelling need for new opportunities in 'immigrant' industries; but eventually Rossendale must experience an economic transformation if it is to survive. Some would question whether the crumbling economy of such a region should be artificially sustained. Rossendale's valleys are frost pockets in winter, and the sun is prevented by their high walls from piercing the persistent inversion fogs. The urban fabric of these towns is becoming worn out and obsolete, and housing conditions are seriously sub-standard: not only back-to-back but even back-to-rock dwellings are to be found in them. Yet the corporate and community life in these old closely knit communities is far richer than in many new housing estates.

In its landscape, as in its economy, Rossendale contains many survivals from the past: indeed the towns threaded along the deep slots of the valleys are something of a museum of urban and industrial Victoriana. Lines of old gritstone mills follow the rivers from which they once drew their power. Streets of sturdy stone houses huddle against the mills of the valley floors and climb the lower slopes in steep, short terraces; gaunt chapels look sternly down over the ill-developed shopping centres straggling along the valley roads. But on the broad, level benches which rise above the narrow slots of the main valleys a quite different landscape is found. The small-holdings of the old farmer-weaver community—now tiny dairy and poultry farms—and the clusters of cottages grouped into weaver's hamlets are an eighteenth century landscape now being invaded by new housing estates for which there is no space in the congested valleys.

The coalfield of south Lancashire

Several economic surveys of the past have identified this sub-region, which has been given a variety both of titles and boundaries. It has been described both as the 'coal-and-cotton district' and as the 'coal-and-chemicals area'. The former fails to distinguish it from the rest of the coalfield, while the latter is plainly inaccurate, for since the death of the St Helens alkali industry in the early 1920s no Lancashire town has coupled chemical manufacture with coalmining. For present purposes the south Lancashire coalfield is defined as a broad east–west belt from the southwestern angle of the Coal Measures near St Helens to the western outskirts of the Manchester conurbation, where the Irwell valley fault provides a convenient geological boundary. On the north it extends to the edge of Rossendale, while the narrow ribbon of concealed Coal Measures on the lip of the Mersey–Irwell valley is its southern limit. This very large sub-region contains a total population of approximately 450,000, in which the three dominant centres are Wigan, St Helens, and Leigh.

In its industrial tradition south Lancashire is a miniature of the county as a whole: the mill and the mine were the twin—indeed the only—bases of its life. Before 1914 this simple economy seemed prosperous, balanced, and secure. The cotton manufacture enjoyed the advantage of cheap fuel of local origin, while the collieries had an assured nearby market for their output. The mills provided the female employment which most coalfields lack, and so most families had a multiple income. But these two basic and interdependent industries were to be shaken to the point of collapse by the economic storms of the depression period, when prosperity was quickly transformed into deep distress.

Even so, the problems of the southern coalfield have been magnified by some writers in the past. This was not, in general, the most distressed area of industrial Lancashire though part of it was declared a Development Area in 1950. Over most of the district the cotton industry has suffered slighter decline than in the county generally, and though coalmining has experienced a radical redistribution it has achieved some stability in the post-war period. And the glass manufacture of St Helens is one of Lancashire's most successful industries. But there are sharp local contrasts within the sub-region: it contains some almost derelict mill-and-pit villages as well as some growing communities with a greater variety of industrial interest. The area is best subdivided, for more detailed

8

description, into three sections: the coal-and-glass area of St Helens, the exhausted coalfield of the north, between Wigan and Bolton, and the active coalfield of the southern border.

(i) St Helens has always had a distinctive industrial structure. The cotton industry made only a weak and ephemeral attempt to establish itself here, though in the smaller pit villages farther east, such as Golborne, it rooted itself deeply and has survived strongly. The death of the old alkali and copper trades at St Helens left coalmining, for a time, in a completely dominant position. In 1929 coalmining employed 24,000 workers, almost exactly twice the number in glass manufacture. But the latter has grown as consistently as the former has declined, and glass making now provides double the number of jobs available in the much-reduced mining industry: the growth of glass making as an indigenous 'replacement' industry has neatly balanced the decline of the old staple, coalmining. And St Helens is quite untroubled by the problems of the declining cotton manufacture. For both these reasons it is difficult to understand the town's inclusion within the South Lancashire Development Area. Certainly, its listing quickened the pace of industrial diversification: a trading estate was established at Parr, and a variety of new trades has come into the district. But even before it acquired this special status the southwestern angle of the coalfield had unusual industrial diversity; for cable making and copper refining at Prescot and locomotive construction at Earlestown are considerable enterprises. Perhaps the most significant achievement of Development Area policy here has been the broadening of the range of work available to women in a district in which the two basic industries are male-employing.

Though St Helens has passed through an industrial transformation it has some serious problems. The halving of mining employment in the 1930s brought intense though temporary distress. Permanent dislocation has resulted from the redistribution of coalmining: all the pits of the shallow coalfield to the north with those of the Skelmersdale outlier have closed, and now a line of large collieries along the southern rim of the field provides almost the entire mining employment. Miners from as far north as Upholland travel to these pits daily by special bus. Land dereliction, too, is a serious problem; in addition to the inevitable pitbanks of an old coalfield there are heaps of alkali waste and of the used sand of the glass industry. Old, congested industrial zones follow the three arms of the derelict Sankey Canal. Though St Helens is particularly short of land, both for industrial purposes and for rehousing the large population in the congested terraced rows of the older parts of the town, there has not yet been any significant reclamation of derelict land. Though it grew slightly between 1931 and 1951, the town has since lost population, but that this is merely local redistribution is shown by the quick growth of some of its smaller neighbours such as Rainford.

214

(ii) The exhausted coalfield of the north has suffered far greater economic decline than the St Helens district for not only is its coalmining virtually extinct and its cotton textile industry a mere remnant, but also the area has conspicuously failed to find any substitute employment. Yet only a small part lay within the limits of a Development Area and no part is now classed as a Development District. In this strip of shallow Coal Measures at the foot of Rossendale surface seams outcropped widely and were worked vigorously from the seventeenth century. No deep reserves existed, and the pits closed as the seams were exhausted. In Westhoughton, a typical instance, mining gave work to 2,200 men in 1929; but by 1947 the industry was dead. Over the same period textile employment declined by one-half, and the total volume of work available in the town fell by 44%. It is surprising that population loss by migration between 1931 and 1951 was as low as 11%, but this is explained by a large daily movement of workers to more fortunate areas to the south and east. Westhoughton typifies the north of the coalfield: mining is almost extinct, and though it has lingered in the faulted Wigan trough the last pits there are soon to close. The cotton industry, too, has suffered more serious losses in the north of the coalfield than in the south, partly because in the older mining communities of the north the mills are small and obsolete, while the newer mills of the south are more easily modernised. Thus the traditional economy of the area has collapsed and serious population losses are general.

Yet there are signs of economic rehabilitation in the derelict coalfield. Part lay within the South Lancashire Development Area, to which governmental guidance has brought many new trades. Some are sited on two trading estates at Wigan, but most are scattered about the area. Tinned foods, metal containers, and cardboard boxes (three obviously associated industries) are among the most important new products; asbestos products and aircraft components are other examples. Wigan and its environs have attracted the bulk of this new employment—a fortunate trend, for this is the area of greatest need. This former 'capital' of the south Lancashire coalfield, still a miners' town though its pits are dead, now has an industrial structure of great and growing breadth. Since its textile industry has survived well and many of its new trades are chiefly employers of women, there is no shortage of female employment. But the problem of the displaced miner remains. The Wigan district daily 'exports' several thousand miners to the collieries between Leigh and Walkden. Apart from this daily journey of 10 miles or more to work (locally regarded as long), mining has left another problem here, that of derelict land. Subsidence flashes cover about two-thirds of a square mile south of Wigan, a town almost ringed by a broad derelict zone; everywhere this landscape of quite unusual hideousness is littered by spoil banks, crumbling pithead gear, and the temporary scars of open-cast coal operations. This is not merely an aesthetic problem, for most of the area is desperately short of land for urban redevelopment and particularly for industrial construction. Indeed the industrial rehabilitation of the derelict coalfield must be preceded by the reclamation of its ravaged landscape for factory sites. In the past reclamation was piecemeal and had chiefly an aesthetic or a social purpose, such as tree planting on spoil heaps or the provision of playing fields. But now much bigger areas are being levelled for housing and industry at Skelmersdale and near Wigan (Fig. 56).

Over the four decades since the industrial difficulties of the exhausted coalfield began, this has been an area of persistent population loss by migration, which until recently more than balanced the high rate of natural increase characteristic of a mining community. But the outward drift of population has slowed progressively; the annual rate of population decline was twice as high in the 1920s as in the 1930s, and it was converted into a slight increase over the period 1939–48. Few towns here have experienced serious population loss in the last decade, and only in Wigan is migration greater now than in the 1930s, owing to short-range movement. The population decline of the derelict coalfield may be halted, though its economic problems are by no means fully solved. Almost certainly the construction of the Preston–Birmingham motorway a little to the west of Wigan will have a favourable—even a dramatic—effect on the inflow of new industry. And the development of overspill towns at Skelmersdale and Westhoughton will guarantee a continuing increase in the area's population in the near future.

(iii) The active coalfield of the south has had slighter problems of decline and readjustment. Here the rich seams of the very thick Coal Measures series plunge steeply southwards and are continued as a narrow 'concealed' ribbon beneath a quickly thickening Permo-Triassic overlay. Despite a multitude of technical difficulties there are deep reserves here adequate to sustain the life of the field far into the future if demand warrants the use of these high-cost resources. Through the decline of the shallow coalfield to the north the mining industry has become concentrated into a narrow line of large pits along the southern edge of the field from Leigh to Manchester. In this linear belt of active mining 22,500 men are at work, 80% of them in nine large collieries which have been modernised since 1942 and in two new pits. Most of these have increased their labour force in the last twenty years, and in their growth they have absorbed the redundant miners of the dead pits farther north. Though both local authorities and the Coal Board have built miners' housing close to these collieries of the south there is still a considerable daily movement to them from areas far to the north and west (Figs. 31, 32, 33, pp. 128–35).

The textile industry, too, has escaped serious decline in the south of the coalfield. In Leigh, the largest centre, mill employment fell by only 5% during the years of crisis between 1958 and 1961. Something of nine-

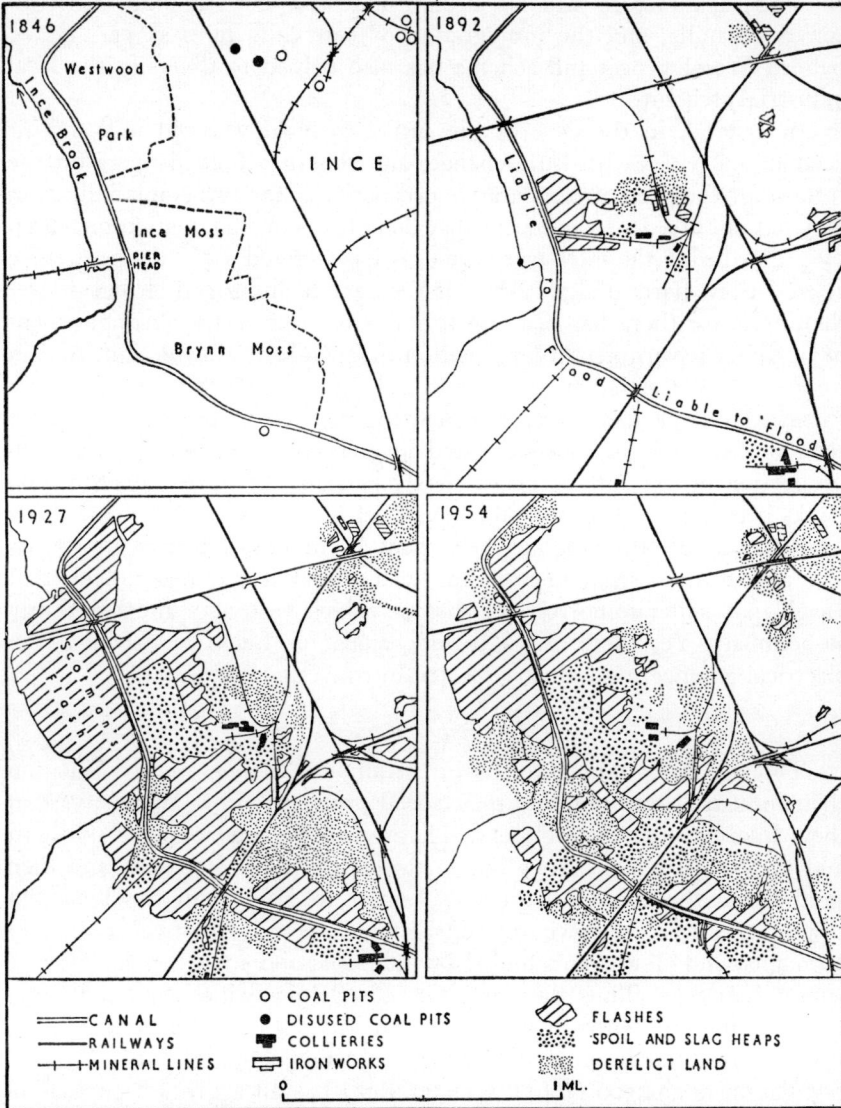

Fig. 56   THE GROWTH OF DERELICT LAND NEAR WIGAN, 1846–1954. This map was first published in *Geography* **45** (1960), 269, by Mr K. L. Wallwork, M.A.

teenth century Lancashire's economic simplicity survives here: in the core of the worked coalfield almost half the occupied men are miners and 44% of the occupied women are mill workers. Apart from a small engineering industry which provides 10% of the total employment there are no new trades of any significance, but farther east, on the fringe of the Manchester conurbation, there is greater industrial variety. Walkden has a large clothing manufacture and an aircraft industry, both housed partly in converted mills, and the immigration of new companies as part of the Salford–Worsley overspill scheme has also helped to diversify the local industrial structure.

In general, in the core of the active coalfield, the old mill-and-pit economy survives with little change; and this may hold dangers for the future, for the present comparative prosperity of the two staple industries may not endure. It is significant that though Leigh's population increased by 7·5% during the inter-war period, it has suffered a 5% decrease since 1951. In few parts of Lancashire is the pace of industrial change slower than here, for there has been no stimulus of either acute unemployment or of direct governmental intervention in its industrial evolution. And in some ways the Leigh district is particularly unattractive to new enterprises: substantial areas have been drowned by subsidence, and in this active section of the field new subsidence damage is commonplace. Only a small proportion of the surface lies uselessly beneath pit waste, but the spoil banks here are still growing and cannot yet be reclaimed. There are many parallels between the Leigh of the present day and the Wigan of forty years ago; and in the absence of new industrial growth it is not impossible that Leigh may suffer tomorrow the distress which yesterday affected Wigan so seriously. Yet there are signs of change, for Leigh has acquired an electrical engineering industry located in converted cotton mills.

The spinning towns

Though the spinning towns lie within the Manchester conurbation their industrial tradition and their social problems are so distinctive that they deserve separate treatment. They form the conurbation's northern and eastern periphery, from Bolton through Bury to Rochdale and then southwards through Oldham and Ashton to Hyde and Stockport, in Cheshire. These are towns of considerable size: all but two are county boroughs, and all are surrounded by industrial and suburban satellites of subservient type. Thus there is a Greater Bolton, which contains Farnworth municipal borough and the urban districts of Horwich, Turton, Little Lever, and Kearsley as well as the county borough itself: its total population is 234,500 (1961). Greater Bury has an aggregate population of 144,300, Greater Rochdale 114,400, Greater Oldham 178,800, the Ashton–Hyde cluster 137,000, and Greater Stockport 213,400. These units resemble those suggested by the Local Government Commission in 1965.

These textile towns of the conurbation's outer girdle are in no sense mere industrial and suburban extensions of Manchester. Most are market towns of some antiquity and all grew strongly as independent manufacturing centres during the Industrial Revolution. Each one has a well-developed commercial focus which offers a broad range of urban facilities; all have a strongly independent corporate life and a robust local patriotism which admits no subordination to Manchester. Indeed, though they are part of the conurbation as a spread of bricks-and-mortar, their social and economic links with Manchester are surprisingly weak.

Though the spinning towns share many common characteristics—for all have declining textile and defunct mining industries—they are sufficiently individual to make it necessary to sketch an industrial profile for each in turn. Greater Bolton is both the largest and the least dependent on Manchester. Only 2% of the county borough's employed population works in the core of the conurbation. This traditional centre of the fine-spinning industry has always had a highly specialised industrial structure: until recently weaving has been of negligible significance, though, in contrast, there is a marked concentration of the finishing trades in the valleys of the Rossendale flank, north of the town. In 1929, 54% of Greater Bolton's employment was in the mills, and since the fine-spinning industry long withstood Asian competition this proportion declined only slowly, to one-third in 1950 and 30% in 1959. But Bolton has faced a quickly worsening problem in recent years, not only through the growth of cotton imports but also through the perfection of synthetic fibres, which has reduced the market for fine cotton yarns. The decline of fine spinning, though delayed, has now become critical. Half Bolton's spindles were scrapped in the reorganisation period, and from 1954 to 1960 the town lost 40% of its mill employment. Since fine-spinning mills employ an exceptionally high proportion of male operatives, the town has faced serious social problems.

Alternative industries are few in Bolton. Coalmining, once the town's second staple, is now represented by a single pit, and, though Bolton still has its mining families, most of the men must make a long daily journey to the pits of the far south. The engineering group of industries provides only 17% of the total work available in Bolton (roughly half of the volume of the town's textile employment), and some of these trades, like textile and railway engineering, are old-established and no longer expanding. Of the 'immigrant' industries aircraft manufacture is among the most significant. The closure of cotton mills has given a new impetus to industrial diversification in Bolton, for they can be bought very cheaply. Unfortunately, most are multi-storey spinning mills, less easily adaptable than single-floor weaving sheds. But—to quote only two examples—a mill at Farnworth was adapted for a domestic equipment company, and one at Walkden for a firm of clothing manufacturers.

Bury differs from Bolton in many respects. Though it is in the spinning belt it has long had a balanced cotton industry, in which weaving gave rather more work than spinning. The recent contraction of the industry has had little effect here; the town lost only 6% of its spindles, and the mills still provide almost 30% of its employment. But Bury has never lacked other work: the old woollen manufacture still survives, and the clean water of the Rossendale streams attracted a paper industry which

219

employs one-tenth of the working population. In turn, the construction of paper machinery has grown considerably. But all of these are old trades, and there has been little recent addition to the range of Bury's industries.

Rochdale shares some, but not all, of Bury's characteristics. It, too, retains a strong interest in woollens and escaped lightly from the concentration of the cotton industry, chiefly owing to its special concern with heavy yarns for industrial uses. In both towns, too, mining has been dead for so long that the social problems of its decline have now resolved themselves. But Rochdale, unlike Bury, is emphatically a spinning town with an insignificant weaving industry; and it is narrower in its industrial basis, for the mills employ 43% of its workers. Not only have new industries avoided Rochdale, but also it lacks established trades outside the textile group except for a growing asbestos-products company and an engineering industry which is still too closely linked with the textile trade. Both Bury and Rochdale are essentially Victorian in their industrial structures, and both would be fortunate to escape great difficulty if the decline of the cotton manufacture spread seriously to the sections in which they specialise.

Of all the spinning towns, Oldham made the fastest growth in the nineteenth century. A mere road-side village in 1800, it contained the largest single concentration of mills in the county by 1920. It lived by the coarse-spinning trade and depended on the export, particularly the tropical, markets, and almost rivalled Blackburn in the speed and severity of its decline as a textile centre. Since 1929 its mill employment has fallen by 70%. Fortunately, Oldham's mills have always provided a much higher proportion of the female than of the male employment of the town: nine out of every ten working women were mill hands in 1929, and even today 36% of the female labour force is employed in the mills but only 26% of the male. The closing of the mills has endangered not the primary but only the supplementary income of most families.

Oldham men have never lacked alternative work. Mining was active in this rich but difficult section of the coalfield, and it vanished only during the 1950s. Oldham, too, had one of the largest of the county's textile-machinery manufactures, but this has declined as mills have closed: indeed, because of this, engineering was a contracting rather than an expanding industry in the Oldham of the 1930s. It was saved by the quick growth of two new branches, electrical engineering and the aircraft industry. Other new trades of many types have come to Oldham in recent decades—many to converted mills. But they are not as important as superficial impressions would suggest: the two largest—clothing and food-stuffs—provide only 3% and 4% respectively of the total volume of work available. And one of Oldham's largest new industries, aircraft construction, is now nationally in a somewhat precarious condition, a reminder that not every 'replacement' industry in a textile town necessarily strengthens its economic security.

Between Oldham and Stockport there is a group of smaller cotton towns which focus on Ashton-under-Lyne and Hyde and extend as broken ribbons into the valleys of the Pennines. Like east Lancashire as a whole, this cluster is an industrial mosaic of great complexity. The smaller towns and industrial villages of the Pennine valleys were grossly over-dependent on their mills: in Stalybridge and Mossley, for example, alternative work was almost absent. Both these single-industry towns have suffered particularly serious losses from the decline of the cotton trade; indeed, the industry is now virtually dead over much of the area. New trades have entered the valleys to take over the abandoned mills, but invariably in inadequate volume; the valley villages are now becoming suburban both to Manchester and to the larger towns immediately to their west, a tendency greatly strengthened by the growth of the large Hattersley overspill estate (in Hyde and Longendale).

These larger towns, particularly Ashton and Hyde, have far broader industrial structures. The heavy-engineering belt of east Manchester extends into them, and they have attracted other, lighter manufactures more recently. Ashton has jam and garments factories; Hyde has rubber works and a large food-preparation plant. Typical of the industrial transformation in progress here is the conversion of a large old print works into an industrial estate housing many small, new enterprises. This contrast between the pace of industrial rehabilitation in the upland valleys and the larger towns of the lowland is repeated throughout Lancashire, and is one of the most significant general trends of the present time.

Stockport's inclusion in a survey of the spinning area is anachronistic, for it is no longer a cotton town. It has long had a tradition of industrial flexibility, for silk, cotton, and now engineering have, in turn, dominated its life. So few of Stockport's spinning and doubling mills have survived the stresses of the last forty years that today textiles provide only 10% of the male and 14% of the total employment, and much of this is not in the county borough but in the smaller towns of the Goyt and Tame valleys. Now one-quarter of Stockport's male labour force is employed in engineering factories, of which the products range from coke ovens and flour-milling machinery to diesel engines and precision instruments. A large clothing industry now rivals the cotton manufacture as the chief source of female employment, and industries as diverse as steel making and biscuit manufacture are strongly developed in the area. Stockport illustrates the direction in which the industrial economies of the other spinning towns must evolve if they are to achieve stability.

This sketch of the industrial contrasts within the spinning area shows that diversification has made varying progress. A simple index of industrial change here is the relative importance of the textile and engineering industries. Only in Stockport is the latter dominant: in Rochdale the ratio of mill work to engineering employment is 3·5:1; in Bury almost 3:1; in Bolton 2:1; but in Oldham the two are almost equal. The population trends of recent years are closely related to these proportions: thus during the last decade (1951–61) Rochdale suffered a 4%, Oldham a 3·5%, and Bolton a 2% loss, but Stockport achieved a 12% increase. All these data are for the 'greater' towns. However, the trends are seriously affected by an increasing but unequally distributed daily outflow of labour from the spinning towns to Manchester. This is the result both of the wider suburban dispersal of the city's population into the spinning belt and the increasing 'export' of the surplus labour of these textile towns to the core of the conurbation. Bolton has been least affected by both these tendencies, and its independence of Manchester is unimpaired. But an increasing daily flow of surplus labour to Manchester has helped to solve Oldham's critical employment problem; without this the town's population loss between 1951 and 1961 would certainly have been larger. Bury's stability of population is the direct result of the northward spread of suburban housing from Manchester, while Stockport's rapid increase has followed the conversion of many of the textile villages of the Pennine flank into dormitory communities. In short, as the traditional industries of the spinning towns have declined and as the surplus population of Manchester has seeped into them their links with the city have become stronger. Whether their old rugged individualism can survive is, at least, in doubt.

Preston, Leyland, Chorley

This northwestern corner of industrial Lancashire is treated as a separate sub-region chiefly because of the great progress it has made in transforming its old textile economy into a better-balanced industrial structure. Yet, in some senses, these towns have little in common. Preston is a market town of very great antiquity—indeed the *de facto* county town —quickly converted into an industrial community by the economic changes of the nineteenth century. Leyland, in contrast, is a mere upstart, a textile village transformed into a thriving factory town of 22,000 inhabitants by the success of the heavy-vehicle company which has adopted its name. Chorley has neither the antiquity of Preston nor the vitality of Leyland; it is a mill-and-mining town of characteristic type, but it was rescued from serious decline by the establishment of a large explosives factory close by. Despite their differences these three towns and their smaller neighbours are an economic unit in the strictest sense, for they exchange large proportions of their working populations daily.

Traditionally the three towns formed the western end of the cotton-weaving belt, but they were never as specialised as Burnley or Blackburn. Preston, particularly, has always had a strong interest in spinning. In general these towns have suffered few serious mill closures in recent years, but over the period since 1920 the cotton industry has declined dramatically in relative importance. Today it provides only 16% of the total employment, and even in Chorley it is significant only as a source of work for women. The other declining staple of industrial Lancashire, coalmining, has always been confined to the Chorley district within this sub-region. Here it has had a curious recent history, for after its near-extinction in the 1930s it experienced a revival after 1945, when new 'panels' of coal were opened up by colliery reconstruction and the sinking of new drift mines: these employ 2,000 Chorley men, 8% of the male labour force.

The remodelling of the industrial geography of the Preston area has been largely the result of the growth of four very large enterprises. Two of these are in the vehicle industry. The English Electric Company has long been established at Preston, but it grew quickly here with the development of its interest in aircraft manufacture, now the chief concern of the Preston factories. A company of similar stature is Leyland Motors, whose factories at Leyland are the largest unit in the British heavy-vehicle industry. Through its acquisition of the Standard car firm of Coventry, Leyland Motors has strengthened Lancashire's quickly growing interest in the British car industry. Though smaller than these two giants, the Courtauld rayon plant at Preston and the government's explosives factory at Chorley are very considerable undertakings; indeed the latter employed 15,000 workers during the Second World War and had its own railway station.

Apart from these new industries of great size, many smaller enterprises have been established in the area. At Leyland paints and rubber products are made; Chorley has a large vehicle-repair factory, while in Preston five minor industrial groups (for example, chemicals and foodstuffs) employ more than 2,000 workers each. In Preston, too, the service industries are much stronger than in the average industrial town of Lancashire, for it is still a minor regional capital and the centre of the county's administration. The Preston sub-region is one of the very few in industrial Lancashire with a continuous increase in both employment and population over the past thirty years. That the 'replacement' industries have grown more quickly than the older trades have declined is shown by a 20% increase in the volume of work available, while the population has grown from 240,000 in 1931 to 280,000 in 1961. Most of this increase has been by immigration, chiefly from other parts of Lancashire, accelerated recently by Leyland's absorption of overspill population. But the rate of natural increase is high too, for this immigrant population is a young one. Thus the sub-region has the social as well as the economic characteristics of a growing community. Though there is no single key to the industrial success of the Preston–Leyland area, its excellent communications have had a powerful influence. It lies on the main London–Glasgow railway; it has its own small but well-equipped port at Preston; it has first-class road links with Merseyside; and its position on the M6 motorway should assist, even assure, its continued expansion.

Conclusion

Whatever the prospects of the cotton industry may be, the economy of the whole of eastern Lancashire must pass through changes broadly similar to those which have already transformed the Preston area and, on a more local scale, fortunate towns like Stockport. A reconstructed cotton industry may well have a permanent place in the industrial life of the Lancashire coalfield, and so, too, will a reorganised mining industry; but these two old staples can no longer, themselves, support a prosperous regional economy. A new industrial revolution has begun in Lancashire, but it has made locally varying progress. Blackburn and Wigan, Oldham and Bolton, are beginning to follow the paths of industrial change already followed by Preston and Leyland. But the old economy lives on in the remoter towns of the uplands and their flanks, like Rochdale, Burnley, and the towns of Rossendale.

The distribution of Lancashire's population is in process of radical change. The nineteenth century pattern was dominated by the coalfield, almost all of which has lost population persistently over the last four decades, though on its western and southern margins there has been a substantial recovery since the Second World War. Beyond the coalfield boundary, west and south Lancashire are areas of persistent population increase. Almost every aspect of current industrial trends suggests that this general remodelling of the population pattern must continue.

CHAPTER 10

North and West Lancashire

THOUGH Lancashire contains an urban population of almost five millions, it is at the same time one of the richest agricultural regions of Great Britain. It is not difficult to divide rural from industrial Lancashire, for with the significant exceptions of Preston and Merseyside the edge of the coalfield sets a northern and western limit to manufacturing on a grand scale and its attendant town growth. Some weakening of this distinction has followed the modern preference for non-coalfield factory sites, but the bulk of this recent industrial growth has been confined to the Mersey–Irwell belt of the south. There is still a contrast of startling clarity between the line of cotton-weaving towns which fills the Blackburn–Burnley lowland and the wooded rural landscapes of the Ribble valley scarcely 5 miles to the north. To stand on the crest of the grit ridge which limits the coalfield here is to see two Lancashires, divided by one of the sharpest economic boundaries in Great Britain. The industrialised coalfield is equally clearly divided from rural west Lancashire. Here, too, a bold cuesta limits the coalfield, and its crest commands views of some of Great Britain's richest farmland, to the west, and, to the east, some of its most hideously ravaged industrial landscapes.

In this chapter an account is given of the essentially rural regions of west and north Lancashire, beyond the margins of the coalfield. Rural Lancashire consists of a number of diverse sub-regions: the Ribble valley and Bowland Forest, the Fylde and the Lonsdale coastlands, the superb farmlands of coastal southwest Lancashire, and, lastly, Furness, Lancashire 'beyond the Sands'. Though all these areas are overwhelmingly agricultural they have not entirely escaped the effects of the industrial and urban revolution. The cotton industry spread weakly to some of the market towns; some, also, have acquired more modern industries. The suburban spread from towns like Preston has affected parts of the region, and its coast is dominated by a line of resorts, now throwing their outer suburbs into their rural hinterland. Indeed, there are few districts left in which the rural population outnumbers the urban.

Fell and plain landscapes

There are vigorous contrasts in the physical landscapes of rural Lancashire; and since these profoundly influence its types of farming they are discussed briefly here to supplement the general account given in Chapter 2. The noble mass of Bowland Forest is the wildest of Lancastria's Carboniferous uplands. Formed from sandstones, grits, limestones, and shales buckled into regular ENE–WSW folds, its bleak, heathy slopes rise to tabular summit plateaux which are one of the very few completely unpopulated parts of Lancastria. The seaward face of Bowland falls abruptly to the drift plain of the Fylde by steep faulted slopes, broken only by the narrow cloughs of the Wyre and Calder valleys. To the north the upland is less clearly limited. The last outpost of the gritstone moorland is the smooth anticlinal ridge of Quernmoor, overlooking Lancaster. But to the north of the broad terraced valley of the Lune, Carboniferous Limestones continue, to form low, broken lines of wooded hills, a varied hinterland to an attractive coastline along which limestone knolls rise above sheets of tidal alluvium, some saltmarsh and a 'raised beach' partly covered by peat.

Bowland's gentlest and most productive face is turned southwards, where the broad valleys of the Loud and Hodder, given over to a varied pastoral agriculture, are scarcely marred by a single red-brick or factory chimney though they lie almost on the threshold of urban Lancashire. Southwards beyond the cuesta of Longridge fell, an outlier of Bowland, lies the Ribble valley, in which the broad shelves of old, uplifted valley floors descend stair-like to the alluvial terraces bordering the meandering stream. The Ribble valley is in some senses a zone of transition between industrial and rural Lancashire. For the most part it has an unspoilt countryside of chiefly pastoral agriculture, but at Clitheroe water power and limestone stimulated the growth of both a cotton industry and a cement manufacture; and elsewhere, at Ribchester and Longridge, smaller industrial villages have grown.

West of Bowland lies the low, blunt peninsula of the Fylde. Seen from the fells this seems a flat, featureless plain fringed by an untidy line of resort building; but closer inspection reveals much variety. In essence it is a drift plain built of boulder clays and isolated sandpatches which totally obscure the underlying Triassic sandstones and marls. In places the clay surface gives a hint of ill-formed drumlins and stadial moraines; but its relief, like that of the very similar clay plain of Cheshire, is chiefly the result of its dissection by an intricate system of brooks. Below the level of the drift surface there are spreads of tidal and river alluvium standing scarcely above sea level. Until their drainage in the last century these were either marshland—of both salt and freshwater types—or peatmoss. Thus extensive areas in the southwestern angle of the Fylde, along the north coast of the peninsula and in the Wyre valley, were waste until improving landlords set to work on them. Today these areas have 'new' landscapes of reclamation, with neat, regularly spaced, brick farmhouses set on straight roads beside the drainage ditches which divide the land into large rectangular fields. The 'old' landscapes of the slightly higher drift surfaces are quite different: settlement is clustered into compact villages of Anglo-Saxon or Norse origin; fields are small, hedged, and irregular; and the system of lanes is old and chaotic. So intricately varied are these landscape contrasts in the Fylde that a climb up a clay scar only 25 feet high will take one from the new countryside to the old, from land which has yet to bear its hundredth harvest to fields which have been tilled, in some cases, from the seventh century.

In the coastlands south of the Ribble contrasts in landscape have similar physical roots but are more regular and less intricately varied than in the Fylde. In southwest Lancashire there are several distinct physical zones aligned roughly parallel with the coast to form a descending staircase of four levels, each with a distinctive landscape. The highest, the eastern limit of the west Lancashire plain, is the faulted Carboniferous cuesta of the Ashhurst–Billinge ridge, the dipslope of which falls eastwards to the ravaged landscapes of the Wigan coalfield. In the crest of the ridge traces of a 500-foot erosion level have been identified, but the scarp-face falls abruptly seawards to a much broader, 250-foot-high platform which is clearly of erosional origin, for it continues without a break from Triassic to Carboniferous materials. A patchy superficial cover of boulder clay Shirdley Hill Sand, and peat obliterates minor irregularities in the 'solid' surface and accentuates its tabular form. In general, especially in the Ormskirk area, the level surfaces and varied soils of the 250-foot platform are superbly farmed, but part of it has the quite different landscape of an abandoned coalfield. Faulting has uplifted the detached Skelmersdale coal basin through the Trias, and this long-dead outlier of the Lancashire coalfield is a perfect example of an abandoned coalfield which has reverted to an indifferent agriculture. Here colliers' rows stand incongruously on country lanes far from the nearest working collieries; the crumbling pitheads are almost lost beneath banks of brambles; and the old mineral lines make convenient footpaths. But this curious landscape will not survive much longer, for the site has been selected as a New Town (Skelmersdale) which will take a substantial overspill population from Liverpool.

The tabular surface of the 250-foot platform terminates abruptly to the west in a pronounced scarp (seen best at Clieve Hill) which is entirely an erosional form, indeed a degraded cliff-line of preglacial age. From its foot extends one of the undulating drift plains so characteristic of Lancastria; in part the surface is so flat that hesitant drainage made possible the growth of peat, which covered a large area in Longton Moss southwest of Preston. A thin veil of Shirdley Hill Sand, too, covers part of the surface. This boulder clay plain lying at about 100 feet above sea level has a clear limit to the west, where a clay cliff rarely more than 20 feet in height separates it from a lower and completely level surface formed of peat-covered tidal silt, which extends to the dunes and salt marshes of the coast. This degraded cliff is an early postglacial shoreline, the 'Hillhouse coast', washed by the sea some 8,000 years ago. With the postglacial rise in land level and the accumulation of beach material in front of it, the sea gradually left this old coastline and retreated to its present position, and between the old and new shorelines a broad belt of estuarine 'Downholland' silt was left. On this dead-flat, ill-drained surface at only 10 to 15 feet above sea level peat developed after a brief period of forest growth to form the continuous belt of mossland from the Douglas to the Alt. Waste and unpeopled for countless generations, this is now farmland of supreme fertility with the open landscape of reclamation agriculture.

Types of farming

Such great differences in altitude, soil, and climate and in accessibility to urban markets have induced a varied pattern of farming types. These range from the intensive arable cultivation of southwest Lancashire to the struggling stock rearing of the upper Bowland valleys, from the glass-roofed tomato houses of the Fylde to the balanced, general farming of the Ribble valley.

The coastlands from the Ribble to the suburban fringe of Merseyside are by far the richest land in Lancashire; indeed, on the official land-classification map they form a block of first-class arable soil second in extent only to the drained fenland of East Anglia. Except for the fragments of undrained peat and the coastal saltmarsh at least four-fifths of the land is cropped, and in a sample of thirty-one farms recently studied by the Department of Agricultural Economics at Manchester University the total arable acreage was 96% of the farm area. Soil rather than climate is the dominant reason for this arable specialisation. Once drained and cultivated the peats have immense fertility, and though the soils derived from Shirdley Hill Sand are less rich their lightness gives them a greater versatility; easy to plough, they warm quickly in spring and are suitable for 'early' crops. Only the heavier boulder clays give damp, cold soils difficult to plough after wet weather. The most favourable elements in climate are the low cloudiness and consequently high sunshine totals; these encourage grain cultivation, an important interest of the west Lancashire farmer.

This region is almost unique in Atlantic Britain as one in which farm income is derived almost entirely from crops—and largely from grain—with no significant contribution from stock. About half the acreage is devoted to the cereals (wheat, oats, and barley), roughly one-fifth to potatoes, and one-tenth to market garden crops. Dairy herds are kept only on a few farms, usually to consume part of the hay worked into the rotation

228

as a rest period. Sheep are unknown except for seasonal flocks in autumn, but pigs and especially poultry are more important enterprises. Fodder roots have little place in the system, but oats and hay are sold to east Lancashire dairy farms, from which farmyard manure is returned to help to sustain the intensity of west Lancashire cultivation.

Such intense arable specialisation has its dangers, of which the most serious is the eel-worm risk to potatoes, especially on peat soils. This has led to a minor agrarian revolution around Ormskirk, where cabbages and other green vegetables have partly replaced the potatoes once grown almost as a monoculture. Sugar beet is a crop of recent introduction, and many farmers have turned to high-value vegetable crops grown almost with nursery intensity for canning and freezing. Market gardening of a very intensive type has long been established near Hesketh Bank, where varied peat and sand soils combine with a mild coastal climate to produce one of the richest farming districts of the country.

It would be misleading to suggest that there is only a single, standard system of farming in west Lancashire of the type described above. In fact the sharp contrasts in soil type are reflected in great differences in farming practice. The drained peats are most completely arable, for permanent grassland here is restricted to tiny paddocks. Yet the rich peats have serious limitations, for they are both highly acid and especially liable to frost, with a significantly shorter growing season than on nearby sand and boulder clays. Only a few crops are suited to the peats, though these yield heavily. Oats and maincrop potatoes are dominant, while rotational grass and special vegetable crops like celery and lettuce occupy smaller acreages. The light, dry, warm soils derived from Shirdley Hill Sands are more versatile; where they were capped thinly by peat they are strong soils, but otherwise they need heavy fertilisation. Many crops compete for space in the complex rotation practised on the sands: early potatoes, peas, and brassicas are all widely grown. These sands are the chief wheat soils of west Lancashire, and clover-grass meadows are grown as short leys. Drift clays give much heavier soils on which such an intensive arable system would be impossible. Here permanent grass occupies a substantial proportion of the acreage; with fodder roots and sown hay it provides feed for the dairy herds which become much more prominent on the clay landscapes.

Since the Fylde has strong physical parallels with west Lancashire one would expect to find here a similar range of farming systems. But this is by no means generally true, in consequence chiefly of the much smaller scale and lower capitalisation of Fylde farming. In patches and pockets of drained peat an intensive arable agriculture of west Lancashire type can be seen, for example in the old mossland of Over-Wyre, where its chief products are oats and potatoes. Behind Blackpool an area of blown sand lying on peat has been developed for market gardening, both to supply the resort and for sale southwards; the immense area of glass for tomato and flower

229

cultivation is the most notable feature. And some of the best-drained tidal and river marshes, the Ribble for example, support intensive cropping in huge fields bounded by the ditches of the reclaimers.

But Fylde agriculture is not as uniformly prosperous and intensive as that of west Lancashire. The boulder clay soils are indifferent in quality. Once Lancashire's granary, they were grossly overworked in oats production, so that by the early nineteenth century they were exhausted and sterile. Slowly farmers on these sticky clays worked out their economic salvation through intensive dairying—once for cheese, but now for liquid milk—coupled with poultry farming, which here reaches its most specialised development in Great Britain. Today the clay grasslands of the Fylde support a dairy system closely similar to that of Cheshire. Most land is under grass in long leys. Before the Second World War this provided only half the feed, and the rest consisted of imported concentrates; now grass-clover crops and roots are grown more extensively, to save the high cost of bought feed. Stocking ratios are high: typically there is one dairy cow to every two acres of land.

Dairy stock are brought to the Fylde from the upland pastoral farms of Lonsdale and Bowland and serve a fairly short period of milk production before being sold. Beef stock are not common in the Fylde except for the rougher country of the Bowland flank, where they may outnumber dairy stock. Sheep are a winter but not a summer feature of the Fylde landscape; most are hill flocks brought down for winter and to lamb, but there are permanent flocks on the coastal saltmarshes. Poultry are found everywhere, especially on the small farms of the glacial soils, and they are kept increasingly on the battery system. A typical holding has a stock of 1,500, kept on about 50 acres of land. Many poultry farms are completely specialised and depend wholly on the purchase of feed; in other cases poultry rearing is an important enterprise on mixed farms. Many of these latter keep pigs, fed partly on the abundant waste food of the Fylde resorts.

On the varied landscapes of extreme north Lancashire, in the Lune valley and the shorelands of Morecambe Bay, agriculture is almost entirely pastoral. The great bulk of the area consists of permanent grassland and rough grazing, on which sheep outnumber cattle by roughly five to one. Crops take only a tiny proportion of the farmland except on the drained lands near the coast and the Lune terraces; but everywhere a high rainfall, which averages more than 70 inches per annum on the fells, limits ploughing.

Traditionally the rearing of beef cattle on the rich pastures of the valleys and lower slopes and of sheep on the fells were the twin supports of north Lancashire farming, and this system has not been radically modified by the passage of time. This is both a fattening and a breeding region, which both 'imports' and 'exports' beasts. Most 'imported' cattle are young stores from Ireland and Scotland; when 'finished' they are sold for beef in south

Lancashire markets. But many of the heifers reared here are sold to farmers in the Fylde and south Lancashire as replacements in dairy herds. Many farmers with access to fellside or saltmarsh keep considerable numbers of sheep; and these, rather than the specialised sheep farmers of the higher ground, are responsible for the area's fat-lamb production. Some lowland farms have developed dairying for the supply of the Lancaster–Morecambe conurbation of some 90,000 people; and close to this considerable market there is intensive vegetable growing on the mild coastlands.

Farming in the Ribble valley is perhaps less specialised and more general than in any other part of Lancashire. In the past a beefstock rearing and fattening area, it has been incompletely invaded by the spread of dairying and, in slighter measure, poultry keeping for the nearby market of the cotton-weaving towns. This growth of dairying has stimulated cropping, chiefly for hay and fodder roots, and the alluvial terraces, especially, are now partly under the plough. But in the remoter recesses of the area these changes have made little progress: in the Hodder valley against the southern flank of Bowland there is scarcely an acre under the plough, except for the re-seeding of pastures. Yet even here change is coming, for the motor truck can collect milk from the remotest farms, so that most now have at least a small dairy herd. At higher levels on the north flank of the Ribble valley sheep displace cattle. Many of these high farms run flocks of 1,000 or more on acreages which range up to 2,000 or 3,000 including their fell rights.

Population trends in rural Lancashire

In general, population changes in the rural areas of north and west Lancashire over the past century have been the reverse of those in the urban-industrial regions of the south. Since the middle of the nineteenth century rural Lancashire has lost population by persistent migration to the towns, except for the non-typical districts in which there was industrial or resort development or in which land reclamation was on a scale large enough radically to modify population trends. Yet during the last thirty years many rural districts have experienced sharp increases of population at a time when very large sections of industrial Lancashire were suffering rapid losses. The decentralisation of industry and the increasingly wide dispersal of dormitory populations are the two chief reasons for this reversal of rural population trends.

The population history of the Fylde is characteristic of that of rural Lancashire as a whole, for after a long period of general decline there has followed, during the present century, a period of rapid and almost universal increase. Rural migration from the Fylde began on a serious scale only after 1851. During the first half of the nineteenth century population was still growing, even in parishes unaffected by improved communications, for this was the period of maximum effort in mossland reclamation. The population increased by more than 50% in some of the remote mossland parishes north of the Wyre between 1801 and 1851. The second half of the century saw a reversal of this trend: now most of the Fylde except the resort coast experienced heavy outward migration. In eighteen completely rural parishes the population declined continuously between 1851 and 1901, in some cases by as much as 40%, and by 1901 eleven of these parishes had smaller totals than in 1801. But on the west coast and in the south of the Fylde rapid growth was taking place: at Lytham, St Annes, and Blackpool the railways created resort towns, while Fleetwood grew as a packet station and fishing port. By 1901 this coastal belt contained a population of more than 80,000, an increase from scarcely 10,000 in 1851. Kirkham and Wesham grew earlier but more slowly for other reasons, for this was the extreme northwestern outpost of the cotton industry.

Over the rural Fylde, with few exceptions, population reached its nadir at the time of the First World War and has grown strongly since. This increase has come chiefly since 1931, for the Fylde Rural District grew by only 3% in the decade 1921–31 but by 76% between 1931 and 1951. The 1951–61 increase was only 6% in this rural district which was seriously affected by the closure of military establishments, for the other rural districts which cover parts of the Fylde—Garstang and Preston—recorded continuing strong increases. This growth has been unequally distributed: it has been strongest in the immediate hinterland of the resort belt and beyond the northern fringes of Preston, where suburbs have begun to penetrate the countryside. But almost every Fylde parish has increased its population at least slightly, in some cases perhaps partly through the intensification of a formerly depressed agriculture, but chiefly by the addition of small dormitory and retired populations. Except for the flanks of Bowland, only the Rawcliffes, remote parishes in the heart of the Over–Wyre mossland, had declines in population between 1931 and 1951. But in the pastoral country of the slopes of Bowland, unaffected by the penetration of an 'adventitious' population, losses continued in most parishes during the decade 1951–61.

Elsewhere in rural Lancashire these same tendencies are repeated with little variation: the rural areas with easy access to the towns have grown through the suburban dispersal but elsewhere, except where a little industry has been established, rural depopulation continues as the mechanisation of agriculture proceeds and as the attractions of town life draw young people from the farms. The population of the West Lancashire Rural District, which now covers 103 square miles, grew by 69% from 1931 to 1951 and by 39% from 1951 to 1961. But almost all of this growth can be accounted for by the peripheral expansion of Merseyside and Southport; parishes beyond their influence have lost a little population or just held their 1931 totals. Thus Maghull parish quadrupled in population over the twenty years 1931–51, while Ince Blundell lost one-quarter of its inhabitants; the 1961

Census confirms that the remoter parishes, for example Hesketh, are still losing population.

In the deeper rural areas of the Lune and Ribble valleys and of Bowland emigration has been continuous and heavy for almost as long as the census has recorded population. Bleasdale and Nether Wyresdale, parishes of the west slope of Bowland, have experienced a 30% population loss since 1821, and of this 5% has occurred since 1931. On the southern flanks of the fells depopulation has been hastened by reservoir construction and afforestation; for example the forty-six farms which existed in the Hodder catchment area in 1912 have been reduced to six. The seven parishes of this valley had almost 4,000 inhabitants in 1831, but by 1931 this had fallen to 2,300. Modest increases since have been confined to the two villages, Chipping and Newton, which have attracted small suburban and retired communities.

Whether these rural population losses will continue seems doubtful even in the most remote parishes. Certainly, farm populations seem bound to decline further; but the present signs are that this will be more than balanced by a growth of 'adventitious' population. Universal car ownership is coming quickly to Great Britain, and it is already virtually established among the middle class. Since no part of rural Lancashire is as much as an hour's drive from a large urban centre, the entire countryside is now open to the townsman. The consequences are already evident in the conversion of farms and cottages for suburban and retired families, and in the small but significant accretions to the villages. Strict planning control will prevent the wholesale invasion of the countryside, but much of it is experiencing social changes which are not expressed in terms of new bricks and mortar (Plate 13).

The changing functions of market towns

Traditionally, the rural areas of west and north Lancashire have been served by a small number of market towns, widely spaced and of substantial size. The market village never had much significance in the commercial life of the county, and these smaller centres were all, in time, overwhelmed by the rivalry of their larger neighbours. Thus Euxton and Croston once had markets, and the hamlet of Inglewhite a cattle fair; but all lapsed long ago. By 1800 there were only half a dozen towns in rural Lancashire with any pretensions to market status and even these were becoming increasingly dominated by the two major regional centres, Preston and Lancaster. Kirkham and Poulton served the Fylde, Garstang the east Fylde and western Bowland, Clitheroe the Ribble valley, and Ormskirk the rich farmlands of west Lancashire. Today few of these are market towns in the sense that they handle the farm produce of their hinterlands, for most goes directly by truck to the great cities; but they are all still important shopping, social, and service centres for the surrounding countryside. Their fortunes over the past century have depended chiefly upon the degree to which they have attracted industry; and today they show sharp contrasts in size and function (Plate 9).

An industrial invasion of the market towns began over a century ago with the growth and dispersal of the cotton industry. Two towns, Kirkham and Clitheroe, were strongly affected by this. In the former an old linen manufacture was replaced by a new cotton industry, sited chiefly in the adjoining township of Wesham, where an industrial suburb which might have been lifted from Bolton or Oldham was planted incongruously beside the attractive Georgian nucleus of old Kirkham. Clitheroe's conversion to a cotton town began earlier and more strongly than Kirkham's. This is reflected in their contrasted population trends, for though both had roughly 3,000 inhabitants in 1821 Clitheroe had become a town of 12,000 a century later, while Kirkham was still below 4,000. Water power from the Ribble was the dominant factor in the quick growth of Clitheroe's cotton industry, and the great Low Moor mills beside the river were one of the largest units in the old water-powered industry.

Like the cotton towns of southeast Lancashire, Kirkham and Clitheroe have suffered from the decline of the textile industry. As remote outliers, their cotton manufactures experienced especially rapid decline; for example, Clitheroe's mill employment fell by 60% between 1931 and 1951, and today cotton provides only 18% of the work in the town. Fortunately, both have other industrial interests. Aircraft manufacture and nuclear research have been established close to Kirkham, which is becoming a dormitory town despite its acquisition of new industries on a small scale. Its market is now dead, except for the customary survival of retail stalls in the old market place. Clitheroe, in contrast, still has the air and the functions of a strong market centre, drawing cattle and sheep to its auction sales from the whole of the Ribble basin despite the strong competition of Hellifield and Skipton. Limestone quarrying and cement manufacture, based on the anticlinal exposure of Carboniferous Limestones in the valley floor, are today its most important sources of male employment. The decline of the once-dominant cotton industry is reflected in the recent population trends of both Clitheroe and Kirkham. The population of the former has been virtually stagnant at a little over 12,000 since 1921, clear evidence that the town has been unable to retain and absorb its own now-dwindling natural increase. Kirkham's population trends are confused by the opening and abandonment of military camps; but the Registrar General's estimates of civil population show virtually no change from 1951 onwards.

Ormskirk, long the chief market centre of the productive plain of west Lancashire, has little in common with Kirkham or Clitheroe. Until recently, it remained more truly a market town which handled much of the produce, and especially the potatoes, of the arable farms of the plain. Though the open market now survives only in a retail form, a substantial trade in agricultural produce still passes through the town, which contains the offices of wholesale merchants and the local headquarters of the Potato Marketing Board. But the patterns of trade in arable products are changing: many crops are now grown under direct contract for canning or freezing; and the merchant has no place in such a system. Thus the town's position as the commercial focus of the west Lancashire plain is weaker than it was in the inter-war period. As a retail shopping centre, too, its influence has been eroded to some degree by the effect of modern road transport in making both Southport and Liverpool much more easily accessible to the country population. Though this loss of purchasing power has been more than balanced by the growth of a dormitory population, there is no doubt that the links between Ormskirk and its countryside have been seriously weakening in the last quarter-century.

Ormskirk is a growing but a changing town. In the twenty years from 1931 to 1951 its population increased by one-fifth to 20,000; and though the rate slackened to 6·5% during the decade 1951–61 this was chiefly because most new building lay just outside the urban district boundaries, where the parish of Aughton grew by over 45% during the decade. Two factors are responsible for this growth: suburban migration to the area from Merseyside, and the development of a wider range of industries. The electrification of the railway line to Liverpool in 1909 was the chief stimulus to dormitory growth, which is focused on the nearby village of Aughton rather than on the town itself, though roughly one-quarter of its occupied population travels out daily, mainly to Merseyside. But Ormskirk's industrial growth has been so strong that this outflow is more than balanced by the inward movement of labour from the countryside and from the old mining village of Skelmersdale, close by, to the factories in and near the town. Most unusually, even for the market towns of Lancashire, the industries are in part associated with an outgrowth from local agriculture; the manufacture of potato crisps and the assembly of farm machinery are two examples of this. Flour milling and confectionery manufacture have more distant local roots, if any, for the raw material is largely imported. Light engineering and clothing are, in a sense, intrusive industries. Today Ormskirk still has something of the atmosphere of a market town but the functions, rather, of a dormitory and light industry centre. The importance of the last of these is somewhat masked, for the chief cluster of factories is not in the town but some 3 miles away at the railway and canal junction of Burscough Bridge. It will be interesting to observe the effect on Ormskirk of the development of a New Town at Skelmersdale, 5 miles away. Certainly this must be to Ormskirk's great advantage as a shopping centre.

Lancaster is best described as the largest of Lancashire's market towns. It is not, in an administrative sense, the county town; and though it now has a wide range of industry its traditional status as the regional centre for north Lancashire still dominates its life. Its livestock market is one of the largest in the Northwest, and it still sends beefstock and store cattle southwards for fattening and slaughter as it has done for centuries. As a shopping, business, and social centre Lancaster has lost little of its traditional importance, for it is too far from its larger southern rivals to feel the effect of their competition. Morecambe, the most northerly of the large resorts, lies immediately to the west, and Lancaster's retail trade benefits from the seasonal influx of visitors. The occupations which derive directly from its service functions—professional, distributive, and service employment—provide work for almost one-third of Lancaster's occupied population; and on a market day, especially, the streets have the air of a busy country town, scarcely affected by industrialisation.

Lancaster's industry is unobtrusive to the casual visitor, yet it provides more work than the service occupations. The town has had a long but a rather uncertain history of industrial development. From its brief years of prosperity as a port engaged in the West Indian and African trade an important furniture manufacture grew; but the largest of the firms has recently closed. The port's links with America, the growth of commercial capital in the town, and the construction of the canal southwards to Preston all contributed to the establishment of the cotton manufacture in Lancaster. But the mills suffered in an extreme degree all the disadvantages of remoteness from both Manchester and Liverpool (the chief market for cloth and the port of entry of the raw material), and the cotton industry has both declined and changed in form. Lancaster has turned from cotton to rayon and to the synthetic fibres which have proved the salvation of a number of the most remote outliers of the Lancashire textile industry. Oilcloth and linoleum manufacture, which succeeded cotton as Lancaster's staple industry, is in two senses the derivative of the older trade, for it uses a coarse textile base, and it took over former cotton mills left empty by depression when it began to grow in the period 1844–70. The linoleum industry, like the town's textile manufacture, has proved itself adaptable to changing trends; for with the development of plastics it has turned to this new material for the production of floor coverings, decorative sheeting, and leathercloth. Two large companies are engaged in this trade; with a total of over 2,000 workers, they are by far the town's biggest employers. Moreover, they have helped to keep the cotton industry alive, for two of the surviving mills produce the textile base for plastic coating.

Lancaster's industrial adaptability has not been able to save it from some slight decline in population, by rather less than 2% during the decade 1951–61. But this loss is more apparent than real. Morecambe is an attractive and convenient dormitory for Lancaster, with which it is connected by electric railway, and the latter's losses are almost exactly balanced by the former's gains. Many of the country parishes beyond the town's boundary, too, have grown during the past decade; and a diffuse straggle of part-dormitory, part-resort development is forming along the coast to the north. Two great changes will have a considerable impact on Lancaster:

TABLE 2

THE LANCASHIRE RESORTS:
SOCIAL AND ECONOMIC STATISTICS FOR 1951 AND 1961

	SOUTH-PORT	LYTHAM ST ANNES	BLACK-POOL	THORNTON CLEVELEYS	FLEET-WOOD	MORE-CAMBE†
Occupied population as percentage of total	43	43	46	41	45	45
Retired population as percentage of total	14	12*	13	17*	8*	15*
Percentage of occupied population working elsewhere (daily outflow)	20	25	16	33	9	29
Percentage of employed population resident elsewhere (daily inflow)	9	23	8	50	15	12
Percentage of labour employed in:						
Manufactures	23	18	19	35	27	25
Distribution	20	15	19	8	18	15
Miscellaneous services	21	22	28	10	8	26
Agriculture and fishing	4	2	2	4	17	1
Transport	7	5	8	2	16	13
Total population:						
1951	84,039	30,343	147,332	15,443	27,537	37,006
1961 ‡	82,004	36,189	153,185	20,648	27,686	40,228
Per cent increase: 1951–61 †	2·4	19·3	4	33·7	0·8	8·7

* Data for the retired female population are not given in the census for towns of lower status than the county boroughs. The figures quoted above are estimates derived by assuming that the ratio of male to female retired population for the county boroughs holds good for the county districts.

† The employment data for Morecambe include figures for the refineries just outside the town.

‡ All the other figures are for 1951.

a university is being built, on a site to the south of the town, and the motorway link to the south brings the town to within a morning's journey of Birmingham. The isolation and remoteness of north Lancashire, never quite destroyed by canal or railway connections, are unlikely to endure.

The resorts and their contrasts

The coastlands of rural Lancashire are much more heavily urbanised than any part of their hinterland, for the broad sandy beaches between the muddy estuaries with their ports were obvious and logical sites for the growth of holiday towns. Between Formby Point and the Kent estuary shallow strips of resort development fringe some 30 miles of coast, nowhere extending inland for more than 3 miles. Though the holiday trade is the dominant factor in the growth of all these towns, no two Lancashire resorts are alike, either in physical appearance or economic character. They have acquired other functions than their tourist industries, and today none is simply a resort. Some, especially Southport, have become dormitories for distant cities; most have large retired populations. All, but especially Blackpool, have become significant centres of industry; indeed, they have found it much easier to acquire new manufactures than the textile towns of eastern Lancashire. Even in their tourist trade the Lancashire resorts differ. Southport, through its very close proximity to Merseyside and central Lancashire, is much visited by the day tripper. Blackpool's superbly efficient holiday industry caters for the working masses, while nearby St Annes is much the most middle class of the resorts. Unlike the others, Morecambe has always looked chiefly to a Yorkshire hinterland, reached by the 'Little North Western' and Midland railways through the Lune–Wenning gap to the upper Aire valley. Two resorts, Fleetwood and Heysham (Morecambe) are minor ports of a specialised type.

Each Lancashire resort has an individual personality, but all have a number of features and problems in common. All have statistically abnormal populations. The working proportions of their populations are far below the average, a reflection of their large retired and dormitory communities. All have an unbalanced age structure with excessive proportions of people aged sixty and above. The sources of local employment are much the same in the six different towns. The percentage in manufacturing industries is low, but in the service industries and distributive trades high, in consequence of the high level of spending among their visitors and their prosperous retired and dormitory elements. In the truest resorts the largest single provider of work is the miscellaneous service group, which includes catering, entertainment, and the other characteristic activities of a holiday town. Every resort suffers, to some degree, from the almost insoluble problem of seasonal unemployment, for the holiday trades offer little winter work. This is one of the attractions of resorts for the manufacturing industries, which can draw upon this surplus of labour but may then create a summer shortage, met by the 'import' of casual workers.

Of all the Lancashire resorts Southport, the oldest, is now least dependent on the holiday trade. Alone among the county's—indeed, also among the country's—resorts, it was in its origins a product of the canal age, for families came by packet boats along the Leeds and Liverpool Canal to Scarisbrick Bridge a few miles inland. The railways to Liverpool and Manchester gave a much greater stimulus to its growth, and during the whole of the nineteenth century this was Lancashire's leading resort. Southport has changed so radically in economic character during the present century that it is no longer correct to describe it simply as a resort. It is an outer suburb of Merseyside, the result of railway electrification and the improvement of the main coastal road. It has, also, a considerable retired population, attracted partly by its reputation for extreme climatic mildness, which has little statistical support. Recently, too, it has made surprising, through inconspicuous, industrial progress (Fig. 57).

A purely physical disadvantage has adversely affected Southport's holiday trade: the enormous supply of silt brought from the south by long-shore drift has led to such rapid coastal accretion that the sea is rapidly retreating from the town. Even by taking a train along the mile-long pier the visitor may catch only a distant glimpse of the sea at low tide, and the prospective bather may have a walk of 2 miles to reach the very gentle waves of the extensive shallows.[1] But the reluctance of the sea to wash Southport has been turned to advantage, for a broad strip of the old beach has been reclaimed at low cost for gardens, pleasure grounds, and a very large boating pool now being extended by further reclamation. Certainly Southport is the most spaciously planned of the resorts, partly for this reason and partly because of the precocious planning controls imposed by its original landowners. The broad tree-lined boulevard of Lord Street—surely one of the finest shopping streets in Great Britain—and the sweep of the promenade overlooking not the sea but magnificent gardens on reclaimed land are enduring achievements of nineteenth century planning. There has been significant but completely unobtrusive industrial growth in Southport, chiefly in well-hidden sites on the landward side. Light engineering, clothing, and food and drink factories employ substantial numbers of workers, many of whom are drawn from the agricultural hinterland. Surprisingly, in this dormitory and resort town the manufacturing industries are the largest employers of labour, and the problem of seasonal unemployment is comparatively slight.

Lytham and its newer neighbour St Annes (they are united as a single municipal borough) closely resemble Southport not only in their appearance and atmosphere but also in their social structure and urban functions. Lytham was Southport's first rival: a railway to Preston was completed by 1846 and gave Lytham, then an insignificant port, access to the developing railway network of the Northwest. After a short period of vigorous growth Lytham has rather languished as a resort, though it has continued to

---

[1] But there are signs of change in the coastline: see footnote on p. 21.

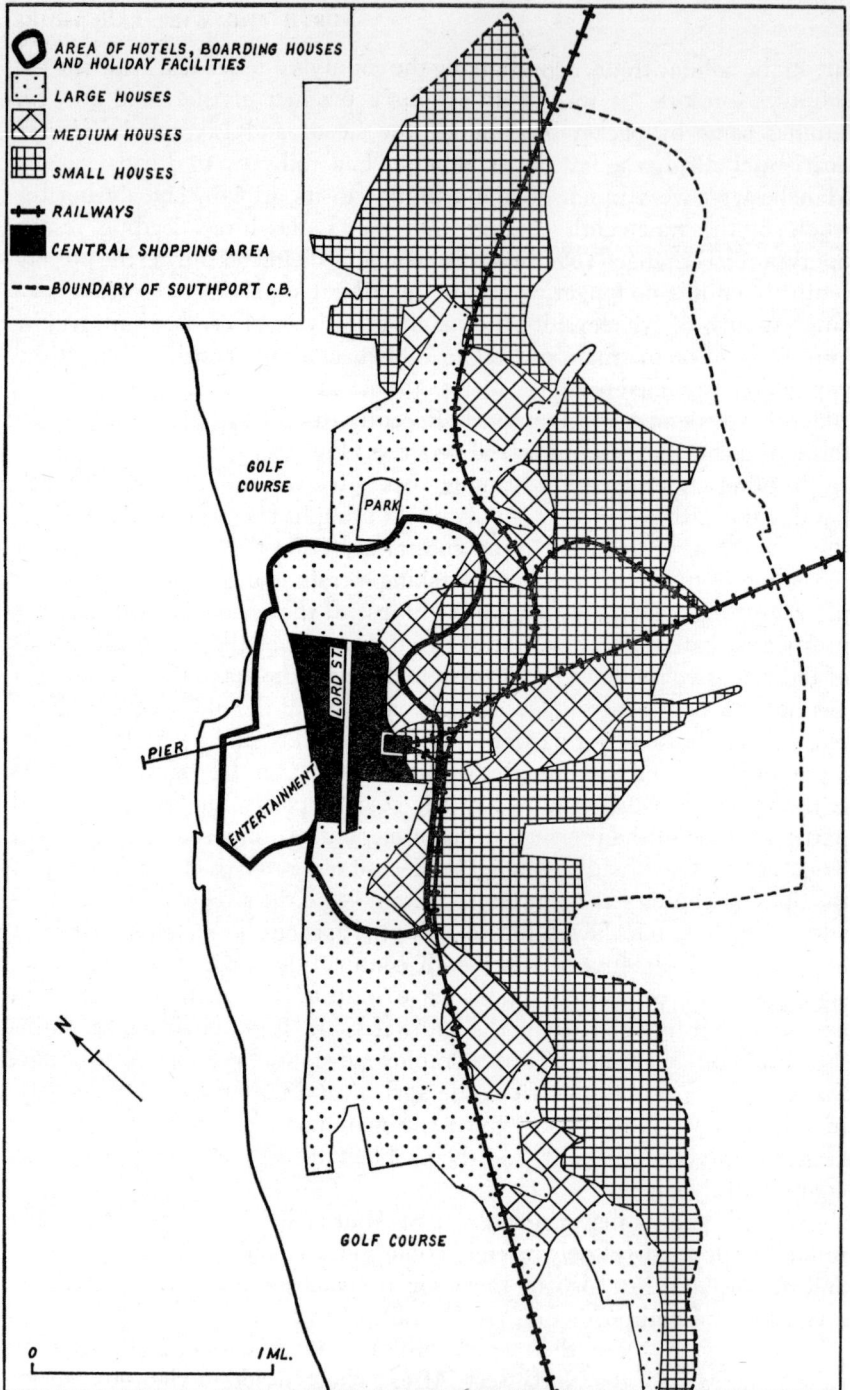

Fig. 57 THE URBAN MORPHOLOGY OF SOUTHPORT. Like most seaside holiday and residential towns, Southport has a linear form along the coast. In the main it is a residential town with a fine shopping quarter and a variety of social and athletic facilities.

develop as a residential town. It could not match what its rivals to the north and south all possessed, a beach of firm clean sand. At Lytham the silting of the Ribble estuary is proceeding so quickly that the town overlooks flat mudbanks whose growth was probably accelerated by the dredging and embanking of the navigation channel to Preston during the nineteenth century (Fig. 58).

St Annes has virtually superseded Lytham as a resort for it grew on a site some 2 miles farther north where the mudbanks are replaced by firm sandy beaches. St Annes is a planned town, developed with close control behind a broad dune-belt on a magnificent site which scarcely contained a single cottage in 1875. Its growth was spectacular: by 1881 it had 1,000 inhabitants, and within thirty years its population had reached 17,000. This was a rate of expansion which made even the growth of the cotton towns of the coalfield seem sluggish in comparison; and it owed much to the energy of the estate company which developed the site.

Edwardian St Annes contrasts with Victorian Lytham in more than merely its architectural character. The former monopolises the holiday industry of the borough, while the latter is largely a dormitory town with a large retired population, though it also contains most of the very limited industrial development. This twin borough, unlike other Lancashire resorts, has attracted little manufacture, and its present tendency is to become progressively more suburban in function. Commuter expresses have long provided a fast link with Manchester, which is only an hour away, and part of the quick growth of population (by 19%) in the decade 1951–61 reflects the increasing popularity of Lytham St Annes as a dormitory for Preston workers. But this suburban expansion is in no sense incompatible with the prosperity of the holiday trade; indeed, St Annes has a distinctive place in the complex of resorts on the Fylde coast, for it is a citadel of middle class respectability where boarding houses style themselves private hotels and serve dinner—that infallible social symbol—rather than the high tea of Blackpool.

Incomparably the largest resort outside metropolitan England, Blackpool is a town of very recent growth which has passed its Lancashire rivals only during the last half-century. Southport was a thriving resort when Blackpool was merely a single short street of fishermen's cottages and small hotels; even Lytham was larger until 1851. But when the railway reached this superb beach in 1846 resort growth was immediate and spectacular. The spread of prosperity down the social scale in the urban populations of the coalfield together with the institution of the annual holiday of the 'wakes week' gave Blackpool an immense stimulus in the closing decades of the nineteenth century, and during the decade 1871–81 its population doubled—from 7,000 to 14,000.

Blackpool is the best favoured of the Fylde resorts by the processes of coastal geomorphology. To the south the shore is one of rapid accretion

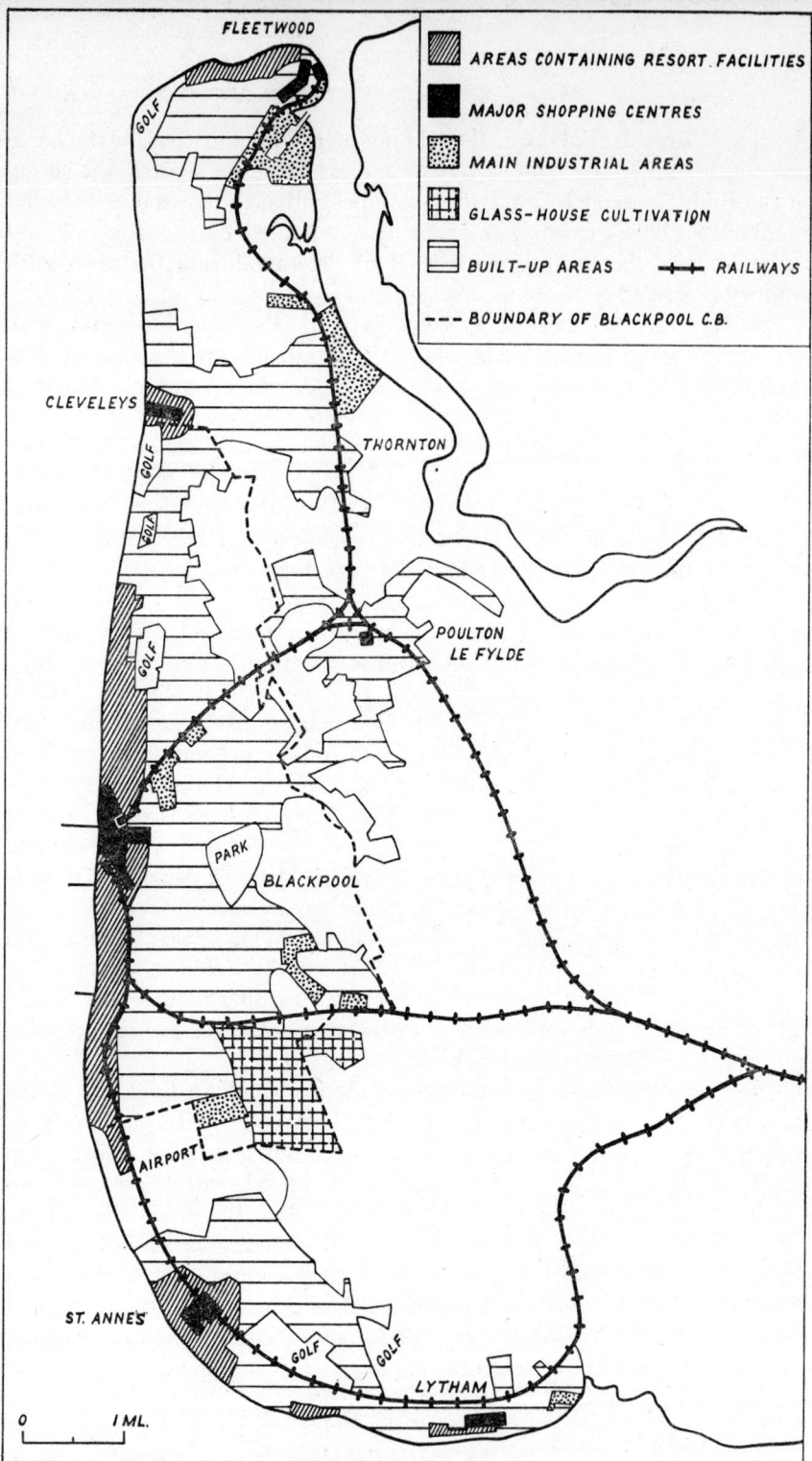

FLEETWOOD

Legend:
- AREAS CONTAINING RESORT FACILITIES
- MAJOR SHOPPING CENTRES
- MAIN INDUSTRIAL AREAS
- GLASS-HOUSE CULTIVATION
- BUILT-UP AREAS
- RAILWAYS
- BOUNDARY OF BLACKPOOL C.B.

GOLF

CLEVELEYS

THORNTON

GOLF

GOLF

POULTON LE FYLDE

GOLF

PARK

BLACKPOOL

AIRPORT

ST. ANNES

GOLF   GOLF

LYTHAM

0   I ML.

Fig. 58 BLACKPOOL AND THE FYLDE COAST. From its beginnings Blackpool catered for 'the humbler creation' and its policy of attracting large crowds has been remarkably successful. Fleetwood combines fishing and industry with holiday catering and the other main centres, Cleveleys, St Annes and Lytham are largely residential with a limited and somewhat discreet provision of resort amenities. The areas away from the sea are favoured by many residents of these Fylde towns for their quietness and relative seclusion.

with a very gently shelving profile, so that at St Annes the sea is scarcely visible at low tide. To the north erosion is much more pronounced, and the quick removal of material of small size by vigorous longshore scouring makes a shingle beach to the south of Fleetwood. But at Blackpool the sandy beach shows no sign either of estuarine mud or shingle, nor is its profile so gentle that the bather needs a bicycle at low tide. Yet the sea has set problems in Blackpool's growth. The boulder clay cliffs of the north shore were suffering active and rapid erosion until expensive coast-defence works were built to protect them (Plate 39).

That the holiday trade is still the foundation of Blackpool's prosperity is shown clearly in Table 2. The combined dormitory and retired population, though numerically large, was in 1951 a smaller proportion than in any other Lancashire resort except for the special case of Fleetwood. Even in the census month of April nearly one-quarter of the employed population was in miscellaneous service industries (most of which depend upon the holiday trade), and at the peak of the season this proportion must rise much higher. Another fifth of the employment in the town is in the distributive trades, the importance of which reflects both the influx of summer visitors and Blackpool's new status as the dominant shopping and commercial centre of the prosperous Fylde. Manufacturing industries have grown in some variety at Blackpool, but their progress has been somewhat uncertain. Consumer goods industries, for example baking, confectionery, and the clothing trades, have developed partly to serve the resort itself; and Blackpool is also a centre for the manufacture of vehicle bodies. But the town's largest industry has deserted it. During the Second World War one of the largest factories in the Northwest was built beside Blackpool airport for aircraft manufacture. Occupied only temporarily since 1945, this is an industrial asset of very great potential importance. There are prospects for its conversion into a vast 'flatted factory' for light manufacturing; if it were reoccupied it would help to cushion the effects of seasonal unemployment in the holiday trades, which is a continuing problem to Blackpool. Unemployment rates regularly rise to high levels during the winter, and the problem is so serious that the town was scheduled as a Development District under the 1960 Local Employment Act.

Thornton Cleveleys and Fleetwood are two contiguous towns to the west of the Wyre estuary, closely linked despite their administrative separation. Fleetwood is almost as new a town as St Annes: it was the product of the railway which reached it in 1840 from Preston coupled with the enterprise of the landowning family from which it takes its name. Fleetwood was intended as a new port, a replacement for the silting harbours of Lancaster and Preston. For a time it was the northern railhead on the London–Glasgow route, and an early steamship, the *Fire King* carried passengers to Scotland. Later packet services operated to the Isle of Man, Dublin, and Belfast; but Fleetwood showed little sign of growing as a cargo

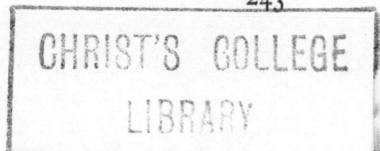

243

port, and the resuscitation of Preston after 1900 ended its hopes. From the closing decades of the nineteenth century it grew as a fishing harbour, and it has now the largest trawler fleet on the west coast of Britain. Today almost exactly half of its occupied male population is employed either in the fishing industry or in the associated handling and transport activities. Marine engineering and fish processing are two other important industries; and Fleetwood depends upon a single dominant activity to a greater degree than almost any other Lancashire town. There is a small holiday trade of slight economic significance, as the low proportion engaged in miscellaneous services (Table 2) indicates. But the catering and entertainment trades usefully absorb some of the surplus female labour which is an economic problem of all ports. Fleetwood has completely failed to attract either a retired or a dormitory population, and it is of little consequence as a shopping and service centre; in all these respects it is unlike its resort neighbours.

Thornton, to the south, has the appearance and atmosphere of a resort but the statistical profile (Table 2) of an industrial town. In fact it has both functions, accommodated on different coasts. The west of Thornton (the Cleveleys area) is a resort with the customary colony of retired people; this is the northern margin of the Blackpool resort conurbation, for to the north the shore becomes shingle and the coastal belt is low with a serious risk of flooding. But the east coast, on the Wyre estuary, is strongly industrial. A chemical manufacture has grown here since 1892, based on brine pumped from salt beds in the Keuper Marls at Preesall on the other bank of the Wyre. This plant, basically an alkali producer, gives employment to about 2,000 workers drawn partly from Fleetwood. The recent announcement that part is to close poses a serious problem for the north Fylde.

The borough of Morecambe and Heysham combines all the functions found in Fleetwood and Thornton Cleveleys, for it is a resort, a port, and a town of some industrial importance. Developed chiefly through its close links with the West Riding by the Midland Railway, Morecambe is the smaller Blackpool of extreme north Lancashire. It has much the same type of holiday trade as its larger rival, which it emulates even to the point of extending its autumn season by offering 'illuminations'. The large retired population and the considerable suburban movement (almost wholly to Lancaster) show that Morecambe has some of the social features typical of the Lancashire resorts. But it has a broader economic base than most. The Midland dock at Heysham, built in 1904 for the Belfast service, adds to the range of local employment; and the development of a complex of oil refining and chemical installations just outside the borough boundary during the Second World War gave it a major new industry.

The resorts of the Lancashire coast vary in age, character, and economic functions, but they have in common a rate of population growth which far exceeds that of the region as a whole; indeed, if the newer suburbs beyond their boundaries are included, this coastal strip is one of the areas of fastest expansion not merely on the regional but also on the national map of population trend. But this growth is not self-sustaining, for it depends on a heavy migration from the rest of Lancashire. Thus the Fylde as a whole grew in population by only 8% from 1951 to 1961, though it experienced a migratory addition of 11%. Its own balance of births against deaths, strongly negative (−3%), reflects the high average age of a population swollen by great numbers of retired people. But there is a strong presumption that the inward migration is not merely of the elderly and that the coastlands are one of the zones of strongest growth in the new Lancashire that is now being shaped.

Furness (Fig. 59)

Lancashire 'beyond the Sands', or Furness, covers some 235 square miles of the Lake District and its margins. It can only be approached from the south by roads or railways which traverse part of Westmorland, but for many centuries the route lay 'across the Sands' of Morecambe Bay. If in 1837 George Stephenson's plan of building a 7-mile embankment to carry the railway from Hest Bank (north of Morecambe) to Humphrey Head in the Cartmel peninsula had been accepted, extensive reclamation would have been possible in Morecambe Bay. From Hest Bank, the one point where the west-coast rail route from London to Glasgow gives one a sea view, the traveller sees the vast expanse of Morecambe Bay, with the lowland areas of Furness, the Furness fells, and the Lake District mountains as a backcloth. From 1781 a regular chaise route operated along with many carts and wagons, which crossed the sands, the Cartmel peninsula through Flookburgh, and then the Leven estuary to Ulverston. The Furness railway, first built as a feeder line to Barrow from slate quarries and ore mines, was extended across the Leven and Kent estuaries by 1857, when the 'sands' route ceased to be significant.

Furness was recognised by the monks of its famous abbey, founded in 1127, as consisting of a plain (in effect a fertile Triassic lowland which rises inland to limestone outcrops rich in iron ore), and an upland, a poor hill-country best suited to sheep farming. By 1163 these monks had acquired virtually all the Furness fells, and as time went on they spread their power farther into the Lake District, establishing granges and parks that were generally sheep farms but in some cases for cattle rearing. Having settled in a sheltered valley near Dalton, like many medieval monks who chose a remote and desolate location, they soon found cause to thank God for having so bountifully provided for them. They organised the mining of iron ore, fostered agriculture, and planted trees in a countryside already partly settled. Millward has suggested that the small clusters of farms in the Furness fells are characteristic of the tenth century Scandinavian settlement, and that from these primary settlements a slow process of agricultural

9

WRYNOSE PASS

R. BRATHAY

△2502
2536△ △2630
2555△ △2635
CONISTON
HAWKSHEAD

WINDERMERE
BOWNESS

R. DUDDON

F u r n e s s   F e l l s

ESTHWAITE

WINDERMERE

CUMBERLAND

BROUGHTON

R. CRAKE

CONISTON WATER

R. LEVEN
BACKBARROW

R. WINSTER

WESTMORLAND

GREENODD

MILNTHORPE

MILLOM

ULVERSTON

CARTMEL

HOODBARROW   ASKAM

CARK

GRANGE-OVER-SANDS

DALTON
B.C.

FLOOKBURGH

HUMPHREY HEAD

BARROW

M O R E C A M B E
B A Y

CARNFORTH

DOCKS
VICKERS-TOWN

HEST BANK

WALNEY
ISLAND

MORECAMBE

R. LUNE

LANCASTER

HEYSHAM

HARBOUR

BLOWN SAND
ALLUVIUM
KEUPER MARL
BUNTER SANDSTONE
MILLSTONE GRIT
CARBONIFEROUS LIMESTONE
SILURIAN & ORDOVICIAN

COUNTY BOUNDARY
RAILWAY

0   10 MLS.

BUILT-UP AREA

B.C.   BIRKRIGG COMMON

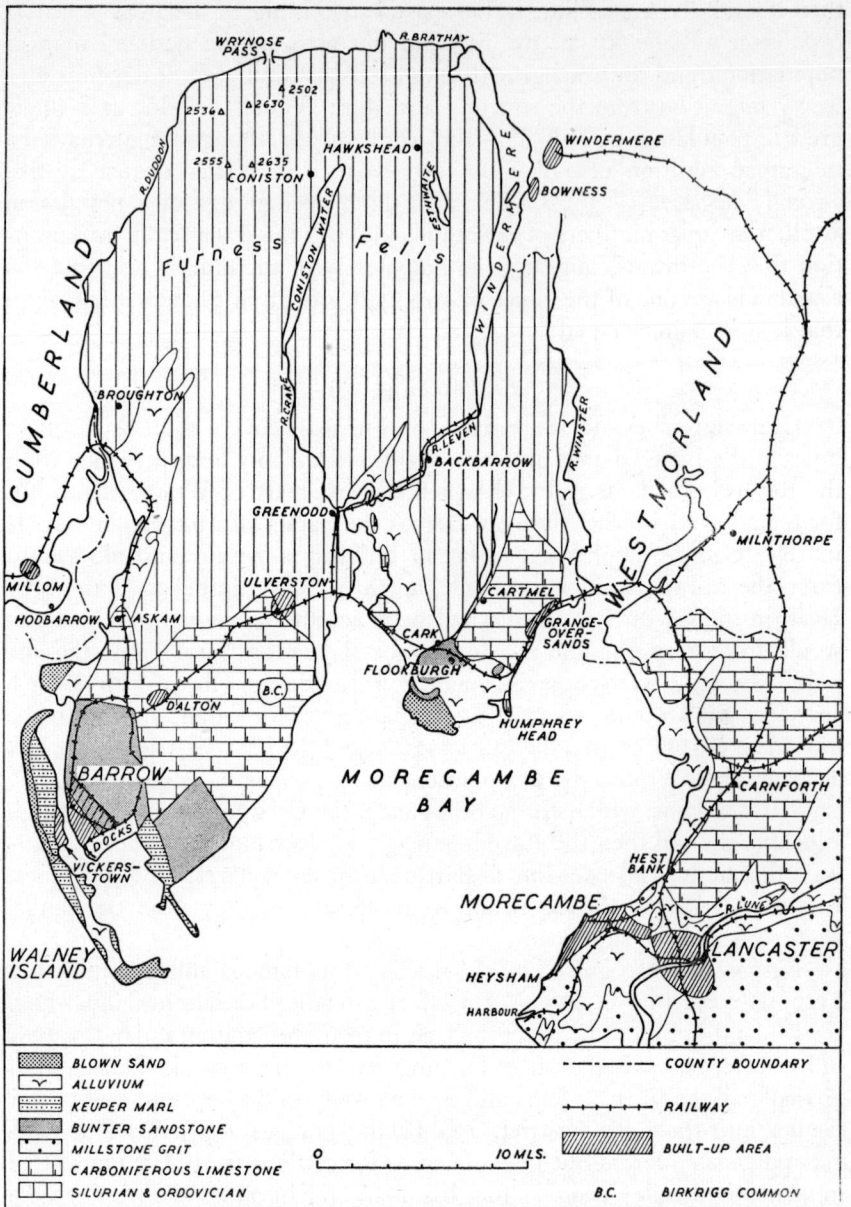

Fig. 59   THE FURNESS AREA. Around the shores of Morecambe Bay there are limited areas of lowland backed by the marginal fells of the Lake District. From Millom there is a similar lowland extending around the west side of the Lake District into the Solway plain in the Scottish Border country.

246

expansion continued for many centuries. It is not necessarily complete yet, for, as noted below, there are areas where further reclamation may be possible. After the dissolution of the monastery in 1537 many yeoman-farmers, locally known as 'statesmen', took over the monastery's land; in time the prosperity of these farmers increased so that their descendants built new houses, especially between 1650 and 1710. In High Furness most of these were of the local slate, generally planned with the stable and barn under the same roof-line as the house. A lime rough-cast was used to plaster the outside walls of the dwelling quarters, which, painted white, stand out prominently in the landscape of green pastures and varied-coloured rough moorland.

The actual boundary of Furness runs through the flat-floored Winster valley and across the wooded fell ridge to Windermere at a point nearly 3 miles south of Bowness. All of the lake water is in Westmorland, but the southeast shores and all the western shores are in Lancashire to the north end of the lake, where the boundary follows the Brathay stream through Little Langdale to Wrynose Pass at the head of the valley (1,281 ft.). The pass has a 'three-shire stone', for there Lancashire meets both Cumberland and Westmorland. From the pass the Furness boundary follows the river Duddon to the long estuary having, on the Cumberland side, the one ore mine still worked, at Hodbarrow, as a prominent feature at Millom. The promised railway bridge between Millom and Askam, a mining valley on the east side, was never built, so for many years one could make the round tour of the estuary for a few coppers, the price the journey would have been had the bridge been built.

Within the Furness fells there are not only the upland sheep farms of the high hillsides but also richer and smaller farms in remote valleys specialising in fat lambs and store sheep, as well as in dairying for the milk depot at Milnthorpe (Westmorland). In the area between Coniston and Windermere there is much poor land, part of which has been taken over by the Forestry Commission, though much of it is in poor coppiced woods. To an increasing extent money is made from the holiday traffic, for both visitors and retired people settling as residents are attracted to this area of fells interspersed by quiet and sheltered valleys. The old town of Hawks-head, in effect a village with Wordsworthian associations, lies in such a valley close to Esthwaite Water, one of the smaller lakes. Little Langdale, far less visited than the better-known Great Langdale farther north, and the Duddon valley are both quiet but attractive to walkers, campers, and climbers, having some farms which are also guest-houses during part of the year. The main tourist centre is Coniston, formerly at the end of a branch railway line from Broughton-in-Furness, and on an A-road from Broughton to Ambleside. The village lies between the lake, 5 miles long but everywhere less than half a mile wide, and the five fine summits of Dow Crag (2,555 ft.), Coniston Old Man (2,635 ft.), Swirl How (2,630 ft.) and Wetherlam

(2,502 ft.), with Grey Friar (2,536 ft.) on the west side overlooking the Duddon valley. In these peaks the Borrowdale volcanic rocks make sharp features comparable with, if less dramatic than, those of the Scafell range farther north in the heart of the Lake District. In general, however, the Furness fells, mainly formed of shales, slates, and grits of Silurian age, are lower, with long ranging summit levels about 800–1,000 feet, having numerous woods, but farmsteads in the valleys and on the lower slopes.

Lowland Furness is divisible into two parts by the estuary of the Crake river, which flows from Coniston; this estuary is crossed by a bridge carrying the railway from Carnforth to Ulverston and Barrow. On its east side lies the Cartmel 'peninsula', and the name Furness is given to the district on the west. In both these areas the landforms show with some clarity the influence of their physical history including that of the glacial phase.

The Cartmel peninsula includes two prominent ridges, made up of Carboniferous limestone on the east side and of Silurian slates farther west, with the Vale of Cartmel, a low-lying area of alluvium, glacial drifts, and drumlins, between them. To the west of the slate ridge, facing the Leven estuary, there is an area consisting largely of peatmoss but in part reclaimed for farming, including some of very good standard. And on the south of the 'peninsula' the flat lowland consists of good farmland behind an embankment, beyond which there are salt marshes which give some excellent sheep pastures. The limestone fells, rising to 600–700 feet, include some areas of limestone pavement and others with very thin soils, not unlike the similar limestone areas across the bay in the Carnforth district. Much of the sheep pasture has been ruined by the spread of bracken. The steep slope facing Morecambe Bay is covered by Grange-over-Sands, a holiday and residential centre of some 3,000 people. In the centre of the peninsula the Vale of Cartmel has some excellent farmland on which some roots and cereals are grown for the stock, though the main source of income is milk. Some farmers also have beef cattle and sheep, especially if they own favoured pastures on the saltmarsh. The main village is Cartmel, clustered with a few hundred inhabitants around its fine church; there is a small woollen industry. The slate ridge to the west has some local patches of drift, but only a small part of it is improved land. Facing the mosses on the west beside the Leven estuary there is a fine wooded scarp 500 feet high. These mosses, mainly peat over alluvium, are largely in a natural state with sub-spontaneous woods of birch, pine, and rowan; they are interspersed by some slate and limestone islands. Given efficient drainage with an embankment, more land could be reclaimed for agriculture; one large farm has a grass-drying plant at which the five or six crops of fescue grass are processed for sale. In the southern plains there is some excellent crop production, with pastures for cattle and sheep. Within this area drainage began during the eighteenth century, but it is still not complete.

Grange seems an exotic element in this area, and the villages, Cartmel,

Cark, and Flookburgh, are small. At Cark there is a factory employing
fifty people, supplying cooked shrimps in cartons; the owners acquire part
of the supply locally but own a fleet of shrimp boats which operate from
Southport to Kirkcudbright. At Flookburgh, cockles are caught on the
sands and either prepared for sale locally or sent to Lytham for processing;
most are sold at seaside resorts such as Blackpool, Southport, or Morecambe. But these strange little industries are minor in comparison with
the iron industry, which long survived at Backbarrow, in the deep Leven
valley south of Windermere. At this works charcoal was used until 1923,
but then coke was brought from Workington and the iron ore imported;
cold blast pig iron was made, mainly for cast-iron rolls to be used in steelworks. In this remote place, where abundant water power was available
from the postglacial Leven gorge, there is an engineering works, and a
factory providing ultramarine which was originally located in a discarded
cotton mill where over a hundred people are employed. At Backbarrow
there is also a small wood industry, originally making baskets for farmers,
but now providing a variety of goods including wood fences, packing cases,
and besoms. Backbarrow, the only place in this area having any sign of a
smoke-polluted atmosphere, provides an excellent example of a remote
industrial area using water power. Traditionally there were various wood-
working industries, but almost all of these have now disappeared, though
there is a large sawmill at Greenodd at the mouth of the Crake and a
smaller one at Near Sawrey, near Esthwaite, which unlike the Greenodd
enterprise relies primarily on local supplies of timber. The bobbin-making
industry survives in a small factory at Stott Park near Windermere and a
much larger enterprise at Spark Bridge on the Crake river.

Low Furness is made up of Carboniferous limestones and red Triassic
sandstones, of which the latter have been used for the red building stones
of Barrow. Bands of Keuper Marl occur in the lower part of Barrow,
including Barrow Island, and also underlie Walney Island, where they are
entirely covered by drift, so that walls and even some of the older houses
are built of seashore pebbles. The drift cover is as much as 150 feet thick
on Walney Island and in places covers preglacial valleys; but generally it
is much thinner, and on Birkrigg common, south of Ulverston (over
400 ft high) it disappears altogether, so that the Carboniferous limestones
form a pavement similar to those that occur in Cartmel. There are some
notable glacial overflow channels, of which one is the Walney channel and
another the valley between Barrow and Dalton in which Furness Abbey
stands, with the railway line.

From the eleventh century, woods were guarded and planted, as the
timber was needed for charcoal in the growing iron industry. The ore
occurred as a high-grade hemetite in 'saps', hollows in the Carboniferous
limestone, of which the largest is the Park sap of Roanhead, 1,400 feet long,
300–600 feet broad, and 600 feet deep. It also occurred in veins, as much as

100 feet wide, 2,000 feet long, and 500 feet deep. In Low Furness the ore was readily accessible, especially around Dalton and Roanhead. Through the enterprise of the abbey's monks both farming and ore mining were fostered, and Dalton became the main town of the peninsula. After the dissolution of the monastery in 1537, which left it a ruin and spread some of its stones through the district, including Ulverston parish church, much of the land went to the Duchy of Lancaster. From the eighteenth century the enclosure movement spread, so that open arable fields were divided and stabilised and marshes were brought under cultivation. Ulverston became a market centre of increasing significance, located at the meeting place of lowland and Fell Furness, though its Ship Canal was never of much significance. The reclamation of saltmarshes, favoured as sheep and cattle pastures, continued into the nineteenth century, for example on the west side facing the Duddon estuary, where some was reclaimed when the railway to Kirkby was built in 1846 and extended to Broughton two years later.

The rise of Barrow is associated largely with the building of the Furness railway from 1846. The original line ran from the slate quarries at Kirkby (providing a blue slate that still sells) and the ore mines near Lindal Moor to Piel Harbour and Barrow; various branch lines and tramlines were constructed to scattered mines and quarries. Immediate success induced the building of the Broughton line to attract the trade in copper and slate from the Coniston area, with an extension to Ulverston in 1854 and—most important of all—the junction with the Lancaster and Carlisle Railway in 1857. This, as noted above, was achieved by the bridging of the Leven and Kent estuaries and brought Furness into incomparably easier communication with the rest of Lancashire; the railway link with Whitehaven was not complete until 1866. Before the railway came, in 1841, Barrow was a village with some 250 people on the sheltered Walney channel, where iron ore was shipped from crude wooden jetties. Blast furnaces were opened in 1859 on Barrow Island and steel making began in 1865. Sand and water were abundant locally; limestone was brought from Stainton by a feeder railway; and the initial idea was to use Durham coke, though in recent years four-fifths of the coke has been brought from Yorkshire. Shipbuilding developed from 1869, and by 1871 the population was nearly 20,000. The buildings included some tenements of the local red sandstone reminiscent of those in Scottish towns, some of them at the very gates of the ironworks. By 1881 the population had increased to nearly 50,000, but during the 1880s there were signs of stability with a small population increase and a heavy outward movement of workers. A jute factory founded in 1870, at one time employing 2,000 women, was closed in 1892, and various engineering works had an unsuccessful career; hopes of making Barrow a port for Irish and Manx traffic failed through the competition of Fleetwood and Heysham. Steel, shipbuilding, and armaments remained the main industries, and Barrow reached its peak population of

74,000 in 1921. In 1951, the town had 67,000 people and in 1961, 65,000. Barrow's future is uncertain, though shipbuilding has so far remained active. But its main ironworks has closed, and its steelworks are threatened with at least partial closure. The remoteness and poor road access are difficulties, though the area is now a Development District. Dalton gradually lost its position as the main market centre of Furness to Ulverston, and its recent increase of population, from 8,000 in 1951 to 10,400 in 1961, is in part due to outward movement from Barrow. In both 1951 and 1961 the two towns together had slightly more than 75,000 people. Ulverston, though still mainly a market centre and having 10,500 people in 1961, has a wide range of industries in the town and district, including electrical engineering, metallurgical trades, oils and chemicals, plastics and textiles.

Furness still retains qualities of remoteness, and Barrow is a town that people visit, if at all, with some deliberate purpose rather than casually on their way somewhere else. 'Teach and relax in Barrow-in-Furness'[1], says an advertising poster exhibited in education departments of universities; inspection shows that virtually any form of physical recreation, including sailing and mountaineering, is available in the town and district. To the northwest, in Cumberland, the expansion of atomic energy is already notable; the town itself has plenty of land available for new industries, and its communications facilities include an aerodrome on a site that is reclaimed saltmarsh on Walney Island. Viewed historically, Barrow's rise is a story of high but only partially realised hopes of the Victorian era; but the Furness countryside shows the imprint of far longer human enterprise and effort. Its high fells merge into the mountains of the Lake District; in Low Furness the red Triassic sandstones form a countryside with red-soiled fields like those of west Cumberland, and its limestones form a physical landscape like that of Lancashire and Westmorland or the other side of the Kent estuary, having bare pavements in driftless areas but patiently farmed lands where glacial deposits provide some cover that has been steadily worked up by fertilisation into the present soils. The reclamation, on anything more than a small local scale, of Morecambe Bay, seems an unlikely prospect in the near future, despite the recent publicity given to the barrage project.

[1] An unknown student in Manchester removed the first two words from the slogan.

CHAPTER 11

The Isle of Man

RISING boldly as a separate mountainous mass in the midst of the Irish
Sea, the Isle of Man 'is not part of the realm of England . . . but an estate
and domain of the Crown of England'. Holding a significant strategic
position, it has had many contacts with England, Scotland, Ireland, and
Wales, which have varied with the ebb and flow of movements along the
western seaways in successive periods of physical and human history.
Today it retains many features of a self-governing community, with its
own government consisting of the Lieutenant-Governor representing the
Crown, the Legislative Council, the House of Keys, and Tynwald, a
unique institution consisting of the Governor and these two branches of
the legislature sitting together to sign bills already passed in the branches,
to levy taxes, and to appoint Boards. The Island is not represented in the
British Parliament, but it is naturally influenced in many fields by England,
while it has particularly close economic and social links with Lancashire.

Relief and structure

The Isle of Man covers some 220 square miles, with a length of 31·5
miles from the Point of Ayre in the north to the Calf of Man in the south,
and a breadth ranging between 8 and 13 miles in its central portion. Its
dominant trend, northeast to southwest, is seen in its mountain axis
running from North Barrule[1] (1,860 ft.) through Snaefell (2,034 ft.) the
highest point, Beinn y Phott (1,790 ft.), Carraghan (1,640 ft.), Colden
(1,599 ft.), Slieau Ruy (1,570 ft.), and South Barrule (1,585 ft.), to terminate
in Bradda Head overlooking Port Erin Bay. Cutting obliquely across the
Island, roughly at right angles to this axis, is a central valley with Peel at
its western end and Douglas at its eastern. There is a low watershed at
about 160 feet in the vicinity of Greeba near the middle of the valley (the
'Greeba gap') which is quite narrow and damp. Clearly the valley is now
of primary importance, since it provides the only easy route across the
interior of the Island, followed by the main road and railway between east

[1] The spelling of place-names is in accordance with the 1:63,360 O.S. sheet 87 (Isle of
Man).

252

and west coasts; in early days, however, before being drained, it was not nearly so significant (Fig. 60).

The line of water-parting following the upland belt has long been of immense significance, for it was the fundamental line of separation in the

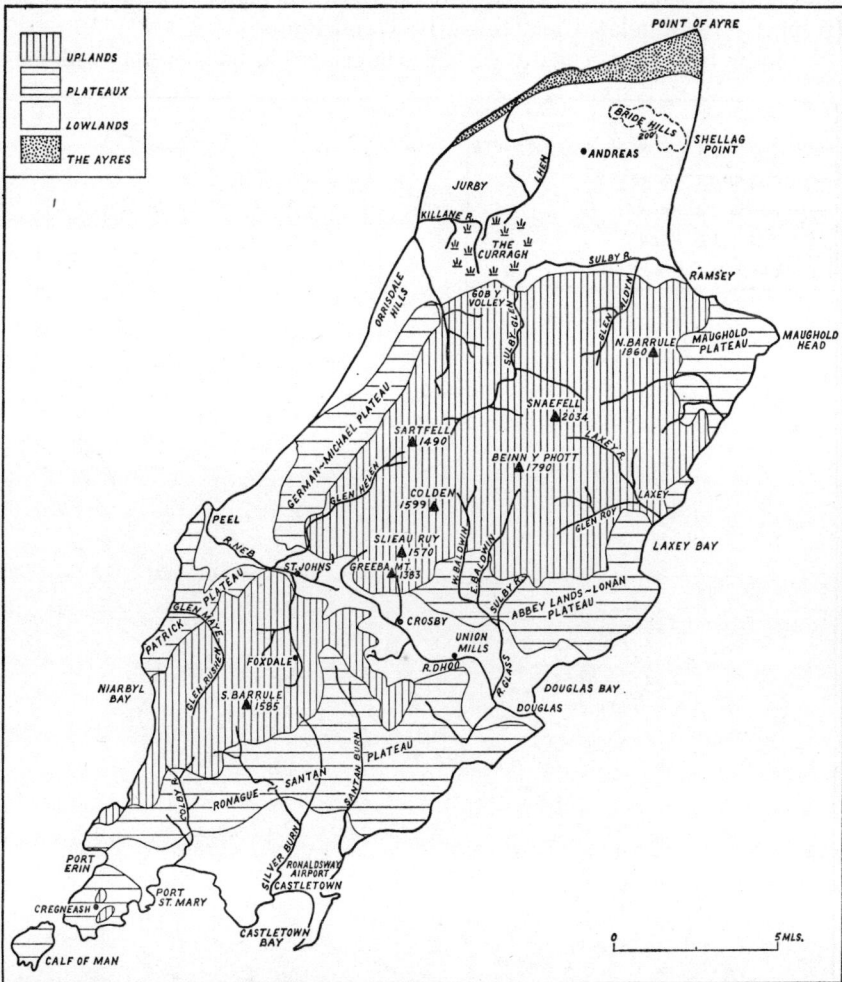

Fig. 60 ISLE OF MAN, PHYSICAL FEATURES. The two major uplands and their fringing plateaux are marked features of the Island. The lowlands are varied in physical form and in agricultural wealth.

division of the Island into the Northside and the Southside (strictly northwest and southeast) which has lasted into quite modern times (Fig. 61). Each division had its own capital (Peel or Castletown), and its own judge (called in Celtic *briw* and in Norse *lagman*), who came to be known as the *deemster* under English influence; and until 1918 there was a Northern

253

Deemster and a Southern Deemster, each with a sphere of jurisdiction based, with certain modifications, on the division indicated. These officials are now termed the First and Second Deemster respectively. For various other purposes four divisions are at present distinguished, Eastern, Southern, Western, and Northern, each with a main town as its focus (respectively Douglas, Castletown, Peel, and Ramsey).

The upland mass constitutes a much crumpled boss of very old slaty

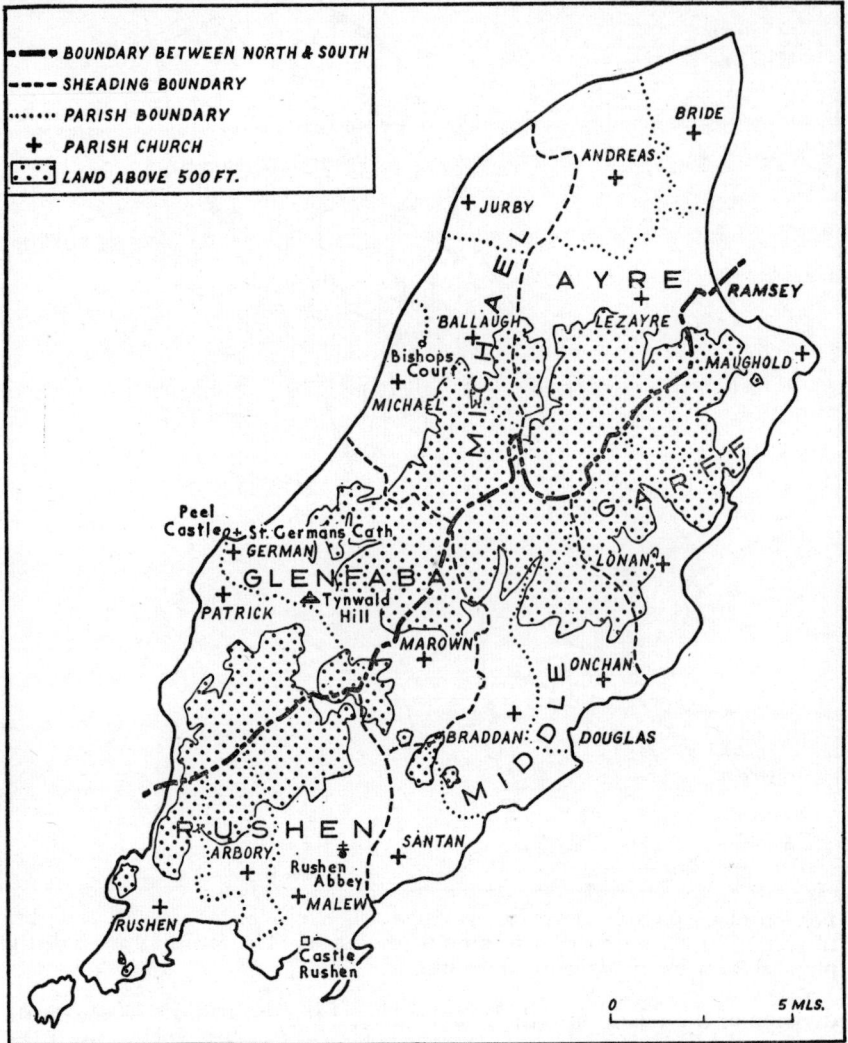

Fig. 61 TRADITIONAL DIVISIONS. Changes made in 1796 blurred the original pattern since the North was decreed to include Michael, Ayre and Garff sheadings, and the South the other three. Marown parish was also transferred to Glenfaba Sheading and Onchan to Middle.

rocks rising above the greatly denuded surrounding belts of newer strata now mainly submerged by the Irish Sea. The earlier rocks, known as the Manx Slate series, consist of clay slates, grits, and flaggy greywackes of indeterminate age, but possibly Ordovician like the Skiddaw Slates of the Lake District. Severely folded and crushed during the Caledonian orogenic period, they outcrop in the axis of the island, and the tough, close-textured slates form the higher ridges. Towards the close of this period of folding the rock mass was penetrated by innumerable veins of molten material forming dykes, seen especially along many sections of the coast where the slates or grits are exposed. In a few places larger intrusive bodies were formed which solidified into massive crystalline rock which, as the result of extensive erosion, are now exposed as granitic bosses. The chief of these are the Dhoon granite with an outcrop nearly a mile and a half long and up to half a mile wide, near the northeast coast south of Maughold Head, and the Foxdale granite, only a little less extensive, near the middle of the Island south of the central valley, while a much smaller area exists at Oatland some 4 miles southwest of Douglas.

Next in age are strata of the earlier Carboniferous period which consist of conglomerates and sandstones at the base of the formation, followed by limestones. The latter underlie the lowland area of the southeast centred on Castletown, extending southwestwards to the outskirts of Port St Mary and northeastwards to a point beyond Ballasalla. In the past the limestone has been extensively worked either as a building stone or for lime at Scarlett and Poyllvaaish on the coast, and inland at the Billown and Ballahot quarries; but most of these workings have now been given up. On the west adjoining Peel a red sandstone of Carboniferous age forms the cliffs for over a mile to the north of the town and extends inland for a little less than this. This Peel sandstone provides, along with the Castletown limestone, the only easily worked building stone in the Island and is abundantly seen in the buildings and walls of the west.

Nowhere else in Man are solid rocks to be seen at the surface, but Carboniferous, Permian, and Triassic deposits lie beneath the lowland north of a line from Ramsey through Ballaugh to Kirk Michael covered by 155 feet or more of glacial drift, with raised-beach material and blown sand in the Ayres of the north. Although borings failed to produce any coal, they revealed the existence of saliferous marls in the Triassic rocks some 600 feet below the surface near the Point of Ayre, and salt was extracted hydraulically from these until 1956.

Glacial features of the landscape

Glacial deposits form the northern drift lowland and are significant almost everywhere else. Three successive glaciations are now thought to have affected the Island, the earliest of which (the Older or Riss) produced the striae on the upper slopes of the Manx mountains which were overridden by ice. This was followed by an interglacial period, after which came another general glaciation (the Main Irish Sea or Würm I) when the ice rose to only about 1,300 feet on the hills. This resulted not only in the thick smooth blanket of drift which swathes the intermediate and lower slopes of the hills, generally below 1,000 feet, but also in the steepening of the valley sides of certain rivers as, for example, in Laxey Glen, where the existing river flows as a misfit stream at the bottom of a broad rounded valley. During the gradual retreat of these conditions a readvance of the ice-front from Scotland (the Scottish glaciation or Würm IIa) brought about a third glaciation which affected only the lowland areas of the Island.

The ice-sheets came mainly from southwest Scotland and northeast Ireland, with some contribution from the Cumbrian region of England, and boulders from each of these areas have been found in the extra-Insular drift. Northern Ireland, as well as the floor of the Irish Sea, are of particular interest as the sources of the flint from the Chalk brought to the coastal deposits north of Kirk Michael, which were used by early man, while granites from southwest Scotland and Ailsa Craig are widespread. Except in the northern lowland much of the drift is of Insular origin.

Boulder clays together with sands and gravels of varying thicknesses are now distributed over most of the Island excepting the very high ground, and the most spectacular of such deposits are found in the Bride moraine. This consists of a chain of mounds, rarely more than half a mile in width, which rise in parts to 300 feet above sea level, and sweep round for nearly 12 miles in a crescent from Shellag Point, on the northeast near Bride, to Jurby and Orrisdale on the west coast. These hills, now regarded as a kame moraine—corresponding to the Fylde (Kirkham) moraine—were formed during a prolonged halt stage in the recession of the ice-sheet, and the characteristic dry valleys within the hills were eroded by melt water from the ice-sheet flowing southward through the moraine into a proglacial lake (Lake Andreas) between the ice-front and the slate hills to the south. The Island then terminated along the edge of the existing abrupt mountain line running east–west just south of Ramsey, with projections like the present Gob y Volley and Sky Hill jutting out north-wards as seacliffs. Material was carried into Lake Andreas both by the drainage from the ice-sheet and by the floods down Glen Auldyn, Sulby Glen, and Glen Dhoo bearing quantities of slaty gravel from the land surface. In the case of the two first rivers their deltaic flats and spits are separated from the drift-gravel platforms left by the retreating ice by lower-lying tracts of alluvium and peatbog constituting the Curragh; but on the western edge the deltaic fan from Glen Dhoo has coalesced with a low-lying drift-gravel platform from the north, so that there is now no effective separation between the two sets of deposits.

Vegetation in post-Pleistocene times

The date at which the Island finally became separated from the rest of Great Britain affects the interpretation of certain aspects of the Manx flora and fauna, and is also bound up with the earliest appearance of man in the area. The older view, as expressed in 1903 by Lamplugh, did not accept the possibility of any postglacial connections. There is now general agreement that land connections persisted for some time after the Pleistocene period, and this is not improbable since the greater part of the Irish Sea basin is less than 300 feet deep, much of it less than 180 feet deep in the stretches between the Island and southwest Scotland, north-west England, and north Wales. It is particularly shallow—only about 60 feet—between the east of Man and the northern part of Lancashire and Cumberland; on the other hand, water is deepest between the west coast and Northern Ireland, where the North Channel has a trough over 300 feet deep. Thus while practically all the organisms, except a few arctic types, must have been extinguished or pushed southwards or southwestwards by the ice-sheets, systematic restocking began very soon after the melting of the ice, and by the time of the final severance it must have proceeded far enough to bring many of the plants and animals that are native to the Island today. On existing evidence the date of this separation is placed about the middle of the Boreal period, a relatively dry and warm spell which lasted from about 7000 to 5500 B.C.

A striking feature of the present Manx landscape, and one that has existed for some centuries, is the extraordinary absence of trees, except in the larger glens and apart from recent afforestation schemes. It has been customary to ascribe this to the frequency of high winds, which, so it was argued, would prevent any dense growth of trees; but it is now thought on ecological grounds that the Island under the prevailing climatic conditions would be covered, in its lower-lying areas at least, with fairly dense forests dominated by the durmast oak. Such a climatic régime did not become established until a considerable time after the glacial period, and the onset of moister and milder conditions associated with the existing Atlantic type of climate came after about 5000 B.C., although there have been various oscillations since then. Before that there had been a pine-hazel woodland which developed during the Boreal period. The drier and cooler conditions of the still earlier pre-Boreal period had seen the return of birch trees to the Island, and this type of vegetation was itself preceded by the tundra and subarctic grassland which had characterised the cold conditions following the actual glacial epoch.

There is sound archaeological evidence for the availability of considerable quantities of oak trees over the lower plateaux and the lowlands of the Island during the earlier centuries of the Christian era for the construction of round houses. Each of these Celtic homesteads required the employment of many hundreds of oak trees to support the turf roofs covering such dwellings, of which seventeen have so far been identified. Some large woodlands apparently existed up to the eleventh century in the north of the Island, but thenceforward records speak of the shortage of timber as a result of the clearance of land for settlement, agriculture, for fuel, boats, and other uses. At present, therefore, many characteristic woodland plants seem to be entirely missing, together with the larger fungi and wood-feeding beetles; animals, too, such as the badger, as well as birds such as the jay and bullfinch, are absent.

Seasonal and regional varieties of climate

As a result of its westerly position, the Isle of Man experiences characteristically equable, windy, cloudy, and humid conditions. The summers are relatively cool, but the winters are mild; calm days are infrequent, and the rainfall is generally heavy for most of the year. These conditions may be illustrated by the small range of only 17·5° F between the mean sea-level temperatures for the warmest and coolest months at Douglas for the period from 1926 to 1950 (August, 59·0° F; February, 41·5° F), as compared with 21·1° F for Blackpool (July, 60·9° F; January, 39·8° F) over the same period. Differences of temperature within the Island are primarily due to variations in altitude. In detail, however, there are other striking differences, such as those between Douglas and Ronaldsway, where the explanation is not so simple. Thus the spring and summer maxima at the latter station are markedly lower than at the former, owing, most likely, to the drainage of cold night air from the long slope of the southern uplands at periods when the mean amounts of cloud are at their lowest and more nocturnal radiation is possible. Similarly there is a greater incidence of ground frost at Ronaldsway than at Douglas, with an average of 7·1 days in April at the former as compared with only 3·2 days at the latter. The Island shares with other areas round the Irish Sea a more favourable sunshine record than most parts of the British Isles at similar latitudes, especially during the spring and early summer months. May and June are the months having the highest mean hours of sunshine at all three stations in the Island (Douglas, Ronaldsway, and Point of Ayre), although, rather unfortunately, July and August are the busiest months of the tourist season.

At Douglas the wettest period is usually from October to January, when some 45% of the total annual rainfall is received and almost two days out of three are rainy. Then comes a period of decreasing rainfall and the driest period is that of late spring and early summer, when Douglas receives less than 18% of its annual precipitation, and rather less than half the days of each month record some rainfall. During July conditions tend to become more rainy, and this change is still more marked during August, the month which has the highest incidence of thunderstorms, and also when the frequency and vigour of depressions are increasing, as they continue to do during September. Regional variations of rainfall are quite appreciable owing to conditions of relief, so that the uplands receive over 50 inches annually with a recorded maximum of 60·2 inches at West Baldwin, while the southern lowland has less than 40 inches with a minimum of 26·6 inches in the vicinity of Port St Mary, and the northern lowland also has less than 40 inches for the most part with a minimum of 32·4 inches in Jurby.

Heavy or prolonged snowfalls are not common, and snow does not persist over the lowlands and lower coastal plateaux. There is, on the other hand, considerable variation, so that whereas snow fell at Douglas on less than five days in five of the thirty-four years between 1924 and 1957, with no snow at all in one year (1953), there were twenty-seven days with snow in the severe winter of 1947. At the Point of Ayre the mean incidence of snowfall is less than that of Douglas (6·5 days as against 8·4 days between 1948 and 1957); at Ronaldsway, on the contrary, the incidence is greater than at Douglas (13·6 days as against 8·4 days over the same period), although the station is over 200 feet lower.

Contrasting natural regions

The natural regions of the Island may be grouped under three main types. (1) The *uplands* comprising all the land above approximately 600 feet, much being over 1,000 feet; (2) the *plateaux* which flank the uplands on the east and west, and range in height between around 350 feet and 600 feet, usually with a sharp drop to the sea; (3) the *lowlands* of the north, centre, and south, generally below 100 feet but rising in the north to 300 feet in the Bride Hills (Fig. 60).

(1) The *uplands* constitute the moorland core, based on Ordovician slates and grits, largely grass covered except at the higher levels. Glacial drift, mainly thin and slaty in character, is widely distributed and produces stony and acid soils of varying depth and texture, but everywhere suffering from the effects of leaching due to relatively mild temperatures and the high annual rainfalls. The upper limit of improved land is usually around 600 to 700 feet, where the annual rainfalls are 50 inches or more, and this, coupled with the lower temperature, means a marked reduction in the feeding value of grassland, while any oats harvest, which is very uncertain, is normally three or four weeks behind that of the lowlands. In certain areas, owing to special factors and despite climatic limitations, enclosure and cultivation have been carried above these limits, as in the former lead-mining area in Glen Rushen; but with the cessation of mining the land has reverted to moorland except where afforestation schemes are in operation. The existence of the central valley causes a division into (*a*) the *northern uplands* rising to over 2,000 feet in Snaefell, and (*b*) the *southern uplands* rising to over 1,550 feet in South Barrule. While the northern uplands do

259

not reach the coast on the west, they actually touch it on the east just north of Laxey and again in the Dhoon area; the southern uplands, on the contrary, descend precipitously right down to the coast, south from the Niarbyl to Bradda Hill, as seen very strikingly at Sloc.

(2) The flanking *plateaux* often present maturely dissected platform surfaces where soil conditions show a good deal of variation, from thin flaggy soils to a fair covering of argillaceous drift. In general, all these areas, together with the lowlands, form the normal agricultural land of the Island; in other words, they are included within the area that was divided into the ancient but now obsolete territorial units known as *treens* which initially represented the cultivable land occupied and developed for agricultural and pastoral purposes by individual families or tribes in very early days. Each treen was divided into *quarterlands*, and these still exist although often much modified. The chief plateaux are, on the west: (*a*) the Patrick plateau, (*b*) the German–Michael plateau, and on the east (*c*) the Maughold plateau, (*d*) the Abbey Lands–Lonan plateau, (*e*) the Ronague–Santan plateau, and (*f*) the Mull peninsula and Calf of Man, where cultivation is on a more restricted scale than formerly.

(3) The three *lowland* areas—northern, central, and southern—naturally comprise the best agricultural land, since they generally possess not only the deepest and richest soils but also the most favourable conditions of relief and climate. In the *northern drift lowland* the lowest section, excluding the Ayres raised beach, is the belt stretching north of the northern uplands which represents the final legacy of the late-glacial Lake Andreas. This is mainly below 50 feet O.D. and is known in general as the northern Curraghs, being poorly drained, especially in the west where much is still bog. The drainage is in three directions, eastwards and westwards by the Sulby and Killane rivers respectively, and northward by the curious Lhen trench which finally curves gracefully to reach the west coast south of Blue Point. Running along the foot of the northern uplands, a series of gravel terraces representing deltaic deposits of slaty material produce drier cultivable sites. The most extensive belt is that lying north of Ballaugh and west of the Curragh, where a loamy clay soil provides some of the best farms in the north of the Island. The area comprising the arc of the Bride kame-moraine has some extensive spreads of sand and gravel providing early soils which are easily worked but which tend to become parched during the drier summer periods. Moister conditions are found over the red boulder clays derived from the Irish Sea bed, which are exposed, for example, north of the Bride moraine at such places as Ballamin, and over many stretches of Andreas and Jurby to the south of the moraine. Such soils are later and more difficult to work, but they produce the heaviest crops and provide the longest periods of grazing.

The *central lowland* is drained both east and west across a fairly broad floor including both drier terrace stretches and damper marshy ones, which impeded traffic until drainage operations were carried out. Flowing eastwards is, first, the Greeba river which joins the Dhoo, later to unite with the Glass from the northern uplands. The combined streams enter the sea at the port of Douglas which derives its name from that of the joint river. Flowing westward from the watershed near Greeba is a tributary of the Neb which comes down from Glen Helen and ultimately reaches the sea at Peel. Around the latter there is a well-marked basin of glacial sands and clays overlying the Peel sandstone which has resulted in a good farming area, but, at the other end, the lowland around Douglas is less clearly defined, and the narrow drift-covered river benches are largely built over.

The *southern lowland* consists, first, of the gently sloping area less than 100 feet high around Castletown, drained mainly by the Silver Burn, with a foundation of limestone, and with soils derived from glacial till, much of it containing limestone material. These conditions, combined with an annual rainfall mainly under 35 inches, have provided some of the most favoured farming districts in the Island. Somewhat similar conditions are continued westwards in a narrower belt through Kentraugh towards Port Erin, but in this section the glacial till rests on a floor of older rocks; again, southeastwards, in the Langness peninsula, thin sandy deposits on outcrops of grit, shales, and igneous rocks have made an area best fitted for a golf links.

It is thus apparent that, despite its restricted area, variety is a keynote of the Island's basic natural conditions, and this is also a feature of its cultural and economic make-up.

The past and its legacy

The Isle of Man illustrates very clearly the shortcomings of the simple two-fold division of Britain as a whole into the lowland zone of the southeast and the highland zone of the northwest, since it is quite misleading to regard the Island itself as uniform from either the physical or human standpoint. In other words, a better understanding of our geography can be attained if the so-called highland division of Britain is subdivided into: (1) an *Atlantic* zone, comprising the coastal lowlands and low plateaux, and (2) a *moorland* zone backing the littoral area which is the real highland area in its physical and human qualities. The contrast is very well illustrated within the Island, where Cregneish provides an excellent example of a moorland village, or rather *clachan* of the Irish type, which formed one of the last strongholds of old Manx country life and traditions. On the contrary, the coastal belt resembles much more closely the lowland section of England, due allowance being made, of course, for the differing space relations of the two sides of Great Britain. Historically, far from being the isolated, passive area waiting to absorb the more backward or traditional elements, this Atlantic belt has frequently been a primary 'receiving' zone of cultures rather than a 'preserving' zone, which was the function of the moorland area. Broadly speaking, when trading conditions have flourished along these western seaways then cultural developments have been vigorous, as during the Neolithic Age (before 2000 B.C.) and the age of the Celtic saints (from the fourth to the eighth century A.D.); but periods of decline along the western sea-routes have resulted in phases of relative backwardness, as in much of the Stanley régime from the early fifteenth to the early eighteenth century, when official policy rather isolated the Island, or during the later phases of the Bronze Age (c.650 B.C. and succeeding centuries), when a deterioration in climatic conditions occurred.

Prehistoric times. The earliest definite evidence of human settlement in the Island dates from the Mesolithic period, when it is quite possible that the link still persisted with the English coast, so that those hunters and food collectors with their microlithic culture (now known as Sauveterrian) were able to cross by dry land, and remains of their temporary resting places have been found at several coastal sites. By Neolithic times (c.2500 to 2000 B.C.) there is no doubt that Man had really become an island, so that the new economy—agriculture and stock-raising—along with the cult of constructing elaborate stone tombs must have come by sea. The characteristic monuments in the Island, known as gallery graves, can be traced to Sardinia, while similar remains are well known at other places around the Irish Sea. These cultivators lived on the lowlands and coastal plateaux in areas which had by then become clothed with forests dominated by the oak; but the clearing of patches of woodland would not be difficult, since Neolithic man was well supplied with good polished stone axes, many of those found in the Island being made of igneous rock (andesitic ash) from the Langdale area in the Lake District. Of the monuments that have survived the outstanding example is Cashtal yn Ard, Ballachrink, on the Maughold plateau, which illustrates excellently the characteristic features of forecourt, porthole, and gallery of tombs; it has indeed become a classic of the gallery-grave type in Atlantic Britain. Moreover, during the extension (1945) of the Ronaldsway airfield on part of the southern lowland, clear evidence was found of a distinctive culture which has been named after the site, and this has been recognised as a secondary culture of the Neolithic age. Many polished axes of Langdale rock were found in addition to evidence of a rectangular house as well as the remains of ox, sheep, and pig; furthermore, the existence of the same type of culture, including the practice of agriculture, has also been proved at Ballateare and many other settlements in the Island. No doubt it was during this period that the original immigration took place of people belonging to the Mediterranean ethnic type, a type which still forms one of the two most important components of the older Manx population. Such people have dark-brown or black hair, brown eyes, and a long narrow head, and are of medium stature. These little dark people are widespread, but according to a survey made some years ago they were then most numerous in the parishes of Onchan, Braddan, and Santan, and many also occurred in Rushen and Patrick.

During the Bronze Age (from 2000 B.C. onwards), when Ireland became of increased importance, trade in gold ornaments and bronze implements was carried on across Britain to Europe, and evidence that the Island was playing its rôle in these activities is provided by the finding of decorated bronze axes and also of some 'food vessels', a distinctive form of pottery well known in Ireland as well as Scotland and northern England during the period. Settlement within the Island continued to expand over the coastal belt, while the northern lowland particularly showed a greater spread of population. The moorlands could hardly have had much in the nature of permanent settlement though parts were no doubt occupied temporarily during the summer season for grazing purposes, as they were in later periods, and also for hunting.

Climatic and cultural conditions deteriorated during the later Bronze Age, and apparently it was not until the earlier centuries of the Christian era that vigorous developments again took place in the Island. This was the time when the Romans were settled in much of Great Britain, and although they never occupied Man they must have had some relations with the Celtic-speaking population there, as in Ireland, and their fleets would pass regularly within sight of the Manx coast, plying from Chester with provisions for the garrison of the Roman Wall. The most interesting discoveries so far made relating to that period in the Island are those of quite large circular houses each of which presumably formed the dwelling-place of a chieftain and his family during what may best be called the Roman Iron Age. The site which now provides the exemplar of this single-homestead unit of Celtic society, partly agricultural but mainly pastoral, was excavated by Gerhard Bersu in 1942 at Ballakeighan (Ballacagen) near Castletown. This round or 'Celtic' house had a diameter of nearly 90 feet and the whole space was covered by a continuous and slightly domed turf roof, about 10 feet high at the centre and supported by a series of massive oak posts arranged in five concentric rings. The living-quarters round the central hearth were shut off from the rest by a circular wattle screen supported by more slender posts of elm or pine, and the remaining and much larger portions of the building were used for the stabling of animals and storage. The seventeen such houses so far recognised are distributed over the lowlands and low plateaux.

Early Christian period (A.D. 450–800). Close contact between the Island and the rest of Atlantic Britain continued after the Roman period, as is proved by the existence of six Ogam-inscribed stones here. This script seems to have originated in Ireland and was carried to Man, as to various parts of western Britain, by colonists from that country; and a point of

263

considerable interest arising from the finding of these inscriptions is that the language then spoken in the Island, while being mainly q-Celtic, or Gaelic, like that in Ireland, also included some p-Celtic, or Brittonic, like that then spoken in Wales and southwestern Scotland. Cultural movements such as these must also have influenced the spread of Celtic Christianity throughout western Britain during the fifth to the eighth centuries, and it seems highly probable that the Isle of Man was on the route of the missionaries concerned.

St Brigit, St Ninian, St Patrick, St Columba, St Cuthbert, and others are commemorated in dedications of early Celtic churches (or *keeills*) and in the names of many ancient parishes, and there can be little doubt that most, if not all, set foot here some time during their lifetime. The Island possesses a remarkable number of keeills whose sites are known—nearly 160 in all—and their distribution has a characteristic pattern over the lowlands and fringing plateaux. There is also a close parallelism with the distribution of treens (see p. 260); indeed, a strong tradition exists that there was originally one keeill on every treen and no doubt the Celtic missionaries had a small church erected on each family estate, or treen, to counteract the influence of ancestor worship which had formerly existed.

The Scandinavian period (A.D. 800–1266). The scene changed dramatically after about A.D. 800 when the conquest of the Island by the Norse Vikings involved many changes in ethnic make-up, religion, administration, and culture generally. Henceforth the long-headed, fair, and tall Nordic race became an important element in the population; and nowadays it is said that people of this type are most frequent in the northernmost parishes of Bride, Andreas, and Jurby as well as the southern parish of Malew, areas with much fertile lowland which the Norse Vikings deliberately chose for their own best settlements.

Although pagan to begin with, the Norse fairly quickly came under the influence of Christianity, and there grew up in the Island a new culture which had a remarkable blend of Celtic and Norse features. This was shown, for example, in the new forms of Celtic crosses with inscriptions in runic script and in the Norse language, commemorating people mainly with Norse but also with some Celtic names, and with decorations based on the old Norse mythology but recorded on Christian memorials. The Norse capacity for administration may be illustrated in various fields in which their work has survived, as in the Manx system of government, which shows the influence of ideas which they introduced, and also in their genius for turning to account customs in existence when they arrived. An essential feature of the Norse life was the annual open-air assembly of all freemen at some central place where new laws were announced and disputes settled. This assembly was called the *thing*, a word which forms the first part of the Manx term Tynwald. The second half is derived from the

Norse for meeting place (*vollr*), so that Tynwald (*Thingvollr*) was originally the place at which this assembly met, as it still does on 5 July to announce new laws. The actual site for this ceremony is Tynwald Hill with the adjoining church at St John's, and this has traditionally been a meeting place for the whole Island from pagan times, when it had a midsummer festival, later associated with St John through the influence of Christianity.

The parishes were probably systematised during the twelfth century by a Manx monarch (Olaf I) who was familiar with the English religious system. Apart from those in the northern lowland (Bride, Andreas, and Jurby), each parish has a frontage along the coast, thence running to the main line of water-parting. The one exception to this is Marown, now entirely inland; but it seems clear that this was originally united to Santan, so that to begin with there were sixteen parishes in all (Fig. 61).

During the Scandinavian period the Isle of Man became the capital of an island realm including all the Hebrides under the general title of the Kingdom of the Isles, with its headquarters on St Patrick's Isle, now joined by causeway to Peel. In the religious sphere this came to be regarded as a separate diocese with the official title of *Ecclesia Sodorensis*, such being the Latin form of the Norse name for Man and the Hebrides (the 'Southern Isles'). The political break-up of the kingdom took place in 1266, when the Hebrides were ceded to Scotland; but the religious link persisted for some time longer. Now there is no connection, but the title of the Manx bishop —Sodor and Man—serves as a reminder of a régime that is past. The Norse language also died away after 1266, leaving Celtic as the chief speech of the Manx, although it was henceforth more closely related to Scottish than to Irish Gaelic. Norse survives in such important terms as Tynwald, but it is chiefly in evidence in a number of place-names (e.g. Snaefell); in this sphere, however, Celtic became so fully restored that in existing names the proportion of Norse to Gaelic in the Isle of Man is roughly only 1 to 6 whereas in Lewis it is nearer 4 to 1.

The Stanley period. For some time after 1266 the Isle of Man was disputed between England and Scotland, but ultimately the former gained control and in 1405 sovereignty was granted to Sir John Stanley, whose descendants, as Earls of Derby or Dukes of Atholl, ruled the Island under the title, initially as *king* but later as *lord*, for over three hundred years. It was a period of consolidation rather than one of new developments, during which the Island was relatively isolated so that it could develop and maintain distinctive features in, for example, its form of government, land systems, and its personal names. Trade was discouraged and strictly regulated; strangers were kept away. Manx was the speech of the mass of the people, but English was used by government officials, the clergy, and well-to-do folk generally. Castletown was the capital and place of the lord's residence until 1869, when it was finally displaced by Douglas. Conditions began to change rather more radically in the later seventeenth century with the increasing significance of smuggling, or 'the running trade', which was carried on along several stretches of the English and Scottish coasts. The Island's strategic position and its low customs duties made it peculiarly well suited for engaging in this traffic, which grew to such proportions during the eighteenth century that the British government took the drastic step of passing the Revesting and Mischief Acts in 1765. This meant that the sovereignty of the Isle of Man was once again vested in the Crown, and the 'smuggling mischief' was gradually brought under control.

After the Revestment (1765). The drastic changes in their constitution by the 1765 legislation came upon the Manx people initially as a humiliation and a disaster. Although Tynwald and its branches still survived, no laws costing money could be passed, since the customs duties were henceforth diverted to the British government. These conditions remained until 1866, when the Manx customs revenue was again transferred from the British Exchequer to the Island's revenue, but with the stipulation that the British Treasury should have the ultimate approval of the spending of that money. These limitations were repealed only in 1958, so the Island has now more real freedom in the conduct of its own affairs. In the economic and social fields conditions gradually became more stable after the abolition of smuggling, and the Island began to benefit by its closer connections with Great Britain in various ways such as the introduction of improved methods into agriculture and more intimate cultural contacts. Indeed, the second half of the nineteenth century saw the development of a period of considerable prosperity which has continued up to recent years.

Modern economic and social conditions

Five main activities are of significance in the existing economic structure of the Island, namely agriculture, fishing, mining, tourism, and manufacturing, and all have reacted on one another in the past as they do at the present. In the early nineteenth century when the population was some 40,000 (the first census in 1821 actually recorded 40,081) the primary sources of livelihood were farming and fishing, neither of which could be regarded as efficient. Agriculture was described in 1812 as 'a recent art'; clover and turnips had not long been introduced, rotation was hardly practised, and implements were very primitive. Moreover, the long-standing connection between farming and fishing still persisted whereby many men were fishermen during the summer, and farmers, or rather crofters, during the rest of the year, with the result that, since the herring fishery clashed with the harvest much of the field labour was performed by women. Most of the persons employed were said by Quayle in his Agricultural Report of 1807 to be 'neither expert at fishing nor skilful cultivators of the earth'. Nowadays farming areas are located on the various lowlands and plateaux up to a height of 600 feet; but cultivation in the early nineteenth century extended for another 100 feet or so above this by taking in *intack* (or *intake*) land in the attempt to feed the population. Not surprisingly, from the 1820s there was considerable migration from the Island, especially from its northern parishes, to the United States after the opening of the Erie Canal, resulting in the original Manx settlements in Ohio and especially Cleveland. Since that period most of this marginal land has gone out of cultivation and there has been a marked downhill movement of population, particularly in the higher parts of the parishes of Rushen, Arbory, and Malew. Whereas, for example, in the area sur-rounding Ronague Chapel (*c.*590 ft.) in the parish of Arbory the tithe maps (about 1840) show at least forty houses, there are now only four which are inhabited, and many *tholtans*, or ruined cottages, still remain here and elsewhere as mute witnesses of the changed conditions.

The tourist industry. Catering for summer visitors has become the main Manx industry and the one on which most of the other activities depend. While its origins may be traced to the third decade of the nineteenth century, its more spectacular growth came after the critical decision in the 1860s to exploit more fully the Island's natural assets. These consist of its attractive landscape both physical and cultural, its position within the Irish Sea in relation to the growing industrial populations, particularly of northern England, and the possession of suitable sites for harbour and resort developments, notably at Douglas. While the number of annual visitors had increased to 90,000 by 1873, when the Victoria Pier was opened at Douglas, the number doubled during the next ten years, and in 1884 over 187,000 arrived. Other developments within the Island included the improvement of roads and the building of narrow-gauge railways in addition to the provision of accommodation and other facilities; and the industry grew with great rapidity, so that a peak was reached in 1913, when no less than 634,512 visitors arrived, representing twelve per head of the resident population (1911=52,016). That figure has never again been equalled, although there was a brief period after the Second World War, from 1947 to 1949, when the annual numbers were over 600,000. The present seasonal total is usually between 445,000 and 500,000, including about 100,000 day excursionists. Of this total the majority come by sea, but in recent years nearly 30% travelled by air, arriving at Ronaldsway, where an up-to-date terminal has been constructed.

This decline of about 10% in the Manx tourist traffic is due to causes of a permanent nature which have reduced the holiday advantages of the Island. Thus while there has undoubtedly been a notable increase in the numbers of British people taking holidays, rising standards of living and improvements in transport have made it possible for many more to go much farther afield, either within Britain or abroad, than formerly. In the Island the industrial contribution from northern England and central Scotland is now higher than ever, probably over 70%, and a recent

267

estimate indicated that the lower-income groups account for as much as 61% of the Manx visitor traffic as compared, say, with 48% for Jersey. This has serious implications, since the visitors stay for a shorter time and spend less, while 90% of the season's traffic (May to September) is concentrated into the months of June, July, and August which include the 'wakes weeks' of the cotton and woollen towns and the 'Glasgow Fair' week. At the present time the gross annual value of the visitor traffic to the Island, excluding receipts from sea and air transport, is some £9 million; moreover, it is probably true that its contribution to the Island's gross income from external sources, apart from investments, can hardly be less than three-quarters. Any diminution of this income therefore must have serious repercussions not only on farming but on the entire economic and social structure, including the ability to finance large-scale winter improvements in coping with the seasonal unemployment problem. As to the future, it is significant that Tynwald recently approved a scheme for the erection of a new modern sea terminal building in Douglas, at a cost of about £400,000, which was completed in 1965. Meanwhile, with a view to stimulating the tourist industry and adding to the Island's revenue, a public Casino was sanctioned by Tynwald and began operations in Douglas during July 1963; similar considerations lay behind the decision to start, in 1964, the first British commercial radio station.

Agriculture. Conditions are fundamentally different now from what they were in the early nineteenth century. The summer visitors help to provide an immense insular market, and the impressive income which they bring makes it possible for the Island to support a density of population sufficient to absorb the greater part of the farm output. The latter now meets most of the local demand for livestock products and potatoes, though not of market garden produce and fruit, for which physical and economic conditions are unsuitable. There is also enough for a small export of oats, turnips, livestock, and meat and for the support of processing manufactures of feed-grains, bacon, and cheese. This high level of production is attained by between 11% and 12% of the working population, with an increasingly mechanised agriculture. While the number of agricultural workers has fallen by nearly a third since 1939 the number of tractors has increased tenfold. There has also been a gradual enlargement of holdings and of fields, although 87% of the farms of more than 20 acres are still under 150 acres, as compared with a corresponding figure of 77% for England and Wales (Fig. 62).

Over 31% of the total surface is in rough grazing, and this figure, which is higher than formerly, includes about 13,000 acres at one time cultivated around the moorland edge, as well as in the marginal stretches of the plateaux and lowlands. In the upland areas sheep grazing is the dominant interest; but many parts of the most favoured hill land between, say, 550 feet and 1,000 feet, are being devoted to government afforestation

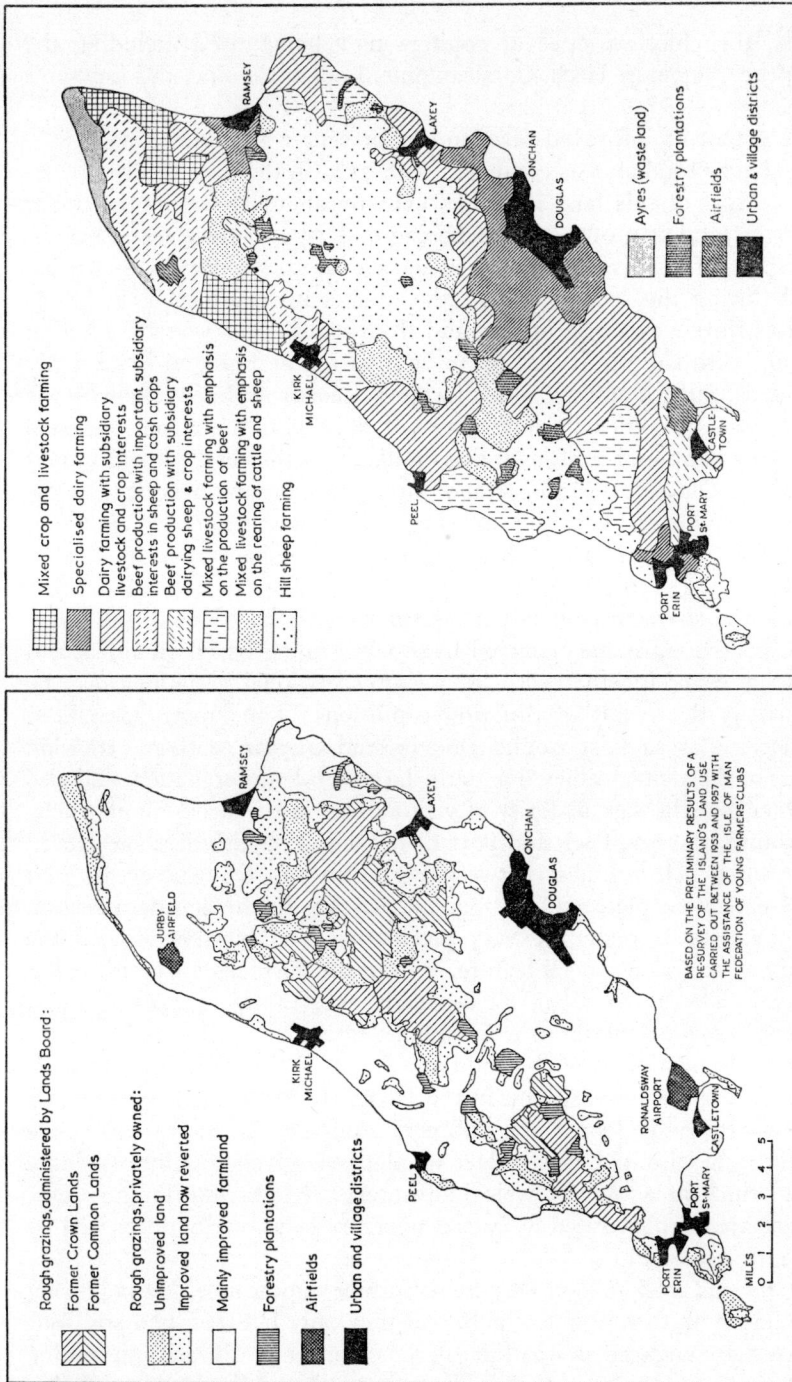

Map 1 legend (left map):

Rough grazings, administered by Lands Board:

- Former Crown Lands
- Former Common Lands

Rough grazings, privately owned:

- Unimproved land
- Improved land now reverted

Mainly improved farmland

Forestry plantations

Airfields

Urban and village districts

Locations: RAMSEY, LAXEY, ONCHAN, DOUGLAS, JURBY AIRFIELD, KIRK MICHAEL, PEEL, RONALDSWAY AIRPORT, CASTLETOWN, PORT St MARY, PORT ERIN

MILES 0 1 2 3 4 5

BASED ON THE PRELIMINARY RESULTS OF A
RE-SURVEY OF THE ISLAND'S LAND USE
CARRIED OUT BETWEEN 1953 AND 1957 WITH
THE ASSISTANCE OF THE ISLE OF MAN
FEDERATION OF YOUNG FARMERS' CLUBS

Map 2 legend (right map):

- Mixed crop and livestock farming
- Specialised dairy farming
- Dairy farming with subsidiary livestock and crop interests
- Beef production with important subsidiary interests in sheep and cash crops
- Beef production with subsidiary dairying sheep & crop interests
- Mixed livestock farming with emphasis on the production of beef
- Mixed livestock farming with emphasis on the rearing of cattle and sheep
- Hill sheep farming

- Ayres (waste land)
- Forestry plantations
- Airfields
- Urban & village districts

Locations: RAMSEY, LAXEY, ONCHAN, DOUGLAS, KIRK MICHAEL, PEEL, CASTLE TOWN, PORT St MARY, PORT ERIN

Fig. 62 TYPES OF LAND USE AND FARMING. These maps by J. W. Birch were originally published in *Great Britain: Geographical Essays*, ed. J. B. Mitchell (Cambridge 1962), 464.

269

schemes, the chief varieties of conifers now being used including the Sitka spruce, Japanese larch, Corsican pine, Lodgepole pine, and Lawson's cypress.

The extent of improved farmland at present constitutes nearly 58% of the Island's total area as compared with 71% in the peak recorded year of 1887. Most of this land is arable, actually about 19% (or just under 14% of the total area of the Island) being under permanent grass, and the greater part of the arable is worked on a five- to seven-course rotation evolved during the second half of the nineteenth century. The system comprises three years of cropping and from two to four years of rotation grassland, with the result that up to 66% of the arable land is normally under grass. Such a practice of ley farming accords well not only with the Island's climatic and soil conditions but also with the strong seasonal demand for lamb and beef, as well as milk, from the resident and tourist populations. Oats, next in importance after grass, occupy over 17% of the arable area, followed by turnips and similar roots with 5% or 6%, potatoes with 2% or 3%, and then barley, wheat, and other crops in smaller quantities.

While the characteristic system prevalent over the whole of the farm-land area is therefore one of mixed livestock-farming based on cereal and root forage crops together with ley pastures, regional variations may be discerned as the result of differing conditions. Thus more specialised dairy-farming areas exist around Douglas and Onchan, with an extension into part of the central valley due to the large resident population, and also to the fact that the vast majority of visitors stay in this area. Similar belts exist around Ramsey, Peel, and Port Erin, while a slightly less specialised dairy-farming belt stretches between Port Erin and Douglas across part of the Castletown plain and the Santan plateau. In the southern section of the Castletown plain the very productive land has encouraged the fattening of beef as a special feature. Within the northern lowland smaller annual rainfalls (33 to 36 in.) favour early and, therefore, more certain, grain harvests, particularly in areas of lighter soils where the quality of the grain tends to be higher. Such conditions prevail in the Ballaugh–Orrisdale region, the earliest harvest land in the Island. Over parts of Andreas and Jurby, where sandy loams are common, summer grazing resources are naturally rather limited and greater emphasis is given to winter feeding for beef. Such areas have physical advantages for growing forage crops, and these are supplemented by cattle concentrates normally purchased by the sale of surplus grain.

Herring and other fishing. Despite its former significance, Manx herring fishing has sunk to a very low ebb, and now only between two and four local boats are engaged in it, while there is increasing difficulty in finding enough crews to man even these. The industry has had a long association with the Island, since its inshore waters are the focus of important feeding and spawning migrations, notably for herring as well as for cod and plaice, while the fish provided a welcome source of food. Indeed, the staple diet for some centuries consisted of 'potatoes and herring', the latter either fresh, kippered, or salted. But herring fishing was not a whole-time occupation for Manxmen, because it lasted normally only during the period from July to October. The usual cycle was for fishing operations to start in the main gathering-ground off Peel (always the chief fishing port), working south as the season advanced, so that in August, the principal month, the most important grounds were to the west and southwest of Calf Island. At one time it was customary for the boats to move eastwards during the later part of the season to fish in the main spawning-ground off Douglas in September and October; but this area was always uncertain, and no serious fishing has taken place there in recent years. During the second half of the nineteenth century many boats went in March and April to the mackerel fishery at Kinsale, and the census returns for 1881, which were taken in April, recorded nearly 2,300 fishermen as being away there. Manx participation in the local fisheries was at its peak from the 1860s to the early 1880s, and it was stated in 1884 that nearly 400 vessels and some 2,600 men and boys were employed. From that date there has been a fairly steady decline, so that now, despite financial help from Tynwald, the Manx herring fishing fleet has been reduced to some half-dozen vessels. This may be attributed partly to the high capital cost of the very specialised modern fishing vessels and competition from English and Scottish enterprises, but also to the fact that the visitor traffic has proved a more profitable alternative to fishing. That there are still herrings to be caught in the area is proved by the annual appearance of between 80 and 150 Scottish and Irish drifters between June and mid-August, their catch being taken mainly to Portpatrick and the County Down ports. Nowadays the production of fish-meal has become a significant object of the herring fishery, and since 1955 a factory for this purpose has been operating at Peel in order to strengthen the local market. It is therefore interesting that, of the herrings landed in the Island in 1959, about 63% were used for reduction to fish-meal, while 26% were processed into kippers and 11% pickle-cured. Fluctuations have occurred since then, so that in 1962 only 5% were used for fish-meal while 54% were kippered, 16% were pickle-cured, and 11% were frozen, none having been returned as such in 1959.

Just as in other areas, with the decline in pelagic fishing, including mainly herrings and mackerel, the demersal and shell fisheries have become of primary importance, and it is these which now together contribute about 80% of the value of all fish landed by local craft. The dredging of escallops from the sandy inshore areas has become especially significant, since the products are almost exclusively for export to London and the other large English cities and the trade began only in 1937. An important feature is that since escallops are in season during winter they then provide employment for men in Port Erin and Douglas, the two main ports involved, who are concerned with running pleasure trips for visitors during the summer or in tending their crab and lobster pots. The chief demersal fish are cod, skate, and plaice; and although the first are taken throughout the year in Manx waters the local fishery is mainly conducted in the winter months from Douglas, and the height of the season occurs in March. Fishing for skate was formerly almost confined to Ramsey, where it was the principal summer fishing; but since about 1940 Douglas boats have taken part, and this port has now become the chief one for landings. Plaice fishing is operated from Peel during the winter and spring months from November to May.

The relative insignificance of the fishing industry as a whole may be judged by the fact that, according to an estimate made for 1956, only 24 boats in all, manned by 70 men, were then actively engaged in the various kinds of the industry. Of these fishermen, less than half, or under 1% of the working male population, are so occupied throughout the year, and the remainder are concerned with visitors during the summer.

Mineral industries. Ores of lead (also containing silver), zinc, iron, and copper occur in veins throughout many portions of the Manx Slates, and have been mined in a number of centres in the past. Two areas of primary importance have stood out, namely Foxdale, producing lead and silver, and Laxey, producing lead, silver, and some copper; but old workings may be seen at Bradda Head, Ballacorkish, and Ballasherlogue, all for lead and silver, in the parish of Rushen, at Langness for copper, and at Maughold Head for hematite.

There is documentary evidence that lead was obtained from Man in the thirteenth century for the roofing of Edwardian castles in Wales, but it was not until the eighteenth century that the search for minerals was carried out systematically, much attention being devoted to the search for coal which was never found. The most prosperous period for mining came after the third and fourth decades of the nineteenth century, when Laxey and Foxdale came into the first rank as producers, and the £80 shares of the Laxey Mining Company reached £1,200 in 1854. It was in this year that the famous Laxey Wheel, said to be the largest in the world, was built for pumping water out of the mines. Mining reached its heyday during the seventies and eighties, when production figures for lead, silver, and zinc reached their highest limits (lead in 1885, 68,68 tons; zinc in 1878, 11,898 tons; silver in 1877, 186,019 oz.). Even 2,256 tons of iron ore were produced in 1873, and 1,317 tons of copper in 1865. It was estimated in 1848 that some 300 were employed at Laxey and 350 at Foxdale; later on the numbers increased, so that well over 1,000 men were absorbed by the mining industry between 1855 and 1880. Since then competition from Broken Hill and elsewhere has compelled even the richest mines to close down, so that an extensive migration of Manx miners has taken place to the goldfields of South Africa and Australia as well as to various parts of America and Canada. In recent years the very high prices of lead and zinc have stimulated investigation into the reworking of waste heaps at Laxey and Foxdale, and a considerable amount of exploratory work has been carried out using modern techniques by Canadian and British, together with Manx, interests. No practical developments have, however, so far been reported. The Manx government, which in 1949 acquired control of the mineral rights, formerly held by the Crown, has given assistance in such developments through the Forestry, Mines, and Lands Board, to whom these rights were transferred in 1950; but the Island's extractive industries employ less than 1% of the working male population.

Manufacturing industries. In earlier days manufactures were on a rather modest scale and were concerned either with working up local materials, such as wool, or catering for the needs of local industries. Thus the herring fishery gave rise to the making of nets, first by hand in cottages, then in small factories in Peel and Port St Mary. Sail making was also important, and a sailcloth factory existed at Tromode near Douglas, while boat- and ship-building were active industries at Ramsey, Douglas, Peel, and Port St Mary, where the building of schooners, sloops, and herring luggers provided employment for a number of shipwrights and other craftsmen. With changing conditions many of these industries disappeared or declined during the nineteenth century.

Under modern conditions increasing attention is being devoted to the compelling need for more manufactures to offset the decline in the tourist industry and to ensure a more stable economy to meet the rising costs of the social services. Active measures have therefore been taken both to stimulate older industries that have survived, and, during the past decade especially, to attract new light industries, inducements being offered by the availability of suitable labour, male and female, the advantages due to lower taxation, assistance in obtaining suitable sites, as well as the residential amenities provided by the Island. Clearly there are obstacles arising from the almost complete lack of raw materials and the expenses of transport, and these emphasise the need for selecting manufactures which require the maximum of skilled labour and yet are light enough to withstand import charges as well as the costs of exporting the finished articles.

Of the traditional industries which survived, the woollen is most significant, and the two mills which exist are almost entirely concerned with exporting. Tynwald mill near St John's is located on the river Neb, although it does not now depend on the power from the stream, and the wool used is mainly of non-Manx origin, from Scotland, together with the Shetlands and Australia. By producing high-grade tweeds and worsteds mainly for the North American market it makes maximum use of local labour to the extent of 45% of total production costs, while the initial dispatch to Liverpool represents a very small proportion of the total ship-

273

ping costs. With one hundred workers, it is now one of the Island's largest factories. Knitting and cloth-garment factories established during the inter-war years still exist at Douglas, Peel, and Laxey, and the first of these in particular illustrates how suitable industries can flourish. This factory in Douglas produces expensive knitted goods in which the labour costs represent 40% or more of the total, while the finished goods are exported by parcel postage. Another very successful modern enterprise, which satisfies the special requirements of the Island, is the nylon-stocking factory at Ramsey, set up only in 1956 and now employing over 120 people, nearly 60% of them women. This, the only major establishment in the agricultural north (until the recent revival of shipbuilding in Ramsey in 1963), makes full use of local labour, while it also enjoys exceptionally low transport charges. Carpet manufacture has also been introduced during the last decade through contact with Kidderminster, and factories located at Laxey and Douglas give employment to 110 workers, of whom half are men. The larger one with 80 employees is located in a new building forming part of a Government Trading Estate on the floodplain of the river Douglas, so that it enjoys the benefits of nearness to the harbour and availability of local labour; the other occupies a former power station in Laxey. Both produce carpets of medium price for export. But since labour costs represent only about 20% of the total, and bulky materials are used, so that shipping charges are apt to be high, the success of the ventures relies very much on such factors as skilful administration and low taxation.

Light-engineering industries, providing employment for the largest manufacturing group (over 400, of whom 80% are men), are located on favourable sites, either on the Douglas Trading Estate or at Ronaldsway, adjoining the airport. Engineering was established in Douglas as long ago as the 1820s by an iron foundry which continued its activity in various ways such as the casting of ship's propellers and the making of crushing rollers for the mining industry. The concern is now engaged in general engineering for the Insular market, while other factories have been intro-duced during the last fifteen years or so with direct government assistance. These are concerned, for example, with precision engineering of aircraft components involving the use of light-alloy castings and bars, with labour costing about 55% of the total production. Indeed, in one Douglas factory producing miniature aero-engines the labour input is as high as 65%, and for the dispatch of exports parcel post is used.

A definite start has therefore been made in the introduction of suitable light industries, and in March 1965 the new factories established during the last ten years were then employing over 1,400 men and women. To these developments must be added a very significant agreement made in 1964 by the Manx Government with an American company for the con-struction of an oil refinery, with related terminal and marketing facilities involving an expenditure of some £4,000,000 in the Island. Land for this purpose has been given free by the Government in the Ayres at the north of the Island, and the buildings should be completed during the next few years. Finally, it should be noted that as the result of the modern industrial drive, the available supply of skilled and semi-skilled labour in the Island is nearing exhaustion, and a recent survey has urged that future policy should aim at strengthening existing industries, as well as stimulating natural resources, and increasing local production of goods which would otherwise have to be imported.

Changes in population and town growth

The figure of 40,081 for the total population of the Island, returned for the first official census in 1821, represented a big increase on the estimate of 14,400 made by the clergy in 1727, and of about 12,000 for the seventeenth century. Not only was the population low in earlier days, but conditions for the mass of the people were very primitive: sanitation was bad, cholera and smallpox were rampant, and the death rate was very high. After 1821 the population generally continued to rise, in spite of considerable emigration from the later 1820s onwards, and in 1891 a maximum of 55,608 was reached for the resident population. A downward movement followed which continued until 1931, when a total of 49,308 was returned, and although a higher figure (55,253) was reached in 1951, the provisional returns for 1961 (48,150) reveal a decrease of 7,103 (nearly 13%) since then.

Apart from changes in the total population, there has been a profound alteration in the distribution between town and country. All four towns in 1726 had a combined figure of 2,530, representing about 17% of the whole Island. Douglas had then become slightly the most populous with 810, Castletown having 785, while Peel had 475 and Ramsey 460. By 1821 the town population had reached 11,500, or 28% of the total, and the movement away from the country districts has continued, so that in 1931 the four towns represented 53% of the total. If the village populations in Onchan, Laxey, Port St Mary, Port Erin, and Michael be added to those for the larger towns, the total 'urban' population is as high as 67% for the whole Island. Douglas with 20,361 has far outstripped the others, being followed by Ramsey with 4,621, Peel with 2,612, and Castletown with 1,755, while Onchan (adjoining Douglas) now has 3,362 (Plates 40–43).

Difficult economic conditions arising from agriculture during the first half of the nineteenth century followed by the decay in mining during the second half, led inevitably to the migration of many of the older-established Manx elements from the Island, not only to many parts of Britain but farther afield to America as well as various parts of the Commonwealth. They have been replaced by people from adjoining parts of Britain who have come either to take part in the tourist trade, in education, or other activities, or else as retired people who have chosen to reside in the Island because of low taxation and the other amenities which are available. The Manx government has welcomed these movements; and the significance of the retired element in the present population may be gauged from the fact that almost 21,000, i.e. over 37% of the total, were returned as 'retired and unoccupied' in the 1951 Census. All this has meant that the population has become more mixed: the distinctive Manx surnames—Karran, Quirk, Kewish, Quine, Qualtrough, Gelling, Kinvig, Costain, Quayle, Collister, Kinrade, and so on—are less frequent than they used to be. Yet the people still cherish the spirit of independence so far as it is compatible within the existing complex economic relationships, and, as previously indicated, the movement for political freedom was carried on so successfully that it secured in 1958 the right to determine its own budget. It will be for the future to show how far the provision of any special local advantages will assist in broadening the economic and social structure of the Island by the encouragement of a larger resident population composed of retired and other people, and also the introduction of suitable industries to enable those displaced by the declining tourist trade to secure alternative and more permanent means of employment. It is at any rate certain that Manx prosperity will continue to be closely linked with that of Lancashire and other lands surrounding the Irish Sea, and also that air transport will be at least a very useful supplement to sea transport in any future developments.

The author wishes to thank the following for help in connection with this chapter: Mr L. Bond (Isle of Man Tourist Board), Mr A. Marshall Cubbon (Manx Museum), and Mr G. E. Lace (I.O.M. Government Employment Division).

CHAPTER 12

Conclusion

ONE cannot maintain that the Northwest has limits so clear as to make it a region apart and distinct from neighbouring regions or that it has a simple and homogeneous personality within its bounds. Its interest lies rather in its variety of scene from one area to another, accentuated rather than diminished by the long and varied imprint of human enterprise. In the north and in the southeast, the region includes sections of the Lake District and the Peak District national parks. By the historical accident that Furness 'beyond the Sands' has remained part of Lancashire, it carries the edge of the county round the shores of Windermere and along the Brathay and Duddon valleys, so that the Furness fells, including Coniston Old Man, and the whole of the Coniston Water are within Lancashire and separated for administrative purposes from the rest of the Lake District. Cumbria, the term used for the Lake District and its margins in both the 1928 volume of essays on the regional geography of Britain and the 1962 successor edited by Jean B. Mitchell, may aptly name the Lake District in one word, but the use of this term may be unfair both to Lancashire and to Westmorland. Even so, one reason among many for establishing national parks was that areas of undeniable beauty and interest should be partly under the control of some board which could integrate the work of separate county councils.

As Lancashire, therefore, bites into the Lake District so too it has at least a foothold in the Pennines. To call it a foothold is perhaps to write with modesty, a quality not always or inevitably associated with Lancashire. But the fact remains that most of the central Pennines is in Yorkshire, and this is nowhere better seen than to the east of Oldham, whereas all the upper Tame valley, as Saddleworth urban district, is in Yorkshire. Cheshire, however, is prolonged into the Pennines, including one section of the national park, though in the southeast the county boundary running along the ridge beyond Congleton is to some extent a regional division between the industrial area and coalfield focused on Stoke-on-Trent on the east, and an agricultural area on the west or Cheshire side. But from the extreme south of Cheshire the lowlands covered with a variety of glacial drifts are continued into Shropshire, the borders of Wales and on towards the

Bristol Channel as the lowland which historically formed the Welsh Marches.

In short, the Northwest hardly possesses an individuality based on natural physical qualities comparable with those that give distinction to such areas as the English Fenlands or upland Wales. Rather one may seek its individuality in the imprint of human enterprise through many generations, both in industry and in agriculture. In the latter half of 1962 Disraeli's phrase 'the two nations' began to circulate as an economic description of Britain, meaning that London with the Midlands and the south stood out as a prosperous or 'fortunate' section of Britain compared with 'the North' as a less prosperous and even 'unfortunate' area, marked by high rates of unemployment at least in certain parts, far graver social problems such as inadequate housing for a considerable proportion of the inhabitants in many towns, a preponderance of declining or at the best unexpanding industries, and a degree of amenity in general living conditions that is below modern expectations or—what expectations become— requirements. These difficulties are not experienced only in the Northwest but are even more acute in the northeast, particularly on Tyneside, Wearside, and generally in the Northumberland and Durham coalfield. To some extent, particularly in relation to housing and general amenities they are also characteristic of much of Yorkshire. Especially difficult is the attraction of new industries to the north, for to many modern industrialists the best area for development appears to be in the London area or within easy reach not only of the metropolitan market but also of the agencies, warehouses, and other factories where supplies may be acquired. Various successful efforts to introduce new industries in the Northwest have been made in the past and are now being made, with governmental incentives, but the difficulties remain.

And many of these difficulties arise from the course of economic history in the Northwest. The marked spread of textile manufacture in the eighteenth century carried industry into remote valleys of the Pennines and Rossendale in the search for water power, and in the uplands also many farmers of a few acres also practised domestic spinning and weaving for a period lasting well into the nineteenth century. In many upland villages and towns weavers' houses still survive, marked by an upper storey with a long range of windows for the home workers. But when machinery became more prevalent, and dependent on steam engines, and when some industrialists became more prosperous and enlarged their premises, the towns began to grow, especially where coal was available. Effectively coal and cotton became the twin supports of industrial Lancastria in the nineteenth century, though some river-side mills survived in strength with water-powered machinery as well as with coal hauled for many miles along roads and canals. And in these towns or industrial villages houses were built of stone within the Pennines and Rossendale, but of brick in the lowlands.

Some of the grits and flagstones in the Pennines provided excellent building material, and a few of them, such as the Haslingden flags, were so valued that they were quarried for sale in a far larger area than Rossendale. Many of the hillsides are scarred with old quarry workings, virtually all of which are now abandoned. The result of the early development of the textile industry was to provide, in Lancashire and northeast Cheshire towns, thousands of houses that are the social embarrassment of a later age. Perhaps the worst problem of all is seen in the deep Rossendale valleys, where the narrow areas between the steep hillsides have back-to-back houses and even back-to-earth houses built into the rock. Nearness to the mill was naturally desired in an age of long working hours, and many houses are overshadowed by the mill, which in some cases also had beside it the spacious home of the proprietor in several acres of grounds and even a Nonconformist chapel varying according to the proprietor's allegiance. To add to the depression of the scene, smoke filled the valleys from the mills and densely packed houses, and the climate was characterised by a high rainfall, frequent fogs, heavy clouds, and a late spring.

Urban sprawl is often spoken of as a phenomenon of the twentieth century, and even of the recent decades. In fact it was widespread from the late eighteenth century, for the mills were scattered along minor water-courses as well as the major rivers. In many instances a new village was spread along a road, one house deep with fields beyond, though in others a few streets of houses were built, notably so in Rossendale, where such a type of development was imposed by natural physical conditions. In either case there was at least access to open country, and a different problem arose in the concentrated larger towns, of which Manchester is the supreme example: tightly wedged round the central city area there were mills and workpeople's houses, and when the Georgian houses near the centre were vacated by the comfortably circumstanced people for whom they were built, some of them—those not taken over for industrial or institutional purposes—became overcrowded tenement dwellings. Many of the towns were developed in so piecemeal a fashion that blocks of streets apparently bear little relation to their neighbours, almost certainly because the pattern of urban development perpetuated field and ownership boundaries derived from the earlier rural landscape; this aspect of town growth has received little attention by research workers in the north but remains obvious on the ground.

Coalmining in the early and middle nineteenth century was mainly in small pits or adit workings, of which the remains may be seen widely in the uplands or in parts of south and central Lancashire. In central Lancashire mining has left derelict areas of great extent, and the subsidence due to the extraction of coal has produced 'flashes' of shallow water that have continued to spread. The devastation of large areas is now rightly regarded as a major planning problem; on a smaller but by no means negligible scale the salt subsidence in Cheshire, especially around Northwich and Winsford, has also made its mark. A local industrial relic of interest is the mounds of chemical waste at St Helens. Given that land is scarce in Britain, one can hope that in time much of the derelict land may be reclaimed for other purposes, such as new industrial estates, parks, playing fields, or housing, but in many areas it is by no means certain that the subsidence has yet ceased. Tip heaps, some of them, such as the 300-foot 'Wigan Alps', a few hundred feet high, can apparently be forested with some success—ironically, but perhaps not inappropriately, with a grant from the National Parks fund. But both the coal and iron waste-heaps are disappearing quickly in parts of Lancashire. Valuable as road metal, their former contents now provide the foundation of long stretches of the M6 motorway.

Throughout industrial Lancashire and Cheshire it is not hard to see the imprint of early-nineteenth century and even earlier industrial growth. Stockport, for example, has many early mills beside the river with large numbers of houses dating from the early nineteenth century and even a vast Sunday School built long before the days of universal education to provide simple literary as well as some religious instruction for the industrial masses. Nor is it difficult to find similar features in other towns, conspicuously in Manchester. In fact few of the major industrial towns were purely creations of the Industrial Revolution, though some, such as Oldham, were mere villages before it. On the other hand, Widnes, Crewe, and Barrow-in-Furness grew only after the coming of the railways. Oldham, however, already seems historic if one thinks in terms of industrial archaeology (obviously a more compelling term than modern economic history); yet its small houses are now being swept away in large numbers, and it already has multi-storey flats that stand out rather strangely against the gaunt outline of the Pennines. Similarly in Widnes and Crewe the mid-nineteenth century houses no longer seem adequate, and redevelopment has begun.

Communications have contributed much to the economic growth of the Northwest, and it is pertinent to remember that many forms of transport were pioneered here. The early efforts to make the rivers into navigations, notably the Weaver with the Mersey and the Irwell, were associated partly with the salt trade, which in time acquired its natural link with the chemical industry. And this involved not only the carriage of salt to a widening market but also the transport of coal to evaporate brine. The Mersey–Irwell improvements were designed to give Manchester, already a major British town by the seventeenth century, access to a port in Liverpool. In the eighteenth century Preston on the Ribble and Lancaster on the Lune were still river ports, but now only Preston's estuary has significance as a port. Chester's major period as a port belongs to medieval rather than modern times, and its final decay was perhaps assured by the building of the first dock at Liverpool in 1715. Road improvement was a clear necessity in the eighteenth century, and the turnpikes were built to link one town with another and with a national system of highways. Manchester was growing in significance at this time not only as a manufacturing centre for textiles but also as a general mart for a wide—and probably widening—tributary area. Its natural nodality of position in the heart of the lowland bounded by the Pennines on the east and Rossendale on the north gave it inherent advantages as a trading town, but these advantages could be made profitable by communications, particularly roads. Especially significant were the roads through Rossendale and the Pennines, where textile working was retained and developed by the inhabitants. Many turnpikes converged on Manchester, and the road system was gradually improved from the early eighteenth century into the nineteenth: by contrast Liverpool had few turnpikes. Although there was much movement of new materials and goods the roads were of only moderate quality. No doubt some of the famous travellers of the eighteenth century, such as Defoe and Arthur Young, were prone to exaggerate a little for dramatic effect in their descriptions of the execrable roads, which were improved in the early nineteenth century through the work of Macadam and Telford.

Canal building in the Northwest flourished for almost a century, from the time of the pioneer Sankey Canal in the 1750s and the widely known Bridgewater Canal. The result was to give Manchester by the early years of the nineteenth century almost as elaborate a network of waterways as a Dutch town. The penetration of the Pennines by three navigable canals was regarded as a great achievement of the time, explicable perhaps in relation to the success of the textile industries and coalmining. Cheshire was traversed by the Trent–Mersey Canal which was a general trunk route, in time connected with the county's other canals and with the Weaver navigation, of continuing importance for the salt industry. The Bridgewater Canal was in competition with the Mersey–Irwell navigation, which suffered from times of neglect. Runcorn became a town dominated by canals, including the Trent–Mersey, the Bridgewater, and the connecting link to the Weaver navigation, but Liverpool acquired only the Leeds–Liverpool Canal, which was connected with the dock system and attracted to its banks a large number of industries; in effect it became an extension of the dockside warehouse and industrial belt.

By the early years of the nineteenth century, the industrial destiny of the Northwest was clear. The river navigations of the Mersey–Irwell and the Weaver, the canals, and the turnpike roads all gave easier communications to the growing factories and even to the homes of the domestic workers. Manchester's rise to the status of a regional capital was gradual, but its progress was strengthened by the provision of improved communications. The marked eighteenth century growth of Liverpool gave the Northwest a great commercial asset, and by the end of the century Lancastria was in the full tide of industrial advance with, by the 1801 Census, almost half its population living in towns of which Manchester with Salford and Liverpool were the largest in the English provinces.

As the towns and industrial villages expanded, so the demand for agricultural produce grew. The simplest form of farming was seen in the uplands, where some at least of the holdings were small and worked only on a part-time basis while the main income came from domestic industry. It is still possible throughout the upland areas to see the small fields made for such holdings, though both the walls and the farmsteads are fast crumbling. The limited areas of grazing in the Pennines were used for sheep, and in Furness, on the much larger extent of rough pasture, sheep were grazed partly for eventual sale to farmers in the surrounding lowlands. But the main concern of farmers on the lowlands during the eighteenth century was to improve the fertility of the soil and to devise suitable crop rotations to conserve fertility. Of the manures, apart from the permanently respected farmyard product, one of the most favoured was marl, ideally a clay impregnated with lime but in fact varied in composition. Close to the towns large supplies of nightsoil were available, of which some was conveyed from Manchester in the same carts that brought the cabbages to market the next morning: boats carried this odiferous fertiliser along the canals. Various chemical manures were tried, including lime and the by-products of industries. To a great extent the relative fertility of different areas was conditioned by their accessibility, and the Fylde, though traditionally rich in agricultural resource, suffered through its isolation. The result of this improvement was to develop and strengthen the regional specialisation that has become characteristic of the Northwest, with dairying in central and south Cheshire, crop farming with some dairying in north Cheshire arable farming in south Lancashire with an extension towards the Ribble east of Southport, dairying with some sheep rearing in the uplands with—in recent times—an increasing production of eggs and poultry, and dairying with stock rearing and poultry in the Fylde and the lowlands of north Lancashire, including Furness. Along with fertilisation of soils that, in the main, were not inherently rich, the practice of drainage steadily developed, but chiefly during the nineteenth century. Before the end of the eighteenth century, some experiments were made in the draining of the peatmosses which in time became rich agricultural areas associated near the towns with market gardening. The present agriculture of the Northwest has gradually developed its economy as a supplier of produce for the town consumers, and though modified in some ways since the earlier years of the Industrial Revolution, it has itself experienced a revolution to its permanent benefit.

In the nineteenth century, Lancastria became one of the great industrial regions of the world, and a great contributor to the export trade of Britain. The main fear of the cotton manufacturers during the nineteenth century was that raw materials would not be available in sufficient quantities, and the cotton famine of the 1860s was one of the black periods in nineteenth century economic history. In the later decades of the century, some Manchester observers noted that Continental and overseas countries were developing the manufacture of cotton but the full menace of this threat was not realised until after the First World War. Coalmining was prosperous also in the nineteenth century, but Lancashire was not self-sufficient in coal, and in the twentieth century the gradual exhaustion of seams in the older parts of the coalfield left a number of miners without work in the immediate vicinity of their homes and compelled them to travel to the newer and deeper pits, of which the most flourishing are on the southern margins of the field near the East Lancashire road. The economic expansion of the nineteenth century was based on coal and cotton, but engineering developed steadily, partly to provide textile machinery. And of other industrial growths, that of chemicals is noteworthy.

The first main line in the Northwest, from Manchester to Liverpool, was constructed in 1830, and within the next twenty years the greater part of the present over-complex system of lines was constructed. In the first half of the century there had been a vast increase in the town population, and this continued sharply throughout the second half of the century. And in this period the towns began to assume their present appearance as they not only expanded but also were partly rebuilt in the central areas. Both Liverpool and Manchester showed a decrease in their central wards during the 1840s as the houses were turned into offices, factories, shops, and warehouses, or pulled down to provide sites for railways, roads, or various non-residential premises. As the present town centres developed they became, especially in the large places, almost entirely non-residential. Suburbs began to grow around railway stations within several miles of the major cities, and notably in the Manchester conurbation, of which the outer limits were at least pegged out by the 1850s. Some of the nearer suburbs were served by horse buses, but these were comparatively expensive, and the main spread of artisan housing was close to the factories and the town centres. Many of the towns in the Northwest are strongly Victorian in appearance, for they were expanding when money was more plentiful than taste. In Manchester the Victorian suburbs such as Withington, Fallowfield, and Didsbury on the south, and Cheetham Hill on the north, have spacious houses apparently designed to give the maximum of domestic work for the minimum of effect, of which the largest are now mainly used as flats. Churches of some elaboration were built, with the tall spires that are characteristic of the skyline in the northern towns, and the older surviving churches of town centres and submerged villages were restored or rebuilt in the latter half of the century, in some cases disastrously. As the areas of artisan houses spread from the central areas, many of the larger houses lost their amenity of situation and were transformed into small factories, warehouses, or offices, or sublet in so-called flats or even in single rooms: the process of change and decay was gradual but inexorable, with the result that some of the worst housing conditions are found in houses originally built for the affluent.

Jealousy of Liverpool's dominant hold over the cotton-importing trade was undoubtedly one motive for the construction of the Manchester Ship Canal in the 1890s, though another was the example of Clydeside and Tyneside, where the rivers had become in fact ship canals. The Mersey and Irwell, however, could not be canalised as easily as the Tyne or the Clyde, and the appropriate analogy for the Ship Canal was rather with the Dutch canals and particularly the North Sea Canal to Amsterdam. Trafford Park, beside the canal at the eastern end, became a major industrial area linked with the docks by an internal train service which still functions, and at one time also by tramways, now superseded by buses. This vast industrial estate has provided sites for numerous modern and growing works, especially those in oil, engineering, timber, and consumer goods, without which the Manchester area would have been less fortunate when the cotton industry began to decline. In time the Ship Canal may become a continuous industrial belt, but that has not been achieved yet, though the concentration of the steel industry at Irlam from 1930 was due in part to the attraction of the canal for the import of ore. In the Manchester area, many port industries such as milling and oil refining have developed: but these are especially prominent on Merseyside, with milling at Birkenhead and oil refining at Stanlow, on the former Gowy marshes close to Ellesmere Port. The chemical industries of Runcorn, the vast petrochemicals plant at Carrington (opposite to Irlam), and other examples show the impetus given to industry by the Ship Canal, although those who travel along it will see that much of it runs through a rural countryside, and possibly further industries will be attracted in time. The East Lancashire road of the 1930s has proved to be attractive to industry, for several of the newer industrial estates, notably that of Kirkby, outside Liverpool, have been located close to it: the new Birmingham–Preston motorway will probably prove to be a magnet for industrial growth in its vicinity, perhaps especially in those areas of central Lancashire where economic development is most desired (Fig. 63).

The image of the Northwest as a region of economic stability, not to say decline, rather than growth, is comparative in more senses than one. Historically, it is comparative because it was long regarded as an area of rapid and unchallenged advance, contributing largely to the economic prestige of Britain through its substantial export trade. For this reason, it might be urged, it should not be allowed to become backward, obliged to export a substantial proportion of its young workers, unable to clear the scars of its past industries and prone to develop what has been called a 'derelict land mentality'. Secondly, the incidence of distress through the decline of coal and cotton is varied, for many other industries have been remarkably successful and a considerable number have settled in abandoned

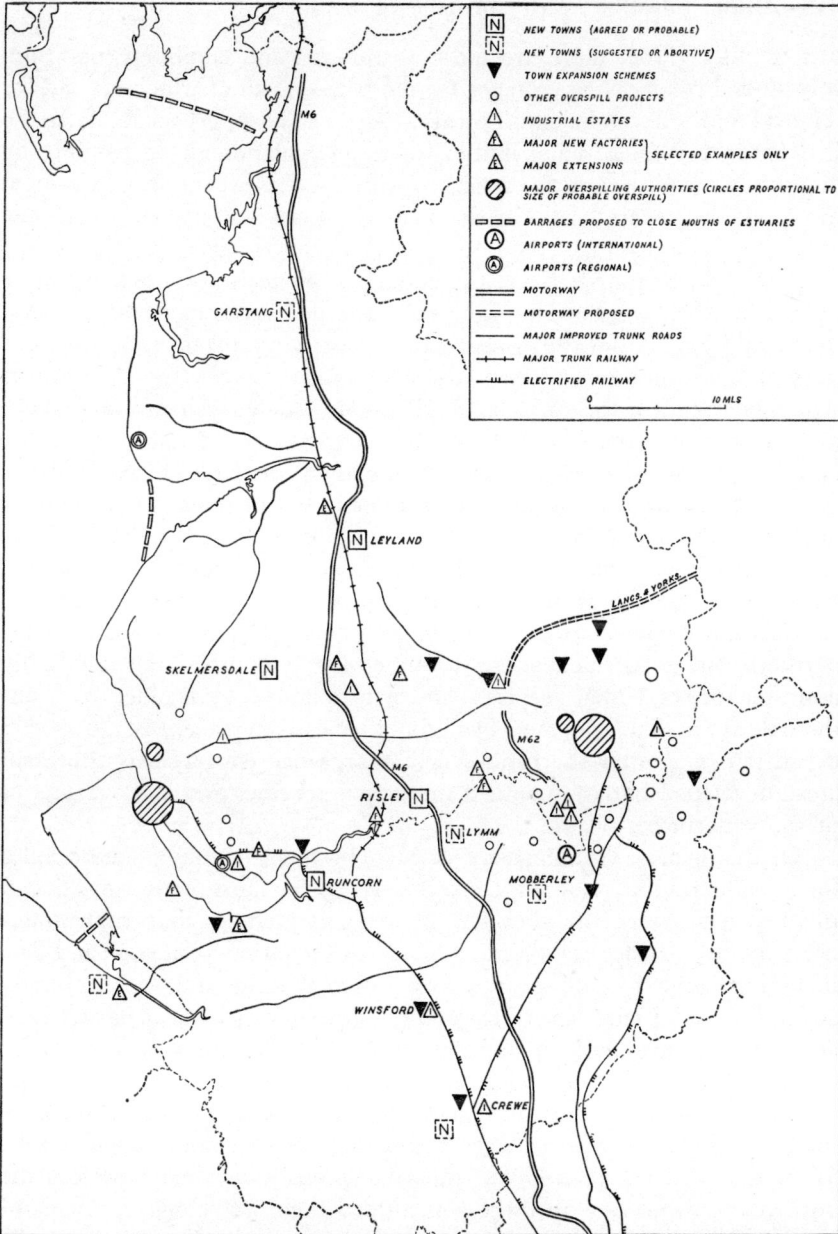

Fig. 63 MAJOR PLANNING PROJECTS IN THE NORTHWEST. Having survived two centuries of industrial life, the Northwest needs regeneration through the replacement of much of its outworn housing and the introduction of new factories. Its communications system now includes a motorway, to which others will be connected in time: Liverpool and Manchester now have quick electric rail communications with London. This map shows some of the schemes projected by the later 1960s: it does not show, though in a modest way it may suggest, that the real need of the Northwest is an effective regional plan. That may mean some modification of loyalties to parish, village, town, and county, in so far as such loyalties involve lack of neighbourly friendship to others.

cotton mills. True, there are mills abandoned and cumbling into ruin, surrounded by decaying cottages for the workers, all of which cry out for removal and redevelopment. Thirdly, there has been, especially since the First World War, a redistribution of the population made possible by motor bus travel, seen in the strong growth of suburbs, and this movement has gradually separated the various social classes more widely from one another.

Although, as noted above, the suburban pioneers were settling some miles from their work as long ago as the middle of the nineteenth century, they could live only within walking or easy driving distances of a railway station, or within the compass of horse omnibus services that were expensive. The effects of this may be seen in an area such as Altrincham, an old market town 8 miles from Manchester, reached by the railway in 1849. New houses were built close to its stations (then two, later united) for business and professional people with a richer type of house as much as a mile or more away, generally furnished with a coachhouse having quarters for the coachman above it. The largest houses, those of the 'cottontots', were on the higher ground near the open country. In time industrial expansion brought factories to the banks of the Bridgewater Canal at the northern end of Altrincham, and to other low-lying areas not noticeably desirable for residential purposes, and artisan houses were added. Without the railway, such developments could not have taken place. But the greater expansion came after the First World War, when entirely new suburban areas developed both as planned municipal schemes and as the fruits of private enterprise.

Of the former, Wythenshawe in Manchester, covering 9 square miles for a population of 90,000–100,000 is perhaps the most interesting. Begun in 1929, it was virtually complete by 1965. It includes industrial estates designed to provide local work and has a wide variety of houses and flats including some for old people, many fine schools and architecturally adventurous churches, several shopping centres of which not all have proved adequate, fine parkways on an American model, express bus services to the city and to Trafford Park, and no railway station of any significance. One aim, of the planners was to prevent the growth of a 'one-class' town by including some more expensive houses for professional and business people. What they did not foresee was the widespread car ownership from the 1950s, so obvious now to those who thread their way along the roads of Wythenshawe. Other areas of new housing, such as Speke within the bounds of Liverpool or Kirkby just beyond it, show similar characteristics. From the late 1920s private enterprise estates were built with houses slightly more affluent in appearance than those of the municipal estates. Less fortunately, some of the widely and rightly condemned 'urban sprawl' developed at this time, as farmers were not unusually glad to sell fields with access to motor roads. But though there are innumerable examples of such haphazard growth, it was less prevalent in the Northwest than in many parts of England as the depression was acute and many pleasant suburban houses could be bought at low prices. It is perhaps best seen in some of the smaller towns along the various main roads.

Sea bathing attracted large numbers of people to the coast long before the railway age, and both Southport and Blackpool were already widely known early in the nineteenth century. And in time the adventure of a trip to the Isle of Man for holidays was favoured. But the main growth came with the railways, and all the seaside towns have holiday and residential functions, with a large number of residents now retired. Of those in the Wirral, New Brighton is the obvious place for a 'day out' by ferry from Liverpool. But Hoylake and West Kirby grew mainly as suburban areas when the Mersey railway was built in the 1880s, though Hoylake, on the open sea, had a tradition of sea bathing going back to the eighteenth century. Southport has a spacious plan and has become both a resort and a favoured residential town for workers in Liverpool, Manchester, and other places. Blackpool has pursued an exceptionally vigorous policy of advertisement, and as long ago as 1879 acquired the right to spend part of its municipal revenues on making its charms known. In effect there is now a minor conurbation on the Fylde coast with, in 1961, nearly 250,000 inhabitants, 16% more than in 1951. A high proportion of the population are in the service trades, but there are marked recent industrial developments also. Morecambe, with Heysham, which are joined on to Lancaster, show qualities similar to Southport and the continuous towns of the Fylde, coast, but on a smaller scale. And the Isle of Man has residential attractions, of which not the least is a lower rate of taxation.

Lancashire and Cheshire had between 1951 and 1961 a population increase of only 2%, compared with a national average of 5%: the present population is just under six and a half millions. Within the same ten years the number of households increased to 2,083,000, +8%, with a national average of +12%; and the number of dwellings (2,104,000) rose by +15% against the national average of +21%. The broad picture is that the older inner Pennine towns, with those of Rossendale and the Blackburn–Burnley 'weaving' towns, are declining in numbers, and so too are most towns of the central coalfield area around Wigan. In fact, of Lancashire's seventeen county boroughs only three—Blackpool, Bootle, and Bury—increased in population, in the two latter cases through the addition of new housing estates on a more substantial scale than in most towns. The decline of population in the county boroughs is due not only to the diminution in the size of household (averaging 3·1 in 1961 but 3·3 in 1951), but to the slow exodus from the central areas as land is cleared by removing old houses to free land for non-residential purposes or rehousing. Large parts of many towns must in the end be rebuilt: perhaps the problem is most dramatically expressed in the figures of unfit houses in Liverpool put at 40% and in

Manchester at 34%. And once these have been cleared, other areas will be ready for redevelopment as the houses in them will have run through their reasonable life. Nor is that all: a recent survey[1] notes: 'The areas with the greatest intensity of poor housing [are] the Rochdale, Oldham, and Staly-bridge groups with their satellites in the Pennine valleys, and the Rossendale towns. The area is contiguous administratively with the greatest concentration of obsolescence in the West Yorkshire survey area and this trans-Pennine group forms the core of the largest area of substandard housing in the country.'

In 1951 Bacup in Rossendale had 6,304 dwellings, of which 36% were said to be unfit in 1954. In 1951, 45% had three rooms or less, 60% no fixed bath, and 31% were without exclusive use of a water closet; in the 1958 rating survey 59% were valued at £10 or less and 28% at £10 to £18. Some 114 basement dwellings were occupied, all with at least one wall back-to-back; 217 dwellings were entirely back-to-earth, or had no rear access because they were overshadowed by a steep hillside or looked over the river; and 1,711 houses (nearly 30%) were back-to-back dwellings. The authors speak of the town as one 'whose fabric is completely outworn and whose economic future is uncertain'.

Is it remarkable that from such places there should be a decline of population—in the case of Bacup not remarkably severe at −6% (from 18,400 to 17,300) in 1951–61? The whole inner-Pennine industrial belt stands out as an area of population decrease; yet it is hard to accept a view that such areas should be allowed to decay into final extinction. The contrary view is that such areas have borne much of the burden and hardship of modern industrial history and that they should share in the industry of a more scientific age with more human conditions of work and more opportunities of leisure. At least they have character. But it is hard to imagine a greater contrast between life in a back-to-back house in Bacup, probably combined with work in an old and dark mill, and life in a neat labour-saving house with a garden in Wythenshawe with work in a modern factory on a well-laid-out industrial estate.

Of the problems of the Northwest there appears to be no end, yet there has been a limited success in the attraction of new industries, of which various examples have been given, including the recent settlement of the motor industry on the edge of the Merseyside conurbation. But the real need at the present time is to induce representatives of the various local government units to co-operate in attracting new industries, in arranging for the removal of the undesirable conditions of living and work which many thousands of people endure, and so making the Northwest more attractive to those of enterprise in the later decades of the twentieth century. It is lamentable that there should be no body to represent the needs and

[1] T. F. Burnett and Sheila F. Scott, 'Housing conditions in the urban areas of England and Wales', *Sociological Review* 10 (1960), 35–79, ref. p. 57.

views of Merseyside, the Manchester conurbation, or the central Lancashire coalfield towns as a whole. True, there is now a Regional Economic
Planning Council to study the development of the Northwest and
regional Economic Planning Boards to co-ordinate the work of the various government departments concerned with economic development:
but many local spokesmen wish to protect the existing administrative
arrangements which have grown up gradually through a series of com-
promise adjustments from the mid-nineteenth century, when the town
expansion made the need for local government clear. Too often, the outlook
expresses a local patriotism that is entirely worthy but completely oblivious
of the needs of a wider area, and even contemptuous of the nearest neighbours. If the fear is valid that England is becoming two nations, of which
that in the north is to be stagnant or even to decline, then the immediate
need is to review, in many different ways, the resources of the Northwest as
a regional unit made to a great extent by past enterprise and, having
reviewed resources, to see in what ways decline or stagnation can be arrested
and progress achieved. This raises the question whether the London region,
together with the southeast and the Midlands, must inevitably be the only
areas of industrial growth while other areas such as the Northwest are
destined to fall back into a subordinate position of 'have-nots'. If this
happens, are areas which have already made a substantial contribution to
the national wealth to receive no national recognition of any obligation or
debt? The very success of Lancastria in the modern industrial history of
Britain has left grave problems for the present time, and one can only hope
that those who study its economic and social geography in the future will
find the picture brighter than it is in the 1960s.

There can be no doubt that in the long term the Bacups must shrink
and the Wythenshawes must grow and multiply, and as these changes
progress the geography of the Northwest must continue to be re-made.
The shape of the region in the future may already be discerned in outline
in Figure 63, on which the major planning projects in progress, agreed or
proposed, are plotted. The developing mesh of modern communications
will be the framework about which the new Lancastria will be shaped.
Already two great axes of improved communication have been fashioned,
one running north–south across the region from the threshold of the
industrial Midlands to the northern extremity of Lancashire, the other the
familiar east–west axis between Manchester and Merseyside. The north–
south axis contains the course on the M6 motorway, which already gives
access to the northern fringes of the Black Country and which will ultimately
connect Lancashire with London by the 'Midland Link' to the M1.
Almost parallel with the M6 and never far from it runs the main line of
the London–Glasgow railway, now electrified to Crewe and thence to
Manchester and Liverpool. This line of superb road and rail communication southwards to the heart of 'fortunate' Britain clearly creates a growth

zone with immense potential for industrial expansion. Already new communities are growing along it. The New Town at Skelmersdale, the proposed 'New City' in the Leyland–Chorley area, the overspill sites at Winsford and Crewe, and the possible overspill developments at Risley and Garstang are all strung along this great routeway, the new main street of the Northwest.

The second great line of movement through the Northwest, the Manchester–Merseyside axis, is to be further improved. To the existing facilities—the Ship Canal, the re-modelled East Lancashire road and the fast train service—are to be added motorways on both sides of the Mersey valley. The first stage of the North Cheshire motorway near Helsby is in the design stage, and this will ultimately link Manchester's international airport at Ringway with south Merseyside. This east–west communications axis, too, is attracting new, planned urban development, the New Town at Runcorn and the overspill sites at Widnes and Ellesmere Port. Motorways are planned elsewhere in Lancastria: the Manchester–Preston and the Fylde motorways will improve communications across parts of Lancashire, where the roads are now overloaded, and the Lancashire–Yorkshire motorway will pierce the somewhat stagnant towns of the north of the Manchester conurbation before striding boldly across the Pennines. By bringing a part of the textile region within easy reach of the national motorway system it may have a dramatic effect on towns whose prospects now seem uncertain. But the motorway network—and indeed all other major planning proposals—avoid the heart of the textile belt in the eastern uplands. There is no creative policy for the future of the remoter textile towns, but apparently an attitude of *laissez faire*. The effect of the proposals summarised in Figure 63 must be to sharpen the already clear contrast between the two Lancastrias, the fortunate areas of growth, prosperity and development in the west and south and the unfortunate districts slowly declining, almost to extinction, through the decay of old industries and the loss of population by migration. Inevitably the next generation of Lancastrians will witness a further stage in the changes already occurring, a shift of industry, employment, investment and population from the uplands of the east to the lowlands of the south and west, from the outworn towns of the Carboniferous outcrop to new types of urban environment on the softer surfaces of the Triassic rocks, from the areas of dank upland climate to the more genial setting of the drier plain. In short the proposals in Figure 63 may be summarised as a suggestion that the Northwest should capitalise its advantages and cut its losses by the planned development of those areas within it which have growth potential.

REFERENCES

The following abbreviated forms are given for the journals listed:

Econ. Geogr.	*Economic Geography* (Worcester, Mass.)
Geogr. J.	*Geographical Journal* (London)
J. Manchr. Geogr. Soc.	*Journal of the Manchester Geographical Society*
Lpool. Manchr. Geol. J.	*Liverpool and Manchester Geological Journal* (Liverpool)
Proc. Geol. Ass.	*Proceedings of the Geological Association* (London)
Proc. Liverpool Geol. Soc.	*Proceedings of the Liverpool Geological Society*
Quart. J. Geol. Soc.	*Quarterly Journal of the Geological Society* (London)
Town Plann. Rev.	*Town Planning Review* (Liverpool)
Trans. Hist. Soc. Lancs. Ches.	*Transactions of the Historical Society of Lancashire and Cheshire* (Liverpool)
Trans. Inst. Brit. Geogr.	*Transactions of the Institute of British Geographers* (London)
Trans. Lancs. Ches. Antiq. Soc.	*Transactions of the Lancashire and Cheshire Antiquarian Society* (Manchester)
Trans. Manchr. Stat. Soc.	*Transactions of the Manchester Statistical Society*

CHAPTER 2

There are few general surveys of the physique of Northwest England, though there are general chapters in the *British Association Handbooks*; Smith, W. (ed.), *A scientific survey of Merseyside* (Liverpool 1953) includes two chapters by Gresswell, R. K. 'Physical landscape and landforms', 37–48, 'The Coast', 49–52, and also Shackleton, R. M., 'Geology', 19–36. The comparable volume, Carter, C. F. (ed.), *Manchester and its region* (Manchester 1962) includes Rodgers, H. B., 'The landscapes of eastern Lancastria', 1–16, and also Simpson, I. M., and Broadhurst, F. M., 'The geological setting of the Manchester area', 61–73. An earlier work is Smith, W., *Physical survey of Merseyside* (Liverpool 1946). The best general statement is Edwards, W., and Trotter, F. M., *The Pennines and adjacent areas* (1954), in the British Regional Geology series, which replaces D. A. Wray's work with the same title, second edition 1948. The sheet memoirs of the Geological Survey 1:63,360 maps include Wedd, C. B., Smith, B., Simmons, W. C., and Wray, D. A., 'Liverpool with Wirral', 1923; Wright, W. B., Sherlock, R. L., Wray, D. A., Lloyd, W., and Tonks, L. H., 'The Rossendale anticline', 1927; Tonks, L. H., Jones, R. C. B., Lloyd, W., and Sherlock, R. L., 'Manchester and the South-east Lancashire coalfield', 1931; Jones, R. C. B., Tonks, L. H., and Wright, W. B., 'Wigan district', 1938; Wray, D. A., and Cope, F. W., 'Southport and Formby', 1948; Earp, J. A., 'Clitheroe and Nelson', 1962; Price, D., Wright, W. B., Jones, R. C. B., Tonks, L. H., and Whitehead, T. H., 'Preston', 1963; Taylor, B. J., Price, R. H., and Trotter, F. M., 'Stockport and Knutsford', 1963.

Studies of specific features include: Johnson, R. H., 'A study of the Charlesworth landslides near Glossop' *Trans Inst. Brit. Geogr.* **37** (1965), 111–26, and Pitty, A. F., 'A study of some escarpment gaps in the southern Pennines' *Trans. Inst. Brit. Geogr.* **37** (1965), 127–45.

Studies of erosion surfaces include Parry, J. T., 'Erosion surfaces of the South-Western Lake District' *Trans. Inst. Brit. Geogr.* **28** (1960), 39–54; Johnson, R. H., and Rice, R. J., 'Denudation chronology of the south-west Pennine upland' *Proc. Geol. Ass.* **72** (1961), 21–31; Moseley, F., 'Erosion surfaces in the Forest of Bowland' *Proceedings of the Yorkshire Geological Society* **32** (1961), 173–96.

On glaciation, detailed studies include Jowett, A., 'The glacial geology of east Lancashire' *Quart. J. Geol. Soc.* **70** (1914), 199–231; Jowett, A., and Charlesworth, J. K., 'The glacial geology of the Derbyshire dome and the western slopes of the southern Pennines' *Quart. J. Geol. Soc.* **85** (1929), 307–34; Owen, D. E., 'The Pleistocene history of the Wirral peninsula' *Proc. Liverpool Geol. Soc.* **19** (1947), 210–39; Owen, D. E., 'The Lower Mersey' *Proc. Liverpool Geol. Soc.* **20** (1950), 137–48; Gresswell, R. K., 'Glacial geomorphology of the south-eastern part of the Lake District' *Lpool. Manchr. Geol. J.* **1** (1952); Rice, R. J., 'Some aspects of the glacial and post-glacial history of the lower Goyt valley, Cheshire' *Proc. Geol. Ass.* **68** (1957), 217–27; Johnson, R. H., 'The glacial geomorphology of the West Pennine flank from Cliviger to Congleton', in Whitlow, J. B., and Wood, P. D. (eds.) *Essays in Geography for Austin Miller* (Reading 1965), 58–93.

On coasts the main work is Gresswell, R. K., *Sandy shores in South Lancashire* (Liverpool 1953). Older pioneer studies include Ashton, W., *The battle of land and sea* (Southport 1909), *The evolution of a coast-line* (Southport 1920).

Articles include: Gresswell, R. K., 'The geomorphology of the south-west Lancashire coastline' *Geogr. J.* **90** (1937), 335–48; 'The post-glacial raised beach in Furness and Lythe, north Morecambe Bay' *Trans. Inst. Brit. Geogr.* **25** (1958), 79–103; 'The origin of the Dee and Mersey estuaries' *Lpool. Manchr. Geol. J.* **4** (1964), 77–88, and Oldfield, F., 'Late Quaternary changes in climate, vegetation and sea-level in lowland Lonsdale' *Trans. Inst. Brit. Geogr.* **28** (1960), 99–117.

On climate, *see* Manley, G., 'The climate of Lancashire' *Memoirs, Manchester Literary and Philosophical Society* **87** (1945–6), 73–95. There are recent accounts in the *British Association Handbooks* noted at the head of this list of references, by S. Gregory in *A scientific survey of Merseyside* (1953), 53–68, and by P. R. Crowe in *Manchester and its region* (1962), 17–46. A recent article is Barrett, E. C., 'Local variations in rainfall trends in the Manchester region' *Trans. Inst. Brit. Geogr.* **35** (1964), 55–71: *see also* Barrett, E. C., 'Regional variations of rainfall trends in Northern England, 1900–59' *Trans. Inst. Brit. Geogr.* **35** (1966), 41–58. The British Association volumes have chapters on plant life; *see also* Bower, M. M., 'The distribution of erosion in blanket peat bogs of the Pennines' *Trans. Inst. Brit. Geogr.* **29** (1961), 17–31. For a general account of water supply with useful maps, *see* Gregory, S., 'Some aspects of water resource development in relation to Lancashire' in *Problems of Applied Geography*, II, No. 3 of *Geographia Polonica* (Warsaw 1963), 263–72.

CHAPTER 3

Camden, W. *Britain* (1637), translated by P. Holland, and L. T. Smith (ed.), *The itinerary of J. Leland* (1909) are contemporary commentaries on the landscape of pre-industrial Lancashire. Dr Charles Leigh's *Natural history of Lancashire, Cheshire and the Peak in Derbyshire* (Oxford 1700) is the earliest known attempt to give a systematic description of the Northwest. The Victoria County History for Lancashire was published in 1906–14.

Prehistoric and Roman periods
Varley, W. J., and Jackson, J. W. *Prehistoric Cheshire* (Chester 1940)
— *Cheshire before the Romans* (Chester 1964)
Watkin, W. T. *Roman Lancashire* (Liverpool 1883)
— *Roman Cheshire* (1886)
Newstead, R. *The Roman occupation of Chester* (1949)
Thompson, F. H. *Roman Cheshire* (Chester 1964)

For later periods, the following works are useful:
Sylvester, D., and Nulty, G. *Historical atlas of Cheshire* (Chester 1958)
Darby, H. C., and Maxwell, I. S. *Domesday Geography of Northern England* (Cambridge 1962)
Hewitt, H. J. *Mediaeval Cheshire*, Chetham Society, **75**, (Manchester 1929)
Walker, F. W. *Historical geography of south-west Lancashire*, Chetham Society, **103**, (Manchester 1939)

Ekwall, E. *The place-names of Lancashire*, Chetham Society, **81**, (Manchester 1922)

Tupling, G. H. *The economic history of Rossendale* (Manchester 1927)

Millward, R. *Lancashire: an illustrated essay on the history of the landscape* (London 1955)

Bagley, J. J. *A history of Lancashire with maps and pictures* (London 1961)

Articles on the pre-industrial period are numerous. Many of them appear in *Trans. Hist. Soc. Lancs. Ches.* and *Trans. Lancs. Ches. Antiq. Soc.* They include the following:

Wainwright, F. T. 'The Anglian settlement of Lancashire' *Trans. Hist. Soc. Lancs. Ches.* **93** (1941), 1–44

— 'North West Mercia' *Trans. Hist. Soc. Lancs. Ches.* **94** (1942), 3–55

— 'The Scandinavians in Lancashire' *Trans. Lancs. Ches. Antiq. Soc.* **58** (1945–6)

Sylvester, D. 'Cheshire in the Dark Ages' *Trans. Hist. Soc. Lancs. Ches.* **114** (1962), 1–22

Tupling, G. H. 'The origin of markets and fairs in medieval Lancashire' *Trans. Lancs. Ches. Antiq. Soc.* **49** (1933), 75–94

— 'An alphabetical list of the markets and fairs in Lancashire recorded before the year 1701' *Trans. Lancs. Ches. Antiq. Soc.* **51** (1936), 86–110

Chapman, V. 'Open fields in west Cheshire' *Trans. Hist. Soc. Lancs. Ches.* **104** (1952), 33–59

Sylvester, D. 'Open field of Cheshire' *Trans. Hist. Soc. Lancs. Ches.* **108** (1956), 1–33

— 'Rural settlement in Cheshire' *Trans. Hist. Soc. Lancs. Ches.* **101** (1949), 1–37

Potter, S. 'Cheshire place-names' *Trans. Hist. Soc. Lancs. Ches.* **106** (1954), 1–22

Rodgers, H. B. 'Land use in Tudor Lancashire' *Trans. Inst. Brit. Geogr.* **21** (1955), 79–97

— 'The market area of Preston in the sixteenth and seventeenth centuries' *Geographical Studies* **3** (1956), 46–55

Auty, B. G. 'Charcoal ironmasters of Cheshire and Lancashire' *Trans. Hist. Soc. Lancs. Ches.* **109** (1957), 71–124

CHAPTER 4

Contemporary sources include:

Holt, J. *General view of the agriculture of the county of Lancaster* (Board of Agriculture, London 1795)

Wedge, T. *General view of the agriculture of the County Palatine of Cheshire* (Board of Agriculture, London 1794)

Young, A. *A six months' tour through the North of England* (London 1770)

Defoe, D. *Tour through the Whole Island of Great Britain* 1724–7, ed. G. D. H. Cole (London 1927)

Aikin, J. *Description of the country from thirty to forty miles round Manchester* (London 1795)

C. Morris, ed. *The journeys of Celia Fiennes* (London 1947)

Ogden, J. *A description of Manchester 'by a native of the town'* (described as 'reprinted from a curious edition of 1783') (Manchester, n.d.)

The first large-scale maps of the counties are Burdett, P. P., 'Cheshire' (1776), and Yates, W., 'Lancashire' (1786). On them *see* Harley, J. B., 'William Yates and Peter Burdett: their role in the mapping of Lancashire and Cheshire during the late eighteenth century' *Trans. Hist. Soc. Lancs. Ches.* **115** (1964), 107–31.

Various books and articles have been published on the eighteenth century dealing with transport and economic growth; a selection is listed here.

Willan, T. S. *River navigation in England and Wales* (Oxford 1936)

— *The navigation of the river Weaver in the eighteenth century*, Chetham Society, **3** (Manchester 1951)

REFERENCES

Harrison, W. 'Development of the turnpike system in Lancashire and Cheshire' *Trans. Lancs. Ches. Antiq. Soc.* **4** (1886), 80–98

Bailey, F. A. 'The minutes of the trustees of the turnpike roads from Liverpool to Prescot, St. Helens, Warrington and Ashton in Makerfield, 1726–89' *Trans. Hist. Soc. Lancs. Ches.* **88** (1936), 159–200

Tupling, G. H. 'The turnpike trusts of Lancashire' *Memoirs, Manchester Literary and Philosophical Society* **94** (1952–3), 39–62

Jarvis, R. C. 'The head port of Chester; and Liverpool: its creek and member' *Trans. Hist. Soc. Lancs. Ches.* **102** (1951), 69–84

Mullineux, F. *The Duke of Bridgewater's Canal* (Eccles and District History Society 1959)

Barker, T. C. 'The Sankey navigation' *Trans. Hist. Soc. Lancs. Ches.* **100** (1948), 121–55

The following papers are more concerned with economic growth:

Bailey, F. A. 'Early coal mining in Prescot' *Trans. Hist. Soc. Lancs. Ches.* **99** (1947), 1–20

Banks, J. H. M. 'Records of mining in Winstanley and Orrell, near Wigan' *Trans. Lancs. Ches. Antiq. Soc.* **54** (1939), 31–64

Barker, T. C. 'Lancashire coal, Cheshire salt and the rise of Liverpool' *Trans. Hist. Soc. Lancs. Ches.* **103** (1951), 83–101

Chapman, S. J. *The Lancashire cotton industry—a study in economic development* (Manchester 1904)

Tupling, G. H. 'The early metal trades and the beginning of engineering in Lancashire' *Trans. Lancs. Ches. Antiq. Soc.* **61** (1949), 1–34

Unwin, G., Hulme, A., and Taylor, G. *Samuel Oldknow and the Arkwrights* (Manchester and London 1924)

Wadsworth, A. P., and Mann, J. de L. *The cotton trade and industrial Lancashire 1600–1780* (Manchester 1931)

CHAPTER 5

Some of the references given under Chapter 4 carry the story forward into the nineteenth century. Those given here deal primarily with agriculture, transport, and industry. A major source is Lewis, S., *A topographical dictionary of England* (London 1831). Baines, E., *History, Directory and Gazetteer of Lancashire* (Liverpool 1824) has useful accounts and excellent maps of most of the larger towns. *See also* Baines, T., *Lancashire and Cheshire Past and Present* (4 vols, London 1869) for the later period. The local *Reports* to the General Board of Health (*c.* 1850) cover most towns in the two counties and describe urban conditions in detail. Almost every town in the region had its early historian: much of their work is worthless, but among the best are Baines, T., *History of Liverpool* (Liverpool 1852) and Hardwick, C., *History of the Borough of Preston* (Preston 1851).

Agriculture

Holland, H. *General view of the agriculture of Cheshire* (Board of Agriculture, London 1808)

Dickson, R. W. *General view of the agriculture of Lancashire* (London 1815)

Garnett, W. J. 'Farming of Lancashire' *Journal of the Royal Agricultural Society* **10** (1849), 1–51

Rothwell, W. *Report on the agriculture of Lancaster* (London 1850)

Binns, J. *Notes on the agriculture of Lancashire, with suggestions for its improvement* (Preston 1851)

Davies, S. *An agricultural history of Cheshire*, Chetham Society, **10**, (Manchester 1960)

Transport

Priestley, J. *Historical account of the navigable rivers, canals and railways of Great Britain* (London 1831)

Kirwan, J. *A descriptive and historical account of the Liverpool and Manchester railway* (London 1831)

Marshall, C. F. D. *Centenary history of the Liverpool and Manchester railway* (London 1930)

Griffiths, E. R. *The Cheshire Lines Railway* (Oakwood Press 1947)

Parkinson, C. N. *The rise of the port of Liverpool* (Liverpool 1952)

Barron, J. *A history of the Ribble navigation* (Preston 1938)

Bailey, W. H. 'Prehistoric Chat Moss and a new chapter in the history of the Manchester and Liverpool Railway' *J. Manchr. Geogr. Soc.* **5** (1889), 119–27

Jackman, W. T. *The development of transportation in modern England*, 2 vols (Cambridge 1916). Revised edition by W. H. Chaloner (1962).

Carter, E. F. *An historical geography of the railways of the British Isles* (London 1959)

Greville, M. D. 'Chronological list of the railways of Lancashire 1830–1939' *Trans. Hist. Soc. Lancs. Ches.* **105** (1953), 187–201

— 'Chronological list of the railways of Cheshire 1837–1939' *Trans. Hist. Soc. Lancs. Ches.* **106** (1954), 135–44

Patmore, J. A. 'The railway network of Merseyside' *Trans. Inst. Brit. Geogr.* **29** (1961), 231–44

— 'The railway network of the Manchester conurbation' *Trans. Inst. Brit. Geogr.* **34** (1964), 159–73

— 'The contraction of the network of railway passenger services in England and Wales, 1836–1962' *Trans. Inst. Brit. Geogr.* **38** (1966), 105–18

Leech, T. Bosdin. *History of the Manchester Ship Canal from its inception to its completion* (London and Manchester 1907)

— 'Tramways and their municipalisation' *Trans. Manch. Stat. Soc.* (1897–8), 127–52

Industry

Baines, E. *History of the cotton manufacture in Great Britain* (London 1835)

Ure, A. *The cotton manufacture of Great Britain* (London 1836)

Love, B. *Handbook of Manchester* (Manchester 1842)

Taylor, W. Cooke. *Notes of a tour in the manufacturing districts of Lancashire* (London 1842)

Dodd, G. *The textile manufactures of Great Britain* (London 1844)

Laird, W. *The export coal trade of Liverpool* (Liverpool 1850)

Faucher, M. L. *Etudes sur l'Angleterre* 2nd ed. (Paris 1856)

Ellison, T. *A handbook of the cotton trade* (London 1858)

Helm, E. 'A view of the cotton trade of the United Kingdom, during the seven years 1862–1868' *Trans. Manchr. Stat. Soc.* (1868–9), 67–94

Greenwood, Alderman. 'The growth of the cotton trade' *J. Manchr. Geogr. Soc.* **3** (1887), 42–52

Niven, J. 'On the statistics of some Lancashire industries' *Trans. Manchr. Stat. Soc.* (1898–9), 107–54

Chapman, S. J. 'The conditions and consequences of market developments in the cotton trade' *Trans. Manchr. Stat. Soc.* (1902–3), 49–67

Modern sources include:

Davies, M. 'A note on an early group of cotton mills' *Geography* **29** (1944), 62–5

Daniels, G. W. *The early English cotton industry* (Manchester 1920)

— 'Industrial Lancashire prior and subsequent to the invention of the mule' *Journal of the Textile Institute* (1927)—a special issue for the Samuel Crompton Centenary

Ogden, H. W. 'The geographical basis of the Lancashire cotton industry' *J. Manchr. Geogr. Soc.* **43** (1927), 8–30

REFERENCES

Jewkes, J. 'The localisation of the cotton industry' *Economic History* **2** (1930), 91–106

Henderson, W. O. *The Lancashire cotton famine* (Manchester 1934)

Redford, A. *Manchester merchants and foreign trade* (Manchester 1934)

Ashton, T. S. *Economic and social investigations in Manchester 1833–1933* (London 1934)

Wadsworth, A. P. 'The early factory system in Rochdale' *Transactions of the Rochdale Scientific and Literary Society* **19** (1937), 136–56

Rodgers, H. B. 'The Lancashire cotton industry in 1840' *Trans. Inst. Brit. Geogr.* **28** (1960), 135–53

Mellows, C. L. 'Geographical basis of the West Pennine silk industry' *Journal of the Textile Institute* **25** (1934), 376–88

Calvert, A. F. *Salt in Cheshire* (London 1915)

Hardie, D. W. F. *A history of the chemical industry in Widnes* (Liverpool 1950)

Taylor, J. A. 'The Wigan coalfield in 1851' *Trans. Hist. Soc. Ches.* **106** (1954), 117–26

Fell, A. *The early iron industry of Furness and district* (Ulverston 1908)

Musson, A. E., and Robinson, E. 'The origins of engineering in Lancashire' *Journal of Economic History* **20** (1960), 209–33

Turton, B. J. 'Horwich, the historical geography of a Lancashire industrial town' *Trans. Lancs. Ches. Antiq. Soc.* **72** (1962), 141–50

Lawton, R. 'Population trends in Lancashire and Cheshire from 1801' *Trans. Hist. Soc. Lancs. Ches.* **114** (1962), 189–200

CHAPTER 6

The years to 1939

Welton, T. A. 'The occupations of the people of England and Wales in 1911, from the point of view of industrial developments' *Trans. Manchr. Stat. Soc.* (1914–15), 47–170

Daniels, G. W. 'The post-War depression in the British cotton industry' *Trans. Manchr. Stat. Soc.* (1923–4), 115–45

— and Jewkes, J. 'The comparative position of the Lancashire cotton industry and Trade' *Trans. Manchr. Stat. Soc.* (1926–7), 55–101

Ellinger, B. 'Lancashire's declining trade with China' *Trans. Manchr. Stat. Soc.* (1927–8), 1–56

H.M. Committee on Industry and Trade. *Survey of Textile Industries* (Part 3 of a Survey of Industry) (London 1928)

University of Manchester, Economics Research Section. *An industrial survey of the Lancashire area* (1932): *Readjustment in Lancashire* (Manchester 1936)

1939 onwards

Department of Economic Affairs. *The North West* (H.M.S.O. 1965)

Royal Commission on the distribution of the industrial population. *Report,* Cmd. 6153 (1940)

Robson, R. *The Cotton Industry in Britain* (London 1957)

Lancashire and Merseyside Industrial Development Association
The Furness area (1948)
The weaving area (1948)
The South-east Lancashire area (1949)
Merseyside (1949)
The spinning area (1950)
The coal–chemical area (1950)
The Lancashire coast area (1951)

More recent statistics and developments are noted in the Association's annual reports and in *The development of Lancashire and Merseyside* (1963)

Smith, W. 'Trends in the geographical development of the Lancashire cotton industry' *Geography* **26** (1941), 7–17

Gibson, G. 'Distribution of industry in the North-West region' *Trans. Manchr. Stat. Soc.* (1947–8), 1–48

Board of Trade. *Working party report on the cotton industry* (H.M.S.O. 1946)

Rodgers, H. B. 'The changing geography of the Lancashire cotton industry' *Econ. Geogr.* **38** (1962), 299–314

— 'Employment and population trends in the North-west of England' (London, Town and Country Planning Association 1962)

— 'Recent industrial changes in Northwest England and their social consequences', in *Problems of Applied Geography* II, No. 3 of *Geographia Polonica* (Warsaw 1964), 211–28

Wallwork, K. L. 'The cotton industry of north-west England, 1941–1961' *Geography* **48** (1962), 241–55

Gibson, J. R. 'The paper industry of north-west England' *The Paper-maker and British Paper Trade Journal* (September 1958–January 1959). Gibson's work appears in five parts in this monthly journal.

Wallwork, K. L. 'Subsidence in the mid-Cheshire industrial area' *Geogr. J.* **122** (1956), 40–53

— 'The mid-Cheshire salt industry' *Geography* **44** (1959)

Gittus, E. 'Migration in Lancashire and Cheshire' *Town Plann. Rev.* **32** (1961–2), 141–56

Pullen, M. J., and Williams, B. R. 'The structure of industry in Lancashire', in *Manchester and its region* (Manchester 1962), 147–55

Mounfield, P. R. *Lancashire* (Naples 1963). Part of a comparative study of Lombardy and Lancashire

CHAPTER 7

Several works relating to Cheshire are mentioned previously. Others listed here include some nineteenth century sources.

Bagshaw, S. *History, Gazetteer and Directory of the County Palatine of Cheshire* (1850)

Ormerod, G. *History of the County Palatine and city of Chester* (London 1882)

Earwaker, J. P. *East Cheshire, past and present* (London 1877–80)

Hewitt, W. *The Wirral peninsula* (London 1922)

Rideout, E. H. *The growth of Wirral* (Liverpool 1927)

Chapman, W. D. *County Palatine: a plan for Cheshire* (Chester 1948)

On agriculture there are some useful sources, notably

King, H. 'The agricultural geography of Lancastria' *J. Manchr. Geogr. Soc.* **43** (1927), 55–73

Boon, E. P. 'Cheshire', Part 65 of *The Land of Britain*, ed. L. D. Stamp (London 1941)

Simpson, E. S. 'The Cheshire grass-dairying region' *Trans. Inst. Brit. Geogr.* **23** (1951), 141–62

Fussell, G. E. 'Four centuries of Cheshire farming' *Trans. Hist. Soc. Lancs. Ches.* **106** (1954), 57–77

On towns, see:

Johnson, E. A., and Russel, R. *A Short history of Nantwich and neighbourhood* (Nantwich 1902)

Chaloner, W. H. *The social and economic development of Crewe* (Manchester 1950)

Two articles deal with Styal, an industrial village near Wilmslow:

Collier, F. 'An early factory community' *Economic History* **2** (1930–3), 117–24

McClure, H. R. 'An historical and regional survey of the village of Styal, Cheshire' *Geogr. J.* **103** (1939), 512–20

REFERENCES

This village is also discussed by a descendant of its founder,
Greg, E. W. 'Foreword' *J. Manchr. Geogr. Soc.* **43** (1927), 1–7

Three recent studies concerned with planning are:

Sylvester, D., and Rodgers, H. B. *Crewe: a geographic, economic and demographic study of the town in relation to S.E. Cheshire* (Crewe 1965)
Rodgers, H. B. *Overspill in Winsford: a social and economic survey of the Winsford Town Expansion scheme* (Winsford 1965)
Ling, A. *Runcorn New Town Draft Plan* (Nottingham 1965)

CHAPTER 8

The main source on the Ship Canal is T. Bosdin Leech, *op. cit.* under Chapter 5. Articles of contemporary interest include:

Condor, F. R. 'The actual and the possible cost of conveyance between Manchester and Liverpool' *Trans. Manchr. Stat. Soc.* (1882–3), 29–44
Tracy, W. B. 'The Manchester Ship Canal: its story in brief from 1708 to 1896' *J. Manchr. Geogr. Soc.* **12** (1896), 205–36
Fletcher, A. W. 'The economic results of the Ship Canal on Manchester and the surrounding districts' *Trans. Manchr. Stat. Soc.* (1896–7), 83–108
McConechy, J. S. 'Economic value of the Ship Canal to Manchester' *Trans. Manchr. Stat. Soc.* (1912–13), 1–126

On agriculture, sources include:

Smith, W. *Lancashire*, Part 45 of *The Land of Britain*, ed. L. D. Stamp (1941)
Taylor, J. A. 'An agricultural borderland in south-west Lancashire' *Geography* **34** (1950), 94–101
— 'Relationships of crop distributions to the drift pattern in south-west Lancashire' *Trans. Inst. Brit. Geogr.* **18** (1952), 77–91
Ministry of Agriculture Technical Report No. 5. *Lancashire: a survey of the uncultivated moss areas* (London 1958)

Merseyside and district

King, H. 'The geography of settlements in south-west Lancashire' *Geography* **14** (1927), 193–200
Jones, D. Caradog (ed.). *Social Survey of Merseyside*, 3 vols (London 1934)
Barker, T. C., and Harris, J. R. *St. Helens: a Merseyside town in the Industrial Revolution* (Liverpool 1954)
Lawton, R. 'The population of Liverpool in the mid-nineteenth century' *Trans. Hist. Soc. Lancs. Ches.* **107** (1955), 89–120
Brenikov, P., and Masser, I. *Housing needs and land availability on Merseyside* (Town and Country Planning Association 1962)
Lloyd, P. E. 'Industrial change in the Merseyside Development Area' *Town Plann. Rev.* **35** (1964–5), 285–98

Manchester and district

Tupling, G. H. 'Old Manchester' *J. Manchr. Geogr. Soc.* **45** (1929), 5–23
Rees, H. 'A growth map for the Manchester region' *Econ. Geogr.* **23** (1943), 136–42
Green, L. P. *Provincial Metropolis* (London 1959)
Cullingworth, J. B. 'Overspill in South-east Lancashire' *Town Plann. Rev.* **30** (1959–60), 189–206
Nicholas, R., and Hellier, M. J. *South Lancashire and North Cheshire advisory plan* (Manchester 1947)
Nicholas, R. *Regional Planning Proposals* (Manchester and district) (London 1945)
— *City of Manchester Plan* (London 1945)

298

Redford, A. *History of local government in Manchester*, 3 vols. (London 1939–40)

Everett, J. *Manchester Guide* (1840); *see also* the guide by Love noted under Chapter 5

Bruton, F. A. *A short history of Manchester and Salford* (Manchester 1924)

Smith, R. 'Manchester as a centre for the manufacture and marketing of goods' *University of Birmingham Historical Journal* 4 (1953), 47–63

Chadwick, G. F., and Medhurst, D. F. *Housing needs and land availability in the southeast Lancashire conurbation* (Town and Country Planning Association 1962)

Rodgers, H. B. 'Employment and the journey-to-work in an overspill community' *Sociological Review* 7 (1959), 213–29

— 'Altrincham: a town of the Manchester conurbation' *Town Plann. Rev.* 33 (1952), 190–202

— 'Suburban growth of Victorian Manchester' *J. Manchr. Geogr. Soc.* 58 (1962), 1–12

CHAPTER 9

Very little published recent material has appeared on this area, but *see*

Wallwork, K. L. 'Land use problems and the evolution of industrial landscapes' *Geography* 45 (1960), 263–75

North, G. 'Industrial development in the Rossendale valley' *J. Manchr. Geogr. Soc.* 58 (1962), 13–29

Valuable nineteenth-century sources include:

Report of the Boundary Commissioners for England and Wales (1837)

Report of the Rivers Pollution Commission (1869–70)

Some of the sources mentioned under other chapters are useful, and material has been drawn from unpublished M.A. theses in the University of Manchester.

CHAPTER 10

Among papers dealing with some aspects of this area are:

Fitzgerald, W., 'The Ribble basin' *J. Manchr. Geogr. Soc.* 43 (1927), 75–96

Thompson, R. E. 'The Fylde' *Geography* 18 (1933), 307–20. But *see also* comment by Smith, W., in *Geography* 19 (1934), 50–4

Smith, W. 'The agricultural geography of the Fylde' *Geography* 22 (1937), 29–43

Wallace, R. 'The paper industry of the Pennines' *Geogr. J.* 86 (1935), 349–56

Thomas, W. J., and Perkins, R. J. 'Land utilisation and agriculture' in *Manchester and its region* (Manchester 1962), 156–70

On the towns, see:

Schofield, M. M. *Outlines of an economic history of Lancaster*, 2 vols (1946)

Armstrong, R. G. 'The rise of Morecambe 1820–62' *Trans. Hist. Soc. Lancs. Ches.* 100 (1948), 157–92

Curnow, W. I. 'The growth of Blackpool as a health and holiday resort' *British Association Scientific Survey* (Blackpool 1946)

Bailey, F. A. 'The origin and growth of Southport' *Town Plann. Rev.* 21 (1951), 297–317

On Furness, see:

Melville, J., and Hobbs, J. L. *Early railway history in Furness* (Cumberland and Westmorland Antiquarian and Archaeological Society Tract Series) 13 (1951)

Marshall, J. D. *Furness and the Industrial Revolution* (Barrow-in-Furness 1958)

Rollinson, W. 'Schemes for the reclamation of land from the sea in North Lancashire during the eighteenth and nineteenth centuries' *Trans. Hist. Soc. Lancs. Ches.* 115 (1963), 133–45

REFERENCES

Harris, A. 'The seaside resorts of Westmorland and Lancashire north of the Sands in the nineteenth century' *Trans. Hist. Soc. Lancs. Ches.* **115** (1963), 147–62

CHAPTER II

The oldest existing society studying most aspects of the Island, physical, biological, and human, is the *Isle of Man Natural History and Antiquarian Society* founded in 1879, which publishes an annual volume of *Proceedings* (abbreviated in the following list as *Proc. I.M. Nat. Hist. & Antiq. Soc.*). The Field Section of this Society now publishes an occasional journal *The Peregrine*. The Manx Museum and National Trust, founded in its present form in 1922, is located in Douglas. Its collections cover all branches of study relating to the Island and it publishes an annual *Journal*, also various guides, e.g. *The Ancient and Historic Monuments of the Isle of Man.*

Allen, D. E., and Cowin, W. S. 'The Flora and Fauna of the Isle of Man and their Geographical Relationships' *North Western Naturalist* **25** (1954)
Allen, D. E. 'Ireland and the Isle of Man: A Floristic Comparison' *The Irish Naturalists' Journal* **12** (1957)
— 'The Vanished Forests' *The Peregrine* **2** (1956)
Annual Reports of Government Boards concerned with: Agriculture and Fisheries; Forestry, Mines and Lands; Tourism, Highways; Harbours, Airports; Social Services
Bersu, G. 'Celtic homesteads of the Isle of Man' *Journal of the Manx Museum* **5** (1945–6)
Birch, J. W. *The Isle of Man: A Study in Economic Geography* (Cambridge 1964)
— 'The Climate of the Isle of Man' *Proc. I.M. Nat. Hist. & Antiq. Soc.* **6** (1959)
Bracegirdle, R. C. 'Post-Glacial Invasions of Man by the animal kingdom' *Proc. I.M. Nat. Hist. & Antiq. Soc.* **6** (1963)
Carter, P. W. 'A History of Botanical Exploration in the Isle of Man' *Proc. I.M. Nat. Hist. & Antiq. Soc.* **6** (1963)
Cubbon, A. M. *Early Maps of the Isle of Man* (Manx Museum), Douglas 1954)
— 'The Ice Age in the Isle of Man' *Proc. I.M. Nat. Hist. & Antiq. Soc.* **5** (1957)
— 'Changing Backcloth; the Manx Environment in Prehistoric and Early Historic Times' *Proc. I.M. Nat. Hist. & Antiq. Soc.* **6** (1959)
Davies, E., and Fleure, H. J. 'Anthropological Survey of the Isle of Man' *Journal of the Royal Anthropological Institute* **66** (1936)
— 'Treens and Quarterlands in the Isle of Man' *Trans. Inst. Brit. Geogr.* **22** (1956)
Kinvig, R. H. *A History of the Isle of Man*, 2nd ed. (Liverpool 1950)
— 'The Isle of Man and Atlantic Britain: A Study in Historical Geography' *Trans. Inst. Brit. Geogr.* **25** (1958)
Kneen, J. J. *Place-names of the Isle of Man*, 6 parts (Manx Society, Douglas 1925–9)
Lamplugh, G. W. *Geology of the Isle of Man* (Memoir of the Geological Survey) (London 1903)
Megaw, E. M., and Megaw, B. R. S. 'The Norse Heritage in the Isle of Man', in *Early Cultures of North-West Europe*, ed. Sir Cyril Fox and Bruce Dickins (1950)
Mitchell, G. F. 'Pleistocene History of the Irish Sea' *Advancement of Science* (British Association) **17**, No. 68 (London 1960)
Pye, N. *The Isle of Man*, Part **41** of *The Land of Britain*, ed. L. D. Stamp (London 1940)
Quayle, T. *General View of Agriculture in the Isle of Man* (London 1812)
Reynolds, G. 'Rainfall in the Isle of Man' *Quarterly Journal of the Royal Meteorological Society* (January 1954)
Skelton, R. H. 'Manx Mines' *Mining Magazine* **92** (1955)
Smith, W. C. *A Short History of the Irish Sea Herring Fisheries* (1923); also 'The Manx Herring Shoals' *Transactions of the Liverpool Biological Society* **51** (1938)

Index

Figures in bold type indicate where the **main** information on the subject will be found

Plate 1 (*top*) PART OF THE CENTRAL PENNINES. Gritstone plateaus overlooking the deep slot of the Etherow valley form a series of stepped slopes between the summits at almost 2,000 feet, and the valley floor. There are poor farmlands on the slopes and a reservoir in the valley.

Plate 2 (*bottom*) BEESTON CASTLE, NEAR TARPORLEY, CHESHIRE. The castle stands on a crag of Triassic sandstone, a dissected fragment of the mid-Cheshire ridge, and looks westwards across the alluvial Dee-Gowy lowlands to the distant hills of north Wales.

Plate 5 (*top*) NANTWICH, CHESHIRE. This old market centre of southwest Cheshire, once the richest of the salt-towns, still preserves much of its traditional half-timbered architecture.

Plate 3 (*top left*) PART OF DELAMERE FOREST, CHESHIRE. Much of this medieval forest, in part replanted, still survives on sterile soils derived from Triassic sandstones and fluvio-glacial sands. The farmed enclosures seen in the photograph have been heavily marled to improve soil texture and fertility.

Plate 4 (*bottom left*) A LARGE FARM IN THE NORTH CHESHIRE ARABLE-DAIRY BELT. Note the ample storage for winter hay, the marl pit serving as a duck-pond, the labourers' cottages and the hamlet of Bucklow Hill beyond. This area was directly threatened by the southwestwards expansion of the Manchester conurbation prior to the passage of town and country planning legislation.

Plate 6 (*top*) THE DEE AT CHESTER. The town walls, here broken by a gate, the Welsh bridge and the weir, which gave power to the city's corn mills but prevented the navigation of the Dee, are all visible. The large modern building is the County Council offices.

Plate 7 (*bottom*) THE ROMAN AND MEDIEVAL NUCLEUS OF CHESTER. The city wall, which can be traced from behind the Cathedral to the upper-left of the picture, contains both Roman and medieval masonry. Two of the great cross-streets are visible, Northgate in the lower left and Eastgate in the bottom right. The Ellesmere Canal with its associated industrialisation and drab terraced housing traverses the background.

Plate 8 (*top*) THE CHESTER 'ROWS'. These galleries above street level give access to a second tier of shops and line the principal streets of the town centre. Traffic congestion in the narrow medieval streets is often much more serious than is shown here.

Plate 9 (*bottom*) POULTON-LE-FYLDE, LANCASHIRE. In few other Lancashire towns has the traditional appearance of the market place survived so well. At Poulton, the market centre for the northern Fylde, the market cross, the stocks and the fishstones stand in the middle of the broad market place, overlooked by the parish church.

Plate 10 (*top*) STONE-BUILT HOUSE IN THE PENNINES. This small country house on the Pennine slopes east of Manchester, typical of many such 'halls' of yeoman rather than of noble families, illustrates the use of local materials in the domestic architecture of the Pennines. The walls are of roughly dressed millstone grit with massive corner stones, while the flagstones of the gritstone sequence serve as the roofing material. The long ranges of mullioned windows are characteristic.

Plate 11 (*bottom*) VICTORIAN HOUSES IN LANCASHIRE. Gritstone and brick housing of middle-Victorian town growth. This is the typical urban environment of the Lancashire textile town, especially in Rossendale, and the Pennine flanks. Such housing is in many respects inadequate by modern standards; yet it by no means constitutes a slum in any official sense, and doubtless another generation or two of children will grow up in it.

Plate 12 (*top*) THE VICTORIAN URBAN SCENE IN BRADFORD, MANCHESTER. The rigidly rectangular pattern of the terraced streets, the scattered industry, the grim and grimy schools (*bottom centre*), the bowling greens, a forlorn children's playground (*left centre*) and the ribbon of shops along the main road (*top left*) are all characteristic of the late-nineteenth century town.

Plate 13 (*bottom*) THE URBAN FRINGE IN SOUTH-WEST LANCASHIRE. This suburban growth, between Widnes and Liverpool, has consumed arable land of first quality, intensively farmed for grass, cereals and vegetables, as the foreground shows.

Plate 14 (*top*) QUARRY BANK MILL, STYAL, CHESHIRE. Begun in 1784, and for long water-powered, this is one of the finest surviving examples of the mills built by the first generation of master spinners. Part of the mill continued to house a small cotton firm until the end of the 1950s. Most unusually for the cotton industry, the water wheel continued in use until 1904 and was then replaced by a turbine.

Plate 15 (*bottom*) A SMALL INDUSTRIAL SETTLEMENT. This industrial hamlet near Rochdale is typical of the tiny settlements created by the dispersed growth of the water-powered textile industries. The small four-roomed cottages are built wholly of crudely dressed gritstone, which serves even for door-posts and the paving blocks. Eighteenth-century in almost every detail, this scene exemplifies the critical housing problems of so many Pennine towns and villages.

Plate 16 (*top*) A MILL-DOMINATED TOWN. Though Glossop, Derbyshire, lies a mile or two outside the boundary adopted for this book, this photograph is included to give a general impression of the appearance of a small textile town, utterly dominated by its mills.

Plate 17 (*bottom*) A CANAL-SIDE FACTORY BELT IN EAST MANCHESTER. The tall cotton-spinning mills with their high chimneys are characteristic. Many have now passed to other industries, though the mill in the lower left was still a spinning mill when the photograph was taken. Pockets of early terraced housing fill the gaps between factories, but there has been clearance on the right.

Plate 18 (*top*) INDUSTRY BESIDE THE SHIP CANAL NEAR IRLAM. The Irlam iron and steel works, Partington power station and (almost lost in the smoke) a petrochemicals plant all occupy canal-side sites. The steelworks' ore-wharf may be seen in the centre. No comment is needed on the problem of air-pollution.

Plate 19 (*bottom*) DERELICT LAND NEAR WIGAN. This wilderness is the only evidence that still survives of the once-flourishing iron industry of the Wigan area.

Plate 20 (*top*) MOSLEY COMMON COLLIERY, NEAR WALKDEN, LANCASHIRE. Though not new, for there was coal-working on this site in 1840, the pit has been largely reconstructed since 1950. In appearance it illustrates features both of nineteenth century mines and the giant modern collieries employing 2,000 to 3,000 men each. The sorting and washing plant (foreground) and the conveyors serving both road and rail loading points are especially prominent.

Plate 21 (*bottom*) CHEMICAL WORKS IN CHESHIRE. The cluster of heavy chemical plants (no longer entirely alkali producers) stands at the edge of the Cheshire saltfield west of Northwich. The river Weaver provides both transport (wharf at bottom left) and process water. Salt in the form of brine is brought from the Holford brinefield some five miles away.

Plate 24 (*top*) A DERELICT CANAL IN MANCHESTER. The short Manchester and Salford
Junction Canal passes through the city centre and was once vitally important as the only
link between the trans-Pennine canals east of the city and the south Lancashire network
to the west.

Plate 22 (*top left*) A RECENT INDUSTRIAL DEVELOPMENT. The Ford Motor Company's
plant at Halewood, on the eastern outskirts of the Merseyside conurbation. The great
size of the factory, its reserves of land for expansion and the excellent access by both
road and rail are all evident.

Plate 23 (*bottom left*) CHEMICAL AND OTHER FACTORIES AT WIDNES, LANCASHIRE. It is
significant to contrast the industrial wasteland on the right with the excellent and
intensively worked farmland in the background. Such contrasts are characteristic of the
Mersey–Irwell belt.

Plate 27 (*top*) SALFORD DOCKS. Though the Manchester Ship Canal continues to the Pomona docks off the lower left of the picture, most ocean-going vessels discharge at the docks shown here. From the left bank of the canal stretches the great industrial estate of Trafford Park.

Plate 25 (*top left*) THE BARTON AQUEDUCTS. Here the Manchester Ship Canal occupies the old course of the Irwell, across which Brindley carried the Bridgewater Canal by means of a masonry aqueduct. This was replaced, on the construction of the Ship Canal, by the swing aqueduct here shown open to Ship Canal traffic. The swing road bridge, until recently the only entrance to the Trafford Park industrial zone from the northwest, was long the worst traffic bottle-neck in the region, but has now been supplemented by a high-level bridge on the motorway (shown in course of construction in Plate 26).

Plate 26 (*bottom left*) THE MANCHESTER SHIP CANAL. The canal traverses the flood plain and terracelands of the Mersey valley east of Warrington. Here it completely replaces the river, part of the old course of which may be seen in the left of the picture, close to the large slag-heap. The M6 motorway crosses flooded land in the middle ground to the canal bridge.

Plate 30 (*top*) THE BIRMINGHAM–PRESTON MOTORWAY. The M6 motorway in north Cheshire, climbing to cross the Ship Canal by its high-level viaduct. Across much of Cheshire, the motorway has brought special problems to farms severed by it. Already open to Carnforth, the motorway provides a quick route not only to industrial Lancashire but also to the Lake District.

Plate 28 (*top left*) THE THREE BRIDGES AT RUNCORN GAP. The massive railway bridge and the elegant but somewhat spidery transporter bridge were long the only links across the narrows of the Mersey estuary and the Manchester Ship Canal. The high-level road bridge, not quite completed here, has now replaced the transporter, which has been demolished.

Plate 29 (*bottom left*) THE PRESTON–LANCASTER SECTION OF THE M6. Here the two great rivals for north-south traffic, the London–Glasgow railway and the motorway, run side by side. The amount of bridgework required, even in a rural area, is striking.

Plate 31 *(top left)* REFINERIES AND OIL WHARVES NEAR ELLESMERE PORT. The two small docks have been supplemented by a new and larger basin at the entrance to the Manchester Ship Canal, but increasingly the needs of the refineries must be met by super-tankers discharging at the deep anchorage at Tranmere.

Plate 32 *(bottom left)* URBAN REDEVELOPMENT IN HULME, MANCHESTER. The renewal of this drab area of early Victorian terraces has taken a variety of forms. Three-storey flats of an early style occur in the centre of the picture, with four-floor 'maisonettes' behind them and, to the left, new terraced houses not radically different from those they are replacing. Industry survives piecemeal, and renewal clearly stops short of the total reconstruction of the urban environment. The whole of the old housing on the right has been cleared since the picture was taken.

Plate 33 (*top*) URBAN RENEWAL IN CENTRAL SALFORD. The balance between tall blocks of twelve to fourteen storeys and lower flats of three or four floors, shown here, is typical of the policies of many northwestern authorities. But industry is rarely cleared or renewed, and this redevelopment area is girdled by old factories, beside the railway and canal in the foreground and the river Irwell in the distance.

Plate 34 (*bottom*) PART OF WYTHENSHAWE, MANCHESTER. The low-density design of the estate is clear, though some parts now have tall flats. The enormous amount of space about the school, the modern church and the small cluster of shops behind it are all typical features. Privet hedges cultivated in the struggle for privacy round almost every back-garden form a striking and perhaps a socially significant pattern.

Plate 37 (*top*) MARKET DAY IN A LANCASHIRE TOWN. Retail markets like this one at Ashton-under-Lyne are strongly developed in most Northwestern towns and contribute significantly to their shopping facilities.

Plate 35 (*top left*) CENTRAL LIVERPOOL. This panorama includes the landing stage and pierhead in the foreground, backed by the Liver building and the other great office buildings, some rebuilt after bomb damage, in the foreground. The chief shopping streets lie in the right-centre of the picture, behind them St George's Hall and the Lime Street station. A section of 'dockland' is included on the left, with its warehouses and congested industry. Little old housing is visible, for flats have replaced terraces over considerable areas of inner Liverpool.

Plate 36 (*bottom left*) LIVERPOOL'S DOCKLAND. The large Gladstone and neighbouring docks in the foreground handle most of the larger vessels. Behind lie the dockside industrial belt and the web of railway communications.

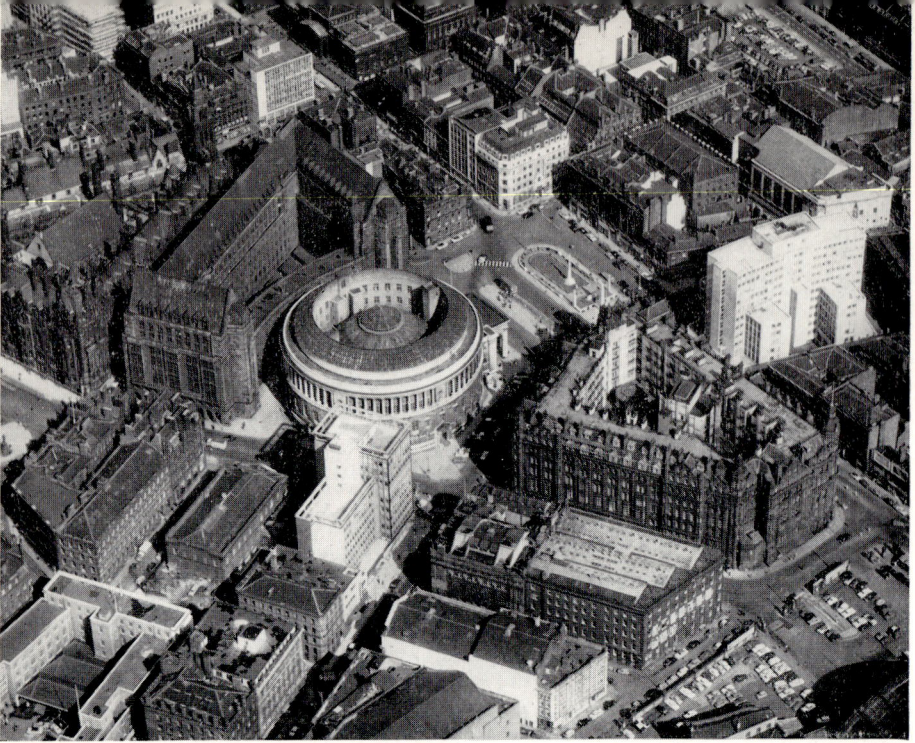

Plate 38 (*top*) CENTRAL MANCHESTER. This photograph includes the Town Hall and its extension, the Central Library and St Peter's Square. In this part of the city centre renewal has been so patchy that the essentially nineteenth century flavour of the urban landscape has been little modified.

Plate 39 (*bottom*) BLACKPOOL AND THE FYLDE COAST. The three piers, the Tower, the 'Pleasure Beach' fun-fair (lower right) and the railways with their vast and now largely disused areas of carriage sidings are the dominant features. In the distance lies the gently rolling drift plain of the Fylde.

Plate 40 (*top*) CASTLETOWN at the mouth of the Silver Burn and the focus of the southern lowland, was the Island's capital until superseded by Douglas in 1869. The fortress of Castle Rushen, overlooking the harbour, dates to Norse times but some of the finest features belong to the fourteenth century, The town still bears little imprint of tourism.

Plate 41 (*bottom*) PEEL began on St Patrick's Isle (the 'Manx Tara') at the mouth of the river Neb, containing much of early religious and civil history. Note the Round Tower (tenth or early-eleventh century) a place of refuge against the Vikings, also ruins of Cathedral Church of St German. The existing town grew up beside the harbour with some newer resort accommodation to the left.

Plate 44   E. BOWEN'S 'COUNTY OF LANCASTER'. This map went through several editions in the middle decades of the eighteenth century, and is the earliest to show the landscape of the county accurately and in some detail.

Plate 42 (*top*)   DOUGLAS, looking NW. The outlet of the river is on the left. Note passenger vessels alongside piers; beyond stretches the long ribbon of hotels, etc. round the shore of the very fine bay. The hills in the background include, from left to right: Slieau Ruy, Colden, Carraghan, and Beinn y Phott.

Plate 43 (*bottom*)   TYNWALD HILL, where new Manx laws are promulgated, and the site of the traditional Mid-summer, or St John's Fair. Note the processional way between the church and the tiered hill, covered for the day with its white canvas pavilion. Its particular location in the central valley is the natural meeting place for the whole Island.

Plate 45   A DETAIL OF BOWEN'S LANCASHIRE. The road system and the location of market towns are shown in detail, as are the great and as yet unreclaimed peatmosses of west Lancashire, with their large shallow lakes, Marton (now Martin) Mere and Black Pool. Both these areas have been drained. See p. 77.

Plate 46 A FURTHER DETAIL FROM BOWEN'S LANCASHIRE. Manchester's position at the focus of an excellent road system, now being improved by turnpiking, stands out clearly. Around the town lesser market centres and large villages clustered thickly, all of them now beginning to turn to the textile industries.

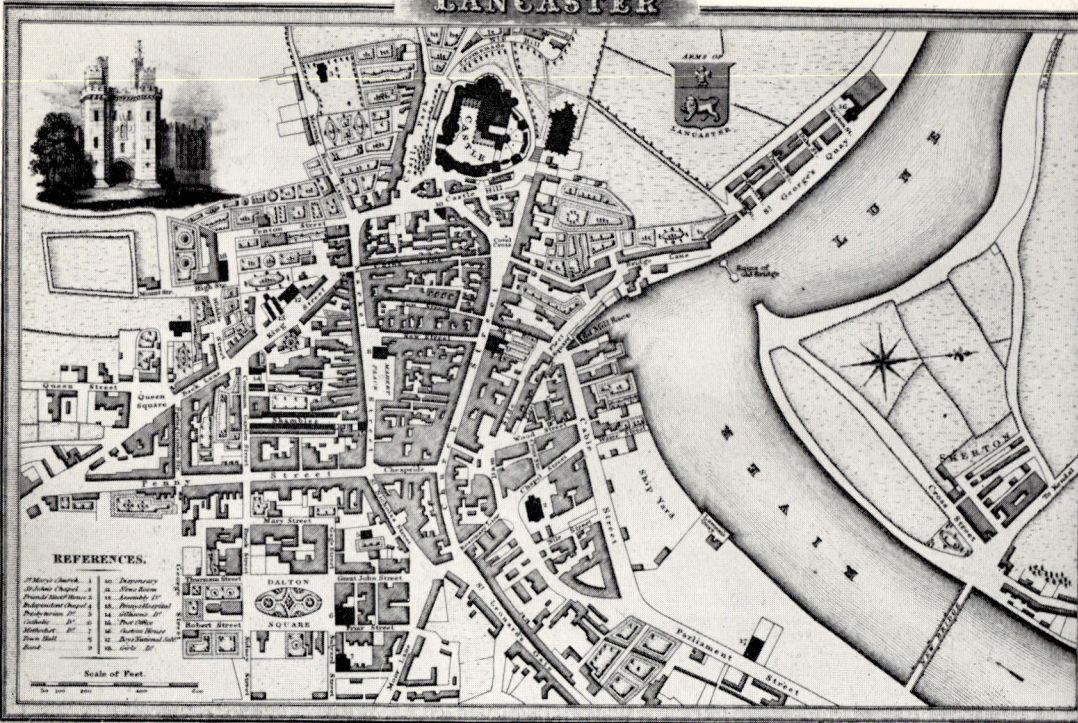

LANCASTER

REFERENCES.

PRESTON

REFERENCES

Market Place from the West

REFERENCE

St Marys or Old Church	1
St Peters Chapel	2
Baptist Chapel	3
Unitarian Chapel	4
Independent Methodist Chapel	5
Methodist Chapel	6
Independent Chapel	7
Primitive Methodist Chapel	8
Methodist Sunday School	9
Grammar School	10
Post Office	11

Scale

Plate 49 (*top*) OLDHAM IN 1824. Alone among Lancashire's great textile towns. Oldham had never been a market centre, but grew as a completely new settlement along the road from Manchester to the West Riding. This late origin explains the formlessness of the town's plan.

Plate 47 (*top left*) LANCASTER IN 1824. The quay and its warehouses, the castle, the market place with a shambles close by and the Georgian extensions made possible by the town's short-lived prosperity as a trading port are all clearly distinguishable.

Plate 48 (*bottom left*) PRESTON IN 1824. Long the *de facto* county town of Lancashire, Preston had large areas of fine eighteenth-century housing set in gardens and squares, but the 'intended streets' in the east illustrate the mean terraced housing which was soon to swamp the town as the cotton industry grew.

Plate 50   LIVERPOOL IN 1824. This map shows something of the growth of industry beside
the contemporary dock system and the wharves at the terminus of the Leeds and

SEAL OF TH

Liverpool Canal. The contrast between the congested artisan quarters and the pleasant
suburbs on the triassic platform at the back of the town is clear.

Plate 51 MANCHESTER IN 1824. The medieval core of the town is visible in the narrow streets near the Collegiate Church. Other notable features are the canal system, the growth of industry along the Irwell and Medlock and the spread of middle-class suburbs to the west and south.

WESTMORLAND

Shap Fells
Ambleside
Windermere
Furness Fells
Bowness-on-Windermere
Coniston
Kendal
Broughton-in-Furness
Kirkby Lonsdale
Millom
Ulverston
Grange over Sands
Dalton-in-Furness
Carnforth
Barrow-in-Furness
MORECAMBE BAY
Morecambe
Walney Island
Heysham
Lancaster

ISLE OF MAN
same scale

Point of Ayre
Ramsey
Snaefell
Peel
54° 10'
Douglas
Port Erin
Castletown
Port St. Mary
Calf of Man
IRISH SEA
4° 30'

54°

YORKSHIRE
Skipton
Ilkley
Fleetwood
Silsden
Forest of Bowland
Cleveleys
Clitheroe
Keighley
Colne
Pendle Hill
Poulton-le-Fylde
Whalley
Nelson
BLACKPOOL
FYLDE
Burnley
Fulwood
Halifax
St. Annes-on-Sea
PRESTON
Accrington
Todmorden
Lytham
BLACKBURN
Haslingden
Bacup
IRISH SEA
Leyland
Darwen
Rawtenstall
HUDDERSFIELD
Southport
Chorley
Rochdale
Holmfirth
Formby Point
Formby
Ormskirk
BOLTON
Bury
Maghull
Wigan
Radcliffe
Crosby
Leigh
Prestwich
OLDHAM
Bootle
Eccles
Ashton-under-Lyne
Glossop
WALLASEY
ST. HELENS
Chat Moss
SALFORD
MANCHESTER
Hoylake
LIVERPOOL
Newton-le-Willows
Stretford
West Kirby
BIRKENHEAD
Widnes
Warrington
Sale
STOCKPORT
DERBY-SHIRE
Bebington
Lymm
Altrincham
Cheadle
Bromborough
Runcorn
Bollin
Wilmslow
Whaley Bridge
Ellesmere Port
Knutsford
Macclesfield
Buxton
Flint
Northwich
Connah's Quay
Queensferry
CHESHIRE
Mold
Chester
Winsford
Middlewich
Congleton
FLINTSHIRE
DOVEDALE
Crewe
Wrexham
Nantwich
DENBIGHSHIRE
FLINT
Whitchurch
SHROPSHIRE

LANCASHIRE

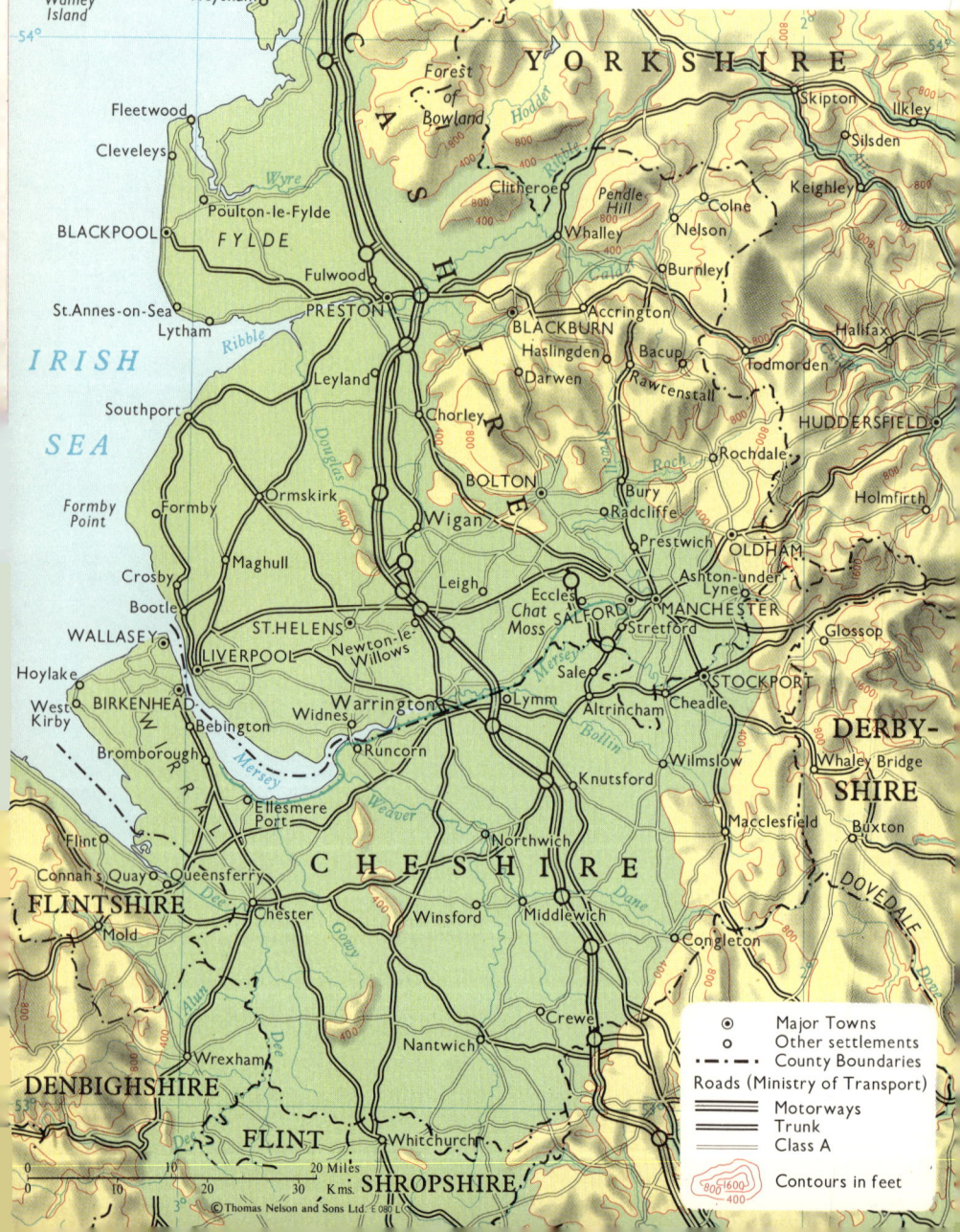

Legend:
- Major Towns
- Other settlements
- County Boundaries
- Roads (Ministry of Transport)
  - Motorways
  - Trunk
  - Class A
- Contours in feet

0 10 20 30 Miles
0 10 20 30 Kms.

© Thomas Nelson and Sons Ltd.

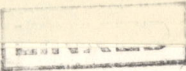